Introductory Topics in Theoretical Physics

Introductory Topics in

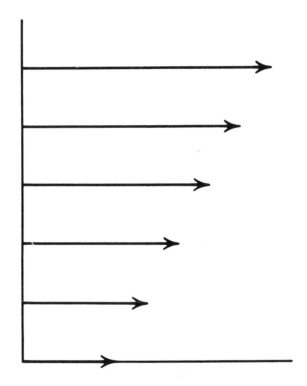

John Wiley and Sons, Inc.

New York · London · Sydney

Theoretical Physics

Relativity, Thermodynamics,

Kinetic Theory, and Statistical Mechanics

Roald K. Wangsness

Professor of Physics, University of Arizona

QC
20
W32

Library of Congress Catalog Card Number: 63-22209
Printed in the United States of America

120495

For Peter and Steven

Preface

The primary purpose of this book is to give a satisfactory introduction to those parts of classical theoretical physics for which a background in mechanics and electrodynamics must be assumed. The level and selection of the material should make it suitable as a senior or beginning graduate text for physics majors. I have, however, constantly tried to keep in mind the needs of the large and growing group for whom a knowledge of this material is continually becoming more necessary. The general and increasing use of solid state devices in engineering makes a familiarity with the thermal properties of materials as described by thermodynamics and statistical mechanics an essential part of the training of the modern engineer. Chemists and metallurgists have really always needed a strong background in these fields, and I hope that the point of view of the presentation I have given will be particularly useful for their general needs as well.

The first part deals with special relativity which is developed from considerations of electromagnetic phenomena in moving systems and the question of whether the inertial system of mechanics is also the correct one for electrodynamics. The formulation of mechanics and electromagnetic theory in 4-vector and tensor form is then developed so that the naturalness and suitability of this description can be emphasized.

In the next part, thermodynamics is developed as an empirical and macroscopic subject. The laws are presented in their "positive" form of definite statements about the existence and properties of state functions rather than in the "negative" manner of describing the impossibility of certain mechanisms. It has been my experience that students obtain a much better understanding of thermodynamic methods and philosophy when this approach is used, and it also becomes much easier for them to appreciate the connection between the various potentials and the choice of independent variables. They also are less prone to develop the attitude that thermodynamics is a branch of physics whose approach and detailed methods are mysterious and foreign as compared to the rest of theoretical physics. The third law is developed and its principal consequences obtained. In the last chapter of this part, I have discussed phase transitions in single component systems and have included consideration of the characteristics of second and higher order transitions.

The brief treatment of the kinetic theory of gases introduces in a graphic way the ideas of probability and distributions as essential features of the calculation of macroscopic properties as averages of molecular properties. Transport processes in non-equilibrium situations are also considered.

The discussion of statistical mechanics which follows is based on the concept of the ensemble as the suitable vehicle for general probability calculations. The considerations are initially based on classical phase space and Hamiltonian systems since this approach involves familiar concepts; the introduction of quantum states is made later by correlating them with elementary cells in phase space. A brief survey of the calculation of the virial coefficients for a real gas is given as an illustration of the use of the Boltzmann distribution and of equating time and ensemble averages. Chapters on semiconductors as well as on fluctuations and noise have been included because of the importance of these subjects for communications and laboratory measurements and because they provide good examples of the applications of general statistical mechanical results to specific situations.

The physics preparation I have assumed is classical mechanics including Hamilton's equations and normal modes of coupled systems and electromagnetism expressed by Maxwell's equations. I have also assumed a mathematical background of calculus through partial differentiation; what little else in mathematical methods has been needed is developed in the text. Most of the exercises will be familiar to those acquainted with the subject and, of course, this is one of the reasons why these time-tested ones were chosen. The symbols $=$, $\simeq$, $\approx$, $\sim$, $\neq$ always mean, respectively: equal to, approximately equal to, of the order of magnitude of, proportional to, and different from.

Much of the organization and content of this book was developed over a period of years in connection with courses I taught at the U.S. Naval Ordnance Laboratory for the University of Maryland and later at the University of Arizona, and I am indebted to the many students and others who have contributed with their questions and comments. I am grateful again to my wife, Cleo Abbott Wangsness, for her encouragement and invaluable aid in all phases of the preparation of this book.

ROALD K. WANGSNESS

Tucson, Arizona
October, 1963

Contents

ix

Introduction

What you have inherited from your fathers
You must earn, in order to possess.

—Goethe, *Faust*

The development of new physical concepts and theories is a continual process and usually proceeds by means of refinement and revision of the old. It is also generally true that the earlier theories rarely disappear completely as a result of such revisions but are present as limiting cases of a more comprehensive theory. Very often the basic physical concepts which are used in the new theory become so broadened in scope as to encompass an astonishing diversity of phenomena.

The special theory of relativity provides the classic example of how the growing inconsistencies with experiment of a previously highly successful theoretical scheme prompted a re-examination of the basic foundations of physical theory. These investigations had profound and far-reaching consequences for physics, and yet the terminology and conceptual notions in terms of which the special theory is formulated are ones such as momentum, energy, charge, and fields which are familiar from the theories of mechanics and electrodynamics for which they were originally devised.

Thermodynamics, which had its origins in the practical problems of developing more efficient machinery for the Industrial Revolution, was soon developed into a macroscopic theory of great generality and power. In its "purest" state, thermodynamics deals only with empirical information, and its independence of models of the structure of matter gives its basic generalizations or "laws" a sense of universality and permanency possessed by no other portion of physics. The interpretation of thermodynamic properties in terms of molecular properties is the task of kinetic theory and statistical mechanics. The basic use of probabilities and averages in statistical mechanics has provided new insight into the microscopic significance of the laws of thermodynamics; yet the original conceptions were general enough that the transition from classical mechanics to quantum mechanics as a basic description of matter was made with comparative ease and required no drastic changes in the methodology of statistical mechanics.

1

Selected references

Throughout this book a background in classical mechanics and electro-dynamics is assumed which is equivalent to the content of

R. K. Wangsness, *Introduction to Theoretical Physics: Classical Mechanics and Electrodynamics*, Wiley, 1963.

Specific references to that book are indicated by the notation (I: 3-13) which in this example is to equation (3-13), the same reference system being used in both that book and this one.

A thorough discussion of both special and general relativity can be found in

C. Møller, *The Theory of Relativity*, Oxford, 1952.

The following book covers many similar topics at about the same level as we do:

A. Sommerfeld, *Thermodynamics and Statistical Mechanics*, Academic Press, 1956.

An outstanding discussion of the fundamentals is contained in

R. C. Tolman, *The Principles of Statistical Mechanics*, Oxford, 1938.

The following six books provide detailed and extensive coverage of their subjects. They include many problems and references.

M. W. Zemansky, *Heat and Thermodynamics* (4th ed.), McGraw-Hill, 1957.

A. B. Pippard, *The Elements of Classical Thermodynamics*, Cambridge, 1957.

H. B. Callen, *Thermodynamics*, Wiley, 1960.

R. D. Present, *Kinetic Theory of Gases*, McGraw-Hill, 1958.

D. ter Haar, *Elements of Statistical Mechanics*, Rinehart, 1954.

T. L. Hill, *An Introduction to Statistical Thermodynamics*, Addison-Wesley, 1960.

A brief introduction to a great many examples of statistical considerations in physics can be found in

C. Kittel, *Elementary Statistical Physics*, Wiley, 1958.

Mathematical methods and results appropriate to the material in this book are well presented in

H. Margenau and G. M. Murphy, *The Mathematics of Physics and Chemistry* (2nd ed.), Van Nostrand, 1956.

P. M. Morse and H. Feshbach, *Methods of Theoretical Physics* (2 vols.), McGraw-Hill, 1953.

Part One

Special Relativity

1 The experimental basis for special relativity

The basic concern of the theory of relativity is the comparison of results obtained by observers of physical phenomena who are moving with respect to each other. The special theory, which is the only form we shall consider, refers only to the case of two observers who have a constant velocity relative to one another. In order to illustrate some of the concepts involved in the general problem, we begin by considering how two moving observers would describe some electromagnetic effects.

1-1 Electromagnetic fields in moving coordinate systems

The vector **E** in the electromagnetic field equations represents the electric field at a given point in space (x, y, z) and at a given time t, all of which are specified in terms of a particular set of coordinate axes. The person who is observing and describing the phenomena is regarded as at rest with respect to these axes.

Suppose now that the same phenomena are to be observed and described by someone else who wishes to use coordinate axes which are moving with respect to the first set. We represent the coordinates and time referred to this second set of axes by x', y', z', t'. The second observer is at rest with respect to his set of axes, and it is assumed to be just as possible to describe the phenomena from his point of view as from the point of view of the first observer. Then there naturally arises the question: Will the two observers describe things in the same way or will their descriptions differ in any essential respects?

The simplest situation of this kind is that in which the two systems, S and S', are moving with constant relative speed v along the common direction of their x and x' axes as shown in Fig. 1-1. The usual formulas relating the two sets of *coordinates and time* for a given "event" are those of the *classical (or Galilean) transformation* (I: 3-13). Since the only component of the relative velocity is $v_x = v$, these transformation equations become

$$x' = x - vt, \quad y' = y, \quad z' = z, \quad t' = t \tag{1-1}$$

if we also assume for simplicity that the two origins O and O' coincide at $t = 0$. If one of these sets of axes is an inertial system, then we know from (I: Sec. 3-5) that the other set is also an inertial system. We know

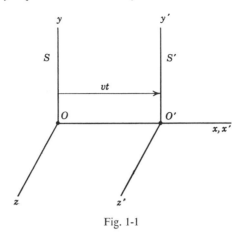

Fig. 1-1

too that these two sets of axes satisfy the *classical (or Galilean) principle of relativity* in that they are both equally good for use in mechanics since the transformation (1-1) ensures that the laws of motion have the same form in all inertial systems. We now want to see whether the *fields* at a given point appear the same or differently to the two observers.

Let us assume that the observer at rest in system S finds that at a given point P there is no electric field but that there is a magnetic induction $\mathbf{B}$. In principle he would learn this by placing a stationary electric charge q at the point P and then noting that the charge experienced no acceleration. On the other hand, if he moves the charge with velocity $\mathbf{v}$, he finds that it is acted on by the force $q\mathbf{v} \times \mathbf{B}$.

Now let the observer associated with and at rest in S', which has a velocity $\mathbf{v}$ with respect to S, perform a similar experiment by placing at the point P a charge q which is at rest. Since q is at rest with respect to the axes S', the charge is therefore moving with velocity $\mathbf{v}$ with respect to the axes S. The observer in S would see this charge accelerated by the force $q\mathbf{v} \times \mathbf{B}$, and the observer in S' must also observe exactly the *same acceleration* according to (I: 3-15) since both systems are inertial systems.

Since the S' observer finds that the charge which is at rest as far as he is concerned is accelerated, he will conclude that the corresponding force must be written $q\mathbf{E}'$, according to (I: 19-34). Thus he decides that there is an *electric field* at P, and, if we equate the accelerations, we find that this field is given by

$$\mathbf{E}' = \mathbf{v} \times \mathbf{B} \tag{1-2}$$

Thus what appeared to one observer as a magnetic field would be interpreted as an electric field by the other observer.

The field given by (1-2) can be expected to be in addition to any electric field **E** already present in *S*. If we assume that we can simply add (1-2) to **E**, we can say that the fields as seen by the two observers are connected by the transformation equation

$$\mathbf{E}' = \mathbf{E} + \mathbf{v} \times \mathbf{B} \tag{1-3}$$

In this equation **E**' is the electric field with reference to axes *S*', while **E** and **B** are the electric field and magnetic induction with reference to the axes *S*. It is to be emphasized that these fields are measured at the same point and at the same time; the difference is entirely due to the different systems of axes to which the observers' descriptions are referred. We shall find later that (1-3) is not quite exact but is a very good approximation when $|\mathbf{v}| \ll c$.

The part of the electric field given by (1-2) is called a *motional* electric field. One can often use (1-3) to express electromagnetic properties of a moving medium in terms of the fields referred to a stationary coordinate system. For example, if the moving medium can be described by a conductivity σ and an electric susceptibility χ_e, the current density and polarization in the medium will be given by

$$\mathbf{J} = \sigma\mathbf{E}' = \sigma(\mathbf{E} + \mathbf{v} \times \mathbf{B}) \tag{1-4}$$

$$\mathbf{P} = \epsilon_0\chi_e\mathbf{E}' = \epsilon_0\chi_e(\mathbf{E} + \mathbf{v} \times \mathbf{B}) \tag{1-5}$$

As another example of the application of (1-2), we can consider the problem of finding the emf induced when a conductor is moving through a magnetic induction where, as in (I: 19-65), the emf is the line integral of **E** around the complete circuit. We shall consider the simple circuit shown in Fig. 1-2. Two straight wires w_1 and w_2 are parallel to the *x* axis in the *xz* plane and are a distance *l* apart. They are connected to each other at one end through a meter *A* which will measure the current in the circuit. Another wire *W* rests on w_1 and w_2 and is parallel to the *z* axis.

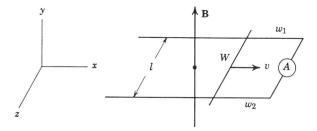

Fig. 1-2

This whole circuit is in a uniform induction **B** which is parallel to the y axis. If W is moved with constant speed v in the direction of increasing x, a current is observed in the circuit. When the current is measured, the emf can be found as the product of the current and the resistance. We want to calculate this emf by using the transformation equations for the fields.

There is no electric field along the wires w_1 and w_2, and the connection through A; hence they make no contribution to the emf. From the point of view of an observer moving with the wire W there is an electric field $E_z' = vB$, according to (1-2), since **v** and **B** are perpendicular. Therefore, from (I: 19-65), the total emf in this circuit is

$$\oint \mathbf{E}' \cdot d\mathbf{s} = E_z'W = BvW \tag{1-6}$$

This result agrees with experiment and is also compatible with the integral form of Faraday's law of induction (I: 19-66) for this case in which the flux is changing only because the area is changing.

1-2 Maxwell's equations and moving coordinate systems

We have just seen that the electric field at a point is not an absolute property of the point but depends on the system of axes to which the observations are referred. The question whether magnetic fields have a similar dependence cannot be answered by the use of simple arguments like those of the last section, since the law of force, $\mathbf{F} = q(\mathbf{E} + \mathbf{v} \times \mathbf{B})$, contains no term that indicates a force acting on a current element which is moving in an electric field. Nevertheless, later we shall find by other means that there is for **B** a transformation equation of a type similar to (1-3).

Since the expressions for the fields change according to the coordinate system one is using, one naturally wonders about the possible effect of a transformation between coordinate systems on the basic equations describing the fields, that is, on Maxwell's equations. Rather than investigate this question for the whole set of Maxwell's equations, it is sufficient for our purposes to consider only one of the consequences of Maxwell's equations—the existence of electromagnetic waves. In free space, according to (I: 30-1), the fields satisfy the wave equation

$$\frac{\partial^2 U}{\partial x^2} + \frac{\partial^2 U}{\partial y^2} + \frac{\partial^2 U}{\partial z^2} = \frac{1}{c^2}\frac{\partial^2 U}{\partial t^2} \tag{1-7}$$

where U can be any of the components of the electric or magnetic fields. As we have seen, (1-7) has solutions in the form of plane waves whose speed of propagation is c. We shall now show that the *form* of this equation is not preserved under the Galilean transformation (1-1); in order to do this we shall want to express (1-7) in terms of the primed variables.

For simplicity, let us confine ourselves to the one-dimensional form of the wave equation:

$$\frac{\partial^2 U}{\partial x^2} = \frac{1}{c^2}\frac{\partial^2 U}{\partial t^2} \tag{1-8}$$

Using (1-1), we see that, if we now regard U as a function of x' and t', then

$$\frac{\partial U}{\partial x} = \frac{\partial U}{\partial x'}\frac{\partial x'}{\partial x} + \frac{\partial U}{\partial t'}\frac{\partial t'}{\partial x} = \frac{\partial U}{\partial x'}$$

so that

$$\frac{\partial^2 U}{\partial x^2} = \frac{\partial^2 U}{\partial x'^2} \tag{1-9}$$

Similarly,

$$\frac{\partial U}{\partial t} = \frac{\partial U}{\partial x'}\frac{\partial x'}{\partial t} + \frac{\partial U}{\partial t'}\frac{\partial t'}{\partial t} = -v\frac{\partial U}{\partial x'} + \frac{\partial U}{\partial t'}$$

$$\frac{\partial^2 U}{\partial t^2} = v^2\frac{\partial^2 U}{\partial x'^2} - 2v\frac{\partial^2 U}{\partial x'\,\partial t'} + \frac{\partial^2 U}{\partial t'^2} \tag{1-10}$$

When (1-9) and (1-10) are substituted into (1-8), we find that the wave equation becomes

$$(c^2 - v^2)\frac{\partial^2 U}{\partial x'^2} = \frac{\partial^2 U}{\partial t'^2} - 2v\frac{\partial^2 U}{\partial x'\,\partial t'} \tag{1-11}$$

which is certainly different from the equation (1-8) for the unprimed axes.

Let us try to find a plane wave solution of (1-11) in the form

$$U = U_0 e^{ik(x'-Vt')} \tag{1-12}$$

where U_0 is a constant amplitude. Substituting (1-12) into (1-11), we find that we must have $V = \pm c - v$ so that the magnitude of the phase velocity of the wave is given by

$$|V| = c \pm v \tag{1-13}$$

and is no longer simply c as it was in the unprimed coordinate system according to (1-8).

Thus we see that, if (1-1) and (1-8) are simultaneously valid, electromagnetic effects would not be the same if they were observed from different reference systems moving with a constant velocity relative to one another, and, in particular, the speed of propagation of a plane wave in a vacuum would not retain its value c. In other words, since (1-7) is a consequence of Maxwell's equations, there would exist *only one* frame of reference in which Maxwell's equations have the form in which we have been writing them and in which electromagnetic waves have the speed c. This preferred reference frame was generally identified with the primary inertial system of mechanics; when this reference system was extended by assuming it to possess electromagnetic properties so that it could also serve as a medium for propagating waves, the augmented system was called the *ether*.

On the other hand, we have seen that the concept of a special reference system is foreign to mechanics because of the existence of the Galilean principle of relativity, that is, the *equivalence* of reference systems moving with constant relative velocity. Since this concept of equivalence has a certain simplicity and attractiveness, we are led to consider the possibility that there may be a *common* principle of relativity (equivalence of co-ordinate systems) for both mechanics and electromagnetism. If this were the case, the Galilean principle of relativity might not actually be the correct one, even though it does hold for mechanics in the Newtonian formulation which we have been using.

The proper choice among these possibilities can only be made on the basis of experimental results. Historically, one method of procedure was to assume that Maxwell's equations were valid in the primary inertial system and were changed according to the scheme illustrated by (1-11) on going to another inertial system—the coordinate transformation being the classical one of (1-1). Thus one could expect noticeable effects due to the motion of the laboratory system with respect to the ether, that is, the primary inertial system. We shall illustrate this procedure by discussing two famous experiments which were performed in order to look for these electromagnetic effects.

1-3   The Trouton-Noble experiment

In this experiment a charged parallel plate condenser was suspended so that it could turn freely about an axis parallel to the plates. It was expected that the effect of the translational motion of the earth with respect to the ether would be a torque tending to align the condenser plates parallel to the direction of motion. In order to derive this expected effect, it will be convenient to simplify the problem by regarding the charges on the plates as concentrated into two point charges whose separation is the same as that of the plates, as illustrated in Fig. 1-3.

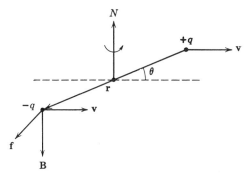

Fig. 1-3

The motion of the charge $+q$ with the velocity $\mathbf{v}$ corresponds to the current element $i\,d\mathbf{s} = q\mathbf{v}$ by (I: 19-32) and produces a magnetic induction $\mathbf{B}$ at the position of the negative charge. According to (I: 19-31), we have

$$\mathbf{B} = \frac{\mu_0 q \mathbf{v} \times \mathbf{r}}{4\pi r^3}$$

so that the force on the negative charge $-q$ is

$$\mathbf{f} = -q\mathbf{v} \times \mathbf{B} = -\frac{\mu_0 q^2 [\mathbf{v} \times (\mathbf{v} \times \mathbf{r})]}{4\pi r^3} \tag{1-14}$$

since the charge $-q$ also has the velocity $\mathbf{v}$. The magnitude of this force is

$$f = \frac{\mu_0 q^2 v^2 \sin \theta}{4\pi r^2} \tag{1-15}$$

Similarly, there will be an equal and opposite force acting on the positive charge as a result of the motion of the negative charge. These two forces together produce a torque parallel to the vertical axis of suspension which tends to rotate the charges until the line connecting them ($\mathbf{r}$) is perpendicular to $\mathbf{v}$. The magnitude of the torque is

$$N = fr \cos \theta = \frac{\mu_0 q^2 v^2 \sin 2\theta}{8\pi r} = \frac{U_e}{2} \left(\frac{v}{c}\right)^2 \sin 2\theta \tag{1-16}$$

where $U_e = q^2/4\pi\epsilon_0 r$ is the electrostatic energy of the system, and where we have used $\mu_0\epsilon_0 = c^{-2}$. [The calculated result which takes into account the charge distribution of the parallel plate condenser is just twice the value given in (1-16).]

Equation (1-16) shows us that this torque is of the order of magnitude of $\frac{1}{2}U_e(v/c)^2$. Taking v as about equal to the speed of the earth in its orbit, which is about 3×10^4 meters/second, one finds that the expected torque would be large enough to be observable. However, the most careful experiments failed to find any indication of this torque. Thus the result of the Trouton-Noble experiment is incompatible with the concept of a stationary ether as a preferred frame for electromagnetism.

1-4   The Michelson-Morley experiment

This experiment was based on the result (1-13) which essentially showed that the phase velocity of light in a given system was the sum of the velocity of the light with respect to the ether plus the velocity of the moving coordinate system with respect to the ether. In other words, (1-13) says that the phase velocity of the wave will depend on the motion of the medium. Since the orbital speed of the earth is so small compared to c, it is not feasible to make a *direct* measurement of the light velocity in various directions with respect to the earth's surface in order to check on (1-13). It is possible, however, to compare these directions and look for this small effect by using the light itself in a particular manner; this idea had been suggested by Maxwell, and the experiment was first performed by Michelson and Morley in 1887.

The experimental arrangement is illustrated in Fig. 1-4. Light from the source L is incident upon the partially silvered glass plate M and divided into two beams which travel normal to each other. Each beam covers the distance l_0 to the mirrors M_1 and M_2 and is reflected back over its original path. Part of the light from each beam passes along the fourth arm toward a detector T. Thus the beams have been recombined, and any

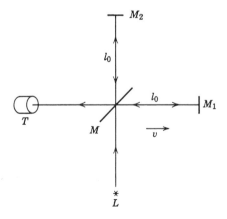

Fig. 1-4

phase difference between them resulting from their journeys back and forth will produce interference effects observable as a variable amplitude in the superimposed beam. In order to calculate the phase difference, we can find the times taken by the light to travel along the arms.

Assuming the arm 1 to be the direction of motion of the apparatus, then, according to (1-13), we find that the speed of the light is $c - v$ on the initial path and $c + v$ on the return path. Thus the time taken to pass to and fro along this arm is

$$t_1 = \frac{l_0}{c - v} + \frac{l_0}{c + v} = \frac{2l_0}{c} \left(1 - \frac{v^2}{c^2}\right)^{-1} \simeq \frac{2l_0}{c} \left(1 + \frac{v^2}{c^2}\right) \qquad (1\text{-}17)$$

In the perpendicular direction along arm 2, the resultant relative light velocity is $\sqrt{c^2 - v^2}$, and the corresponding time for the double journey is

$$t_2 = \frac{2l_0}{\sqrt{c^2 - v^2}} \simeq \frac{2l_0}{c} \left(1 + \frac{v^2}{2c^2}\right) \qquad (1\text{-}18)$$

Thus the two times are not equal, the difference being obtained from (1-17) and (1-18) as

$$\Delta t = t_1 - t_2 \simeq \frac{l_0}{c} \left(\frac{v}{c}\right)^2 \qquad (1\text{-}19)$$

Taking $l_0 = 30$ meters and $v \simeq 3 \times 10^4$ meters/second as before, we find from (1-19) that $\Delta t = 10^{-15}$ second. This corresponds to a phase difference

$$2\pi\nu \, \Delta t = \frac{2\pi c \, \Delta t}{\lambda} = 0.6(2\pi) \simeq 3.8 \text{ radians}$$

for visible light with wavelength of 0.5 micron. This is a sizable relative phase shift and could lead to detectable changes in the interference pattern as the apparatus is rotated to interchange the two arms. However, no such effects were observed, either in the original Michelson-Morley experiment or in subsequent experiments of a similar nature. Thus these optical experiments contradict the result (1-13) which followed from combining the concepts of a preferred frame for electromagnetism with the Galilean relativity principle for mechanics.

There was one famous attempt to preserve the preferred ether frame, however. The *Lorentz-Fitzgerald contraction* hypothesis proposed that, for all bodies, motion relative to the stationary ether frame produced a contraction in the dimensions parallel to the direction of motion by the factor $\sqrt{1 - (v^2/c^2)}$. Accordingly, the length for arm 1 should actually be $l_1 = l_0\sqrt{1 - (v^2/c^2)}$, while $l_2 = l_0$ since arm 2 is at right angles to the direction of motion. The time t_1 given in (1-17) then becomes

$$t_1 = \frac{2l_1}{c}\left(1 - \frac{v^2}{c^2}\right)^{-1} = \frac{2l_0}{c}\left(1 - \frac{v^2}{c^2}\right)^{-\frac{1}{2}} = t_2$$

so that $\Delta t = 0$ and there should be no effect, exactly as was observed. However, although the contraction hypothesis would explain the original Michelson-Morley experiment, it does *not* explain the subsequent Kennedy-Thorndike experiment which used an apparatus with arms of unequal length, l_{10} and l_{20}. Taking account of the contraction, one can show that then

$$\Delta t = \frac{2(l_{10} - l_{20})}{c}\left(1 - \frac{v^2}{c^2}\right)^{-\frac{1}{2}} \tag{1-20}$$

which was not observed either.

These experiments contradict the concept of a preferred reference frame for electromagnetism. Accordingly, we are led to assume that there is a common principle of relativity for mechanics and electromagnetism, but it cannot be that corresponding to the transformation expressed by (1-1). The concepts which we introduce to replace those we have used up to now are those supplied by the postulates of special relativity.

Exercises

1-1. A magnetic induction **B** is parallel to the axis of a cylinder of radius a and dielectric susceptibility χ_e. If the cylinder is rotated about its axis with an angular velocity ω, show that the resultant polarization produced is $P = \epsilon_0\chi_e\omega Br$ and that the charge per unit length which appears on the surface of the cylinder is given by $2\pi a^2\epsilon_0\chi_e\omega B$.

1-2. A brass disk of radius a is mounted on an axle which is parallel to the uniform induction **B**. A current I enters the disk at a contact on the circumference and leaves the disk along the center of the axle. Show that the torque on this system, called a Faraday disk, is $\frac{1}{2}IBa^2$.

1-3. Derive (1-20).

2 *The basic postulates and the Lorentz transformation*

In the preceding chapter we have seen that experiment contradicts the concept of a preferred system for electromagnetism. We have also seen it to be plausible that the concept of relativity (equivalence of moving coordinate systems) holds for electromagnetism as well as for mechanics. In 1905 Einstein extended these ideas even further by proposing the equivalent of the two following postulates.

POSTULATE ONE. *All* systems of coordinates are equally suitable for the description of physical phenomena.

This postulate literally refers to all systems of coordinates, although we shall restrict ourselves to those systems which are moving with constant velocity relative to one another. When we use this restriction, we are discussing the *special theory* of relativity; an unrestricted discussion would correspond to the *general theory* of relativity.

The postulate also says that there is a common principle of relativity for all of physics, although we shall be discussing it only in terms of mechanics and electromagnetism. Another way of stating the first postulate is to say that no theory can contain any reference whatsoever to an *absolute* speed of translational motion of the coordinate system which is being used. We saw in (1-13) that Maxwell's equations combined with the Galilean transformation did indicate the possibility of effects due to an absolute velocity, but such a prediction is not borne out by experiment. This could mean that Maxwell's equations are not exact but are only approximations, or it could mean that the Galilean transformation is not correct. Einstein preferred the second possibility; instead of postulating that Maxwell's equations must be covariant (unchanged in form) to the proper transformation of coordinates, it is *sufficient* (and equivalent) to state:

POSTULATE TWO. The speed of light in vacuum is the same for all these observers and is independent of the motion of the source.

It is this second postulate which leads to the more unfamiliar results of the Einstein theory of relativity. The postulate implies that Newtonian mechanics is not the correct form for the exact representation of mechanical phenomena, since the transformation (1-1) representing the relativity principle natural to mechanics is incompatible with this second postulate, as is illustrated by (1-13). First it will be necessary for us to find the transformation rules for the coordinates which will satisfy the second postulate; then we shall have to find such laws of mechanics as will satisfy the first postulate when we use these transformation laws. The actual applicability of these two postulates to the description of physical phenomena can then be appraised by seeing how well results deduced from them agree with experiment.

2-1   The Lorentz transformation

The transformation of coordinates which is quantitatively compatible with the second postulate is called the Lorentz transformation and is what we now want to find. We still consider two coordinate systems in relative motion. For a given point event the first observer will assign the spatial coordinates and time (x, y, z, t), and those obtained by the second observer will be (x', y', z', t'). Thus our transformation equations must give the position (x', y', z') and the time t' of the event if the first observer assigns the values (x, y, z) and t to it. Although our derivation is somewhat oversimplified, it will lead to the correct result and will include the principal features of a more elaborate and exact treatment.

Suppose that, at the instant the two origins of the coordinate systems coincide, a small pulse of light is produced at the origin. The second postulate requires that both observers see the light propagating outward with the same speed c in all directions. Thus, with respect to his own coordinate system, each observer must see the wavefront as a sphere of radius equal to c times the time. The equations of the wavefront are, therefore,

$$x^2 + y^2 + z^2 - c^2 t^2 = 0 \qquad (2\text{-}1)$$

$$x'^2 + y'^2 + z'^2 - c^2 t'^2 = 0 \qquad (2\text{-}2)$$

and we must satisfy the identity

$$x^2 + y^2 + z^2 - c^2 t^2 = x'^2 + y'^2 + z'^2 - c^2 t'^2 \qquad (2\text{-}3)$$

An equivalent way of saying this is that the quantity on either side of (2-3) must be *invariant* with respect to the transformation leading from one system to the other.

Again, for the sake of simplicity, we take the x and x' axes in the direction of the relative velocity of the systems S and S' as in Fig. 1-1. First we make the fairly evident assumption that the transverse coordinates remain unchanged, that is, $y = y'$, $z = z'$, so that (2-3) becomes

$$x^2 - c^2t^2 = x'^2 - c^2t'^2 \qquad (2\text{-}4)$$

Since there is only *one* relative velocity v, the transformation formulas must further fulfil the condition that the origin O' has the coordinate vt in S and that O has the coordinate $-vt'$ in S', since the two origins coincided at $t = t' = 0$. Thus we must have

$$x = vt \qquad \text{when } x' = 0$$
$$x' = -vt' \qquad \text{when } x = 0 \qquad (2\text{-}5)$$

as is also illustrated in Fig. 2-1. We shall try the simplest relations which will satisfy (2-5), that is, the linear equations

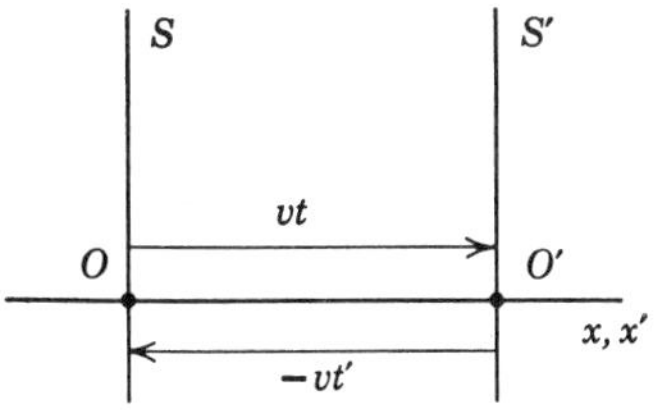

$$x' = \gamma(x - vt), \quad x = \gamma'(x' + vt') \quad (2\text{-}6)$$

Fig. 2-1

where γ and γ' are constants to be determined. We can express t' in terms of the unprimed quantities by eliminating x' from (2-6); the result is that

$$t' = \gamma\left[t - \frac{x}{v}\left(1 - \frac{1}{\gamma\gamma'}\right)\right] \qquad (2\text{-}7)$$

Putting these expressions for x' and t' into (2-4) and rearranging, we obtain

$$x^2\left[1 - \gamma^2 + \frac{\gamma^2 c^2}{v^2}\left(1 - \frac{1}{\gamma\gamma'}\right)^2\right] + 2xt\left[\gamma^2 v - \frac{c^2\gamma^2}{v}\left(1 - \frac{1}{\gamma\gamma'}\right)\right]$$
$$+ t^2[c^2(\gamma^2 - 1) - \gamma^2 v^2] = 0 \quad (2\text{-}8)$$

In order that (2-8) will always be zero for all possible values of x and t, it is necessary that the coefficients of x^2, xt, and t^2 vanish separately.

Equating the coefficient of t^2 to zero, we find that

$$\gamma = \frac{1}{\sqrt{1 - (v^2/c^2)}} \qquad (2\text{-}9)$$

We also find from the coefficient of xt and from (2-9) that $\gamma = \gamma'$. We can now easily verify that these values of γ and γ' also make the coefficient of x^2 in (2-8) vanish.

Combining all these results, we obtain the *Lorentz transformation* formulas

$$x' = \gamma(x - vt), \quad y' = y, \quad z' = z, \quad t' = \gamma\left(t - \frac{v}{c^2}x\right) \qquad (2\text{-}10)$$

$$x = \gamma(x' + vt'), \quad y = y', \quad z = z', \quad t = \gamma\left(t' + \frac{v}{c^2}x'\right) \qquad (2\text{-}11)$$

where γ is given by (2-9), and the equations (2-11) can be obtained from (2-10) by solving for the unprimed quantities in terms of the primed ones.

If we let $c \to \infty$ in (2-10), we obtain in the limit the Galilean transformation (1-1) which we now see as a first approximation to the Lorentz transformation for finite values of v. The results (2-10) and (2-11) also have the desired symmetry since, by interchanging primed and unprimed symbols and changing the sign of v, we go from one set to the other.

Actually, any linear transformation of coordinates and time which satisfies (2-3) is called a Lorentz transformation. The one given in (2-10) is the particular one which applies only to the special case in which the relative motion of the systems is along their common x direction. We shall return to the consideration of more general Lorentz transformations later, but for the present we shall restrict ourselves to the one given in (2-10).

Exercise

2-1. Show by direct substitution of (2-10) into (1-8) that the Lorentz transformation preserves the form of the wave equation, that is, if $\partial^2 U/\partial x^2 = \partial^2 U/c^2\,\partial t^2$, then $\partial^2 U/\partial x'^2 = \partial^2 U/c^2\,\partial t'^2$.

3 Some kinematic consequences of the Lorentz transformation

Now that we have obtained the Lorentz transformation equations, we want to see what sort of physical results are implied by them. We confine ourselves in this chapter to effects which are basically kinematical, that is, which involve only the geometrical and temporal descriptions of events given by our two observers.

We shall let

$$\beta = \frac{v}{c} \tag{3-1}$$

so that (2-10) becomes

$$x' = \gamma(x - \beta ct), \quad y' = y, \quad z' = z, \quad t' = \gamma\left(t - \frac{\beta x}{c}\right) \tag{3-2}$$

where

$$\gamma = \frac{1}{\sqrt{1 - \beta^2}} \tag{3-3}$$

3-1 Relativity of simultaneity

Suppose that two events occur at the points x_1 and x_2 in the S system and are simultaneous so that $t_1 = t_2$. The times at which these events are observed in S' as obtained from (3-2) are

$$t_1' = \gamma\left(t_1 - \frac{\beta x_1}{c}\right), \quad t_2' = \gamma\left(t_2 - \frac{\beta x_2}{c}\right) \tag{3-4}$$

Therefore the time interval between these events is

$$\Delta t' = t_2' - t_1' = -\frac{\gamma\beta}{c}(x_2 - x_1) \neq 0 \tag{3-5}$$

This result shows that two events which occur at *different points* x_1 and x_2, and which are simultaneous for an observer at rest in S, will no longer appear to be simultaneous to an observer at rest in S', and who is therefore moving relative to S. In other words, simultaneity is not an absolute property of a pair of events but is also a function of the state of motion of the observer.

3-2 The Einstein time dilation

Suppose that we have a clock located at the point x_1 and that it is emitting signals of some sort at regular intervals Δt, where

$$\Delta t = t_2 - t_1 = t_3 - t_2, \quad \text{etc.} \tag{3-6}$$

The corresponding times in the primed system are given by (3-4), except that now $x_2 = x_1$ since the clock is fixed in the unprimed system. Therefore, when seen from the system which is moving relative to the clock, we find from (3-4) that these signals will be separated by the time intervals $\Delta t'$ given by

$$\Delta t' = \gamma \, \Delta t > \Delta t \tag{3-7}$$

since $\gamma > 1$.

Thus the time interval appears to be longer to the moving observer than it does in the system in which the clock is at rest.

3-3   The Lorentz contraction

In principle, we measure a length by placing a measuring rod along the distance to be measured and then finding the difference between the scale marks which *simultaneously coincide* with the ends of the length of interest. This detailed specification, which seems trivial when the measuring rod and the length are relatively at rest, is essential when they are moving with respect to each other.

We let $L = x_2 - x_1$ be the distance between two points as found with a scale which is at rest with respect to them. The length as found by the moving observer who assigns coordinates x_2' and x_1' to the ends is found from (3-2) to be

$$L' = x_2' - x_1' = \gamma[x_2 - x_1 - \beta c(t_2 - t_1)] \tag{3-8}$$

However, the points x_2' and x_1' must have been determined simultaneously in the S' frame, so that $t_2' = t_1'$; this means that the time interval $(t_2 - t_1)$ appearing in (3-8) must be given by

$$t_2 - t_1 = \frac{\beta}{c}(x_2 - x_1) = \left(\frac{\beta}{c}\right)L \tag{3-9}$$

according to (3-4). When (3-9) is substituted into (3-8) and (3-3) is used, we find that

$$L' = \gamma(1 - \beta^2)L = \frac{L}{\gamma} = L\sqrt{1 - \beta^2} < L \tag{3-10}$$

Thus, as found by the moving observer, the length in the direction of motion will be contracted by the factor $1/\gamma$.

Although we derived these quantitative results (3-5), (3-7), and (3-10) by means of the Lorentz transformation, it should be emphasized that it can be shown that these effects are qualitative consequences of the two postulates only, and thus the existence of these effects does *not* depend on the specific formulas given in (3-2) and used above.

3-4 Einstein's velocity addition formulas

In Newtonian mechanics, which depends on the Galilean transformation, relative velocities are found by simple addition of components as is shown explicitly in (I: 3-14). In a mechanics which depends on the Lorentz transformation, the combining of velocities is somewhat more complicated.

Suppose that a point has the velocity $\mathbf{u}'$ as observed in S', where

$$\mathbf{u}' = u_x'\hat{\mathbf{i}}' + u_y'\hat{\mathbf{j}}' + u_z'\hat{\mathbf{k}}' \tag{3-11}$$

and

$$u_x' = \frac{dx'}{dt'}, \quad u_y' = \frac{dy'}{dt'}, \quad u_z' = \frac{dz'}{dt'} \tag{3-12}$$

We now want to find the components u_x, u_y, u_z of the velocity of this same point when its motion is observed with respect to the system S.

Differentiating (2-11) and (3-2), we find that

$$u_x = \frac{dx}{dt} = \gamma\left(\frac{dx'}{dt'}\frac{dt'}{dt} + \beta c \frac{dt'}{dt}\right)$$

$$\frac{dt'}{dt} = \gamma\left(1 - \frac{\beta}{c}u_x\right) \tag{3-13}$$

so that, when these are combined and dt'/dt is eliminated, we obtain

$$u_x = \gamma^2(u_x' + v)\left(1 - \frac{\beta}{c}u_x\right)$$

which can be solved for u_x, yielding

$$u_x = \frac{u_x' + v}{1 + (vu_x'/c^2)} \tag{3-14}$$

We can now express the right side of (3-13) completely in terms of primed quantities by substituting (3-14); the result is that

$$\frac{dt'}{dt} = \frac{1}{\gamma[1 + (vu_x'/c^2)]} \tag{3-15}$$

Similarly we find from (2-11) and (3-15) that

$$u_y = \frac{dy}{dt} = \frac{dy'}{dt'}\frac{dt'}{dt} = \frac{u_y'}{\gamma[1 + (vu_x'/c^2)]} \tag{3-16}$$

$$u_z = \frac{u_z'}{\gamma[1 + (vu_x'/c^2)]} \tag{3-17}$$

which are the remaining relations needed to convert velocity components observed in one system to those observed in another.

These equations have the interesting property that the sum of two velocities can never exceed c. Let us consider an extreme case as an illustration: Suppose that the system S' has relative speed $v = c$, while the velocity of the point with respect to S' is also $u_x' = c$. According to the Galilean transformation, the resultant speed observed in S would be $u_x = u_x' + v = c + c = 2c$. The Einstein formula (3-14) gives, instead,

$$u_x = \frac{c + c}{1 + (c^2/c^2)} = c$$

as was asserted.

We also note that, if $\beta = v/c \ll 1$, then (3-14), (3-16), and (3-17) become approximately

$$u_x \simeq u_x' + v, \quad u_y' \simeq u_y, \quad u_z' \simeq u_z \tag{3-18}$$

so that the simple addition of components which follows from the Galilean transformation is an approximation which holds quite well for low relative velocities of the coordinate systems.

Application. *Index of refraction of moving media*

The classical experiment on the propagation of light in moving media was performed by Fizeau, who measured the small difference in the indices of refraction of stationary and flowing water by an interference method. It is clear that the flow velocity of the water cannot simply be added to the phase velocity of the light, as this would require the effect to be independent of the density of the medium and thus result in a sharp discontinuity between the properties of an extremely tenuous flowing medium and those of a vacuum for which the effect cannot occur. Such a discontinuity is never observed, and, in fact, the actual result of the experiment can be expressed in terms of the wave velocity u in the flowing medium as

$$u = u_0 + v\left(1 - \frac{1}{n^2}\right) \tag{3-19}$$

where v is the flow velocity of the medium of index of refraction n, and $u_0 = c/n$ is the wave velocity in the stationary medium. The factor multiplying v is called the *Fresnel coefficient*; it approaches zero as $n \to 1$, as we would expect. Although (3-19) can be derived from a theory based on the ether concept, it is most easily obtained from the relativistic formulas for combining velocities.

If we assume that $v/c \ll 1$ and neglect second order terms in v/c, we find from (3-14) that the phase velocity u found by an observer at rest in the stationary system is given by

$$u = \frac{u_0 + v}{1 + (vu_0/c^2)} \simeq (u_0 + v)\left(1 - \frac{vu_0}{c^2}\right)$$

$$= u_0 + v - \frac{vu_0^2}{c^2} - \left(\frac{v}{c}\right)^2 u_0 \simeq u_0 + v\left(1 - \frac{u_0^2}{c^2}\right)$$

$$= u_0 + v\left(1 - \frac{1}{n^2}\right)$$

which is exactly the experimental result in (3-19).

3-5 The Doppler effect and aberration

In this section we want to investigate how the frequencies and directions of propagation of a wave will appear to our two observers. Suppose that a light source Q', which is at rest in S', emits a spherical wave. According to (I: 32-5), we can represent this wave by

$$U' = \frac{U_0'}{r'} e^{i(k'r' - \omega't')} \tag{3-20}$$

where U_0' is an amplitude factor and the frequency ν' is found from

$$k' = \frac{\omega'}{c} = \frac{2\pi\nu'}{c} \tag{3-21}$$

Suppose that there is an observer P at rest in S and located in the xy plane at the point (x, y), while the coordinates are x' and y' with respect to S'. As illustrated in Fig. 3-1, the direction of propagation from Q' to P

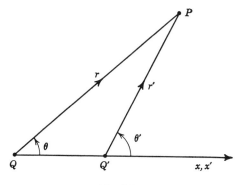

Fig. 3-1

makes the angle θ' with the x' axis so that

$$r' = x' \cos \theta' + y' \sin \theta' \qquad (3\text{-}22)$$

The observer in S will interpret the wave as a spherical wave originating from a point source Q in his system so that he must write the equation for the wave in the form

$$U = \frac{U_0}{r} e^{i(kr - \omega t)} \qquad (3\text{-}23)$$

where

$$k = \frac{\omega}{c} = \frac{2\pi\nu}{c} \qquad (3\text{-}24)$$

$$r = x \cos \theta + y \sin \theta \qquad (3\text{-}25)$$

Now the *numerical* value of the phase of the wave must be the same and independent of whatever system is used to express it; consequently, the values of the exponents in (3-20) and (3-23) must always be equal. In addition, the coordinates and the times of the two systems must be connected by the Lorentz transformation (3-2). Equating these exponents, substituting from (3-21), (3-22), (3-24), (3-25), and (3-2), we find that we must have

$$\nu\left(\frac{x \cos \theta + y \sin \theta}{c} - t\right) = \nu'\left[\frac{\gamma(x - \beta ct)\cos \theta' + y \sin \theta'}{c} - \gamma\left(t - \frac{\beta x}{c}\right)\right]$$
$$(3\text{-}26)$$

This equality must hold for all possible values of x, y, and t; this is possible only if the coefficients of these quantities are separately equal.

Equating the coefficients of t on both sides of (3-26), we find that

$$\nu = \nu'\gamma(1 + \beta \cos \theta') \qquad (3\text{-}27)$$

which is the exact relativistic Doppler effect formula and relates the two frequencies. We note that, if $\beta \ll 1$, then $\gamma \simeq 1$, and (3-27) becomes the classical formula

$$\nu \simeq \nu'(1 + \beta \cos \theta') \qquad (3\text{-}28)$$

Equating the coefficients of x on both sides of (3-26), we find that

$$\nu \cos \theta = \nu'\gamma(\cos \theta' + \beta) \qquad (3\text{-}29)$$

and, if we use (3-27) to eliminate the frequencies, we find that

$$\cos \theta = \frac{\cos \theta' + \beta}{1 + \beta \cos \theta'} \qquad (3\text{-}30)$$

which relates the two directions of propagation and is the aberration formula.

The relativistic Doppler formula (3-27)′ differs from the acoustical formula (3-28) in that it predicts a *transverse* effect. Suppose that one observes the frequency at right angles to the motion, that is, $\theta = \pi/2$. Then $\cos \theta = 0$ and $\cos \theta' = -\beta$, according to (3-30). When this is substituted into (3-27) and (3-3) is used, we find that

$$\nu = \nu'\sqrt{1 - \beta^2} \tag{3-31}$$

The effect predicted by (3-31) has been observed by studying the radiation from an electric discharge in hydrogen; it provides some experimental evidence for the basic correctness of the relativity postulates.

3-6   Another point of view

The Lorentz transformation holds for coordinate differentials, of course, so that from (3-2) we obtain

$$dx' = \gamma(dx - \beta c\, dt), \quad dy' = dy$$
$$dz' = dz, \quad dt' = \gamma\left(dt - \frac{\beta}{c}\, dx\right) \tag{3-32}$$

We also know from (2-3) that the Lorentz transformation corresponds to the equality

$$(dx)^2 + (dy)^2 + (dz)^2 - c^2(dt)^2 = (dx')^2 + (dy')^2 + (dz')^2 - c^2(dt')^2 \tag{3-33}$$

Therefore, dividing out $(dt)^2$ and $(dt')^2$ and taking the square root, we find that the quantity $d\tau$ given by

$$d\tau = dt\left\{1 - \frac{1}{c^2}\left[\left(\frac{dx}{dt}\right)^2 + \left(\frac{dy}{dt}\right)^2 + \left(\frac{dz}{dt}\right)^2\right]\right\}^{\frac{1}{2}}$$
$$= dt\sqrt{1 - \frac{u^2}{c^2}} = dt'\sqrt{1 - \frac{u'^2}{c^2}} \tag{3-34}$$

has the same value for all frames of reference connected by the Lorentz transformation; this invariant $d\tau$ is called the *proper time interval*. We see from (3-34) that $d\tau = dt_0 = $ the time interval measured in the system in which the particle is at rest ($u = 0$).

Suppose we divide both sides of the infinitesimal Lorentz transformation (3-32) by $d\tau$; the result is

$$\frac{dx'}{d\tau} = \gamma\left(\frac{dx}{d\tau} - \beta c\,\frac{dt}{d\tau}\right), \quad \frac{dy'}{d\tau} = \frac{dy}{d\tau}$$

$$\frac{dz'}{d\tau} = \frac{dz}{d\tau}, \quad \frac{dt'}{d\tau} = \gamma\left(\frac{dt}{d\tau} - \frac{\beta}{c}\,\frac{dx}{d\tau}\right) \tag{3-35}$$

Using (3-34) and comparing (3-35) with (3-2), we see that the four quantities

$$\frac{dx}{d\tau} = \frac{dx}{dt\sqrt{1 - u^2/c^2}} = \frac{u_x}{\sqrt{1 - u^2/c^2}}$$

$$\frac{dy}{d\tau} = \frac{u_y}{\sqrt{1 - u^2/c^2}}$$

$$\frac{dz}{d\tau} = \frac{u_z}{\sqrt{1 - u^2/c^2}} \tag{3-36}$$

$$\frac{dt}{d\tau} = \frac{1}{\sqrt{1 - u^2/c^2}}$$

transform in exactly the same way as do x, y, z, t. Therefore, since we know that

$$x = \gamma(x' + \beta ct'), \quad t = \gamma(t' + \beta x'/c)$$

we can immediately write the transformation equations for the analogous quantities $dx/d\tau$ and $dt/d\tau$ as

$$\frac{u_x}{\sqrt{1 - u^2/c^2}} = \gamma\left[\frac{u_x'}{\sqrt{1 - u'^2/c^2}} + v\,\frac{1}{\sqrt{1 - u'^2/c^2}}\right] \tag{3-37}$$

$$\frac{1}{\sqrt{1 - u^2/c^2}} = \gamma\left[\frac{1}{\sqrt{1 - u'^2/c^2}} + \frac{v}{c^2}\,\frac{u_x'}{\sqrt{1 - u'^2/c^2}}\right] \tag{3-38}$$

and, on dividing (3-37) by (3-38), we obtain

$$u_x = \frac{u_x' + v}{1 + (vu_x'/c^2)}$$

which is exactly the velocity transformation formula (3-14). The remaining two formulas (3-16) and (3-17) can be derived in exactly the same way.

The point of view implied by our use of (3-37) and (3-38) is quite different from our previous method of derivation, which depended on differentiating the transformation equations and then eliminating terms.

We were able to obtain (3-14) in this second way because we knew how the quantities (3-36) were affected by a Lorentz transformation, that is, because *we knew their transformation properties.*

Thus this example has shown us that we should be able to write the transformation equations for certain quantities quite easily, provided that we know something about their general properties. Accordingly, it appears that this whole question is worth looking into more deeply and is the motivation for what we are going to do next.

Exercises

3-1. The average lifetime of a μ-meson before radioactive decay as measured in its "rest" system is 2.22×10^{-6} second. What will be its average lifetime for an observer with respect to whom the meson has a speed of $0.99c$? How far will the meson travel in this time?

3-2. A rigid rod of length L makes an angle θ with the x axis of the system in which it is at rest. Show that, for an observer moving with respect to the rod, the apparent length L' and angle θ' are given by

$$L' = L[(\cos \theta/\gamma)^2 + \sin^2 \theta]^{1/2}, \quad \tan \theta' = \gamma \tan \theta$$

3-3. Show that two successive Lorentz transformations corresponding to speeds v_1 and v_2 in the same direction are equivalent to a single Lorentz transformation with a speed $v = (v_1 + v_2)/[1 + (v_1 v_2/c^2)]$. What relation does this result have to (3-14)?

3-4. Derive (3-16) and (3-17) by the methods used to obtain (3-37) and (3-38).

3-5. Find the transformation laws for the components of the acceleration, $a_x = du_x/dt$, etc. Show from these results that, if $\mathbf{a_0}'$ is the acceleration in the system in which the particle is momentarily at rest,

$$a_x = a_{x0}/\gamma^3, \quad a_y = a_{y0}/\gamma^2, \quad a_z = a_{z0}/\gamma^2$$

4 General Lorentz transformations

Let us consider the two rectangular coordinate systems shown in Fig. 4-1. They have a common origin but otherwise differ by a rotation; that is, if we rotate one set of axes as a rigid body, it can be brought into coincidence with the other. The exact rotation could be specified, for example, by giving the direction cosines of the primed axes with respect to the unprimed axes.

Let us consider a point which has the coordinates x, y, z in one set of axes, while in the other set it has the coordinates x', y', z'. Both of these different sets of numbers locate the same point P.

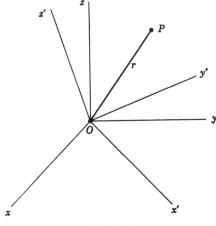

Fig. 4-1

It is evident that the distance r of P from the origin is an *invariant*; that is, it has the same numerical value regardless of which coordinate system we are using. Thus we have

$$r^2 = x^2 + y^2 + z^2 = x'^2 + y'^2 + z'^2 \tag{4-1}$$

If we introduce the notation

$$x_1 = x, \quad x_2 = y, \quad x_3 = z \tag{4-2}$$

then (4-1) can be written

$$r^2 = \sum_{i=1}^{3} x_i{}^2 = \sum_{i=1}^{3} x_i'^2 \tag{4-3}$$

The equations which relate the two sets of coordinates can be expected to be linear, so that we can write

$$x_i' = \sum_{j=1}^{3} a_{ij} x_j \qquad (i = 1, 2, 3) \tag{4-4}$$

That is, the three equations

$$
\begin{aligned}
x_1' &= a_{11}x_1 + a_{12}x_2 + a_{13}x_3 \\
x_2' &= a_{21}x_1 + a_{22}x_2 + a_{23}x_3 \\
x_3' &= a_{31}x_1 + a_{32}x_2 + a_{33}x_3
\end{aligned}
\tag{4-5}
$$

The set of nine numbers a_{ij} characterizes the rotation connecting the primed and unprimed axis systems, and, in fact, the a_{ij} can be related to the various direction cosines. It is also clear that these a_{ij} cannot all be independent because the transformation equations (4-4) have not yet been required to satisfy the condition of keeping r^2 invariant as given in (4-3); that is, they must yet satisfy a fundamental requirement that (4-4) describe a *rotation*. We could go on to elaborate this treatment of the three-dimensional case which we have begun, but it is just as easily done for a more general situation to which we now turn.

4-1   Lorentz transformations as rotations

We recall from (2-3) that the basic condition for the Lorentz transformation was the invariance of the quantity s^2 given by

$$s^2 = x^2 + y^2 + z^2 - c^2t^2 = x'^2 + y'^2 + z'^2 - c^2t'^2 \qquad (4\text{-}6)$$

If we introduce the notation

$$x_1 = x, \quad x_2 = y, \quad x_3 = z, \quad x_4 = ict \qquad (4\text{-}7)$$

then (4-6) can be written

$$s^2 = \sum_{\mu=1}^{4} x_\mu{}^2 = \sum_{\mu=1}^{4} x_\mu{}'^2 \qquad (4\text{-}8)$$

On comparing (4-8) and (4-3), we see that the *most general* Lorentz transformation can be interpreted as a *rigid rotation of axes in a four-dimensional space* whose axes are $x_1, x_2, x_3, x_4 = ict$.

We can write the transformation equations relating the two sets in the general linear form

$$x_\mu{}' = \sum_{\nu=1}^{4} a_{\mu\nu} x_\nu \qquad (\mu = 1, 2, 3, 4) \qquad (4\text{-}9)$$

The transformation must be linear for, if it were not, it would give a preferred status to whatever origin we happened to choose, and this would violate the first postulate by providing an objective way of distinguishing one coordinate system from the other.

In order that (4-9) represent a Lorentz transformation (four-dimensional rotation), (4-8) must be satisfied; we would like to learn what requirements are thus imposed on the sixteen coefficients $a_{\mu\nu}$. Substituting (4-9) into (4-8), we obtain

$$\sum_\lambda x_\lambda{}'^2 = \sum_\lambda \left(\sum_\mu a_{\lambda\mu} x_\mu \right)\left(\sum_\nu a_{\lambda\nu} x_\nu \right) = \sum_{\mu\nu} \left(\sum_\lambda a_{\lambda\mu} a_{\lambda\nu} \right) x_\mu x_\nu \qquad (4\text{-}10)$$

Since (4-10) must also equal $\sum_\mu x_\mu{}^2$, we see that we must have

$$\sum_\lambda a_{\lambda\mu} a_{\lambda\nu} = 0 \qquad \text{if } \mu \neq \nu$$

$$\sum_\lambda a_{\lambda\mu}{}^2 = 1 \qquad \text{if } \mu = \nu$$

or, expressed more simply,

$$\sum_{\lambda} a_{\lambda\mu} a_{\lambda\nu} = \delta_{\mu\nu} \tag{4-11}$$

which is our condition for the rigid rotation.

We can also write

$$x_\nu = \sum_{\lambda} b_{\nu\lambda} x_{\lambda}' \tag{4-12}$$

where the $b_{\nu\lambda}$ are a set of coefficients which are evidently related to the $a_{\mu\nu}$ of (4-9). To determine this relation, we substitute (4-12) into (4-9) and find that

$$x_{\mu}' = \sum_{\nu} a_{\mu\nu} \Big(\sum_{\lambda} b_{\nu\lambda} x_{\lambda}' \Big) = \sum_{\lambda} x_{\lambda}' \Big(\sum_{\nu} a_{\mu\nu} b_{\nu\lambda} \Big) = \sum_{\lambda} x_{\lambda}' \, \delta_{\mu\lambda} \tag{4-13}$$

after we have expressed x_{μ}' in terms of a sum in the last step. Comparing the last two terms in (4-13), we see that

$$\sum_{\nu} a_{\mu\nu} b_{\nu\lambda} = \delta_{\mu\lambda} \tag{4-14}$$

The last result can be solved for the b's by multiplying both sides of (4-14) by $a_{\mu\rho}$, summing over μ, and using (4-11):

$$\sum_{\mu\nu} a_{\mu\rho} a_{\mu\nu} b_{\nu\lambda} = \sum_{\mu} a_{\mu\rho} \, \delta_{\mu\lambda} = a_{\lambda\rho} = \sum_{\nu} b_{\nu\lambda} \sum_{\mu} a_{\mu\rho} a_{\mu\nu} = \sum_{\nu} b_{\nu\lambda} \, \delta_{\rho\nu} = b_{\rho\lambda} \tag{4-15}$$

Thus $b_{\rho\lambda} = a_{\lambda\rho}$, and we can therefore say that

$$\text{if } x_{\mu}' = \sum_{\nu} a_{\mu\nu} x_{\nu}, \quad \text{then } x_{\mu} = \sum_{\nu} a_{\nu\mu} x_{\nu}' \tag{4-16}$$

and also that

$$\sum_{\lambda} a_{\mu\lambda} a_{\nu\lambda} = \delta_{\mu\nu} \tag{4-17}$$

which can be found by substituting (4-15) into (4-14) and interchanging the indices λ and ν.

When the notation of (4-7) is used, the transformation equations for the particular Lorentz transformation (3-2) which we have been using up to now become, respectively,

$$\begin{aligned} x_1' &= \gamma x_1 + i\beta\gamma x_4, \quad x_2' = x_2 \\ x_3' &= x_3, \quad x_4' = -i\beta\gamma x_1 + \gamma x_4 \end{aligned} \tag{4-18}$$

By comparing (4-18) and (4-9) we see that the coefficients $a_{\mu\nu}$ for this special transformation can be written as the matrix

$$a_{\mu\nu} = \begin{pmatrix} a_{11} & a_{12} & a_{13} & a_{14} \\ a_{21} & a_{22} & a_{23} & a_{24} \\ a_{31} & a_{32} & a_{33} & a_{34} \\ a_{41} & a_{42} & a_{43} & a_{44} \end{pmatrix} = \begin{pmatrix} \gamma & 0 & 0 & i\beta\gamma \\ 0 & 1 & 0 & 0 \\ 0 & 0 & 1 & 0 \\ -i\beta\gamma & 0 & 0 & \gamma \end{pmatrix} \tag{4-19}$$

It will be left as exercises to verify that (4-19) satisfies (4-11) and (4-17).

It should be mentioned that a rigid rotation of the axes in three-dimensional space will also keep the expression $x^2 + y^2 + z^2 - c^2t^2$ invariant because of (4-1) and its independence of the time. Thus such a physical rotation of coordinate axes should be included in the group of general Lorentz transformations described by (4-9).

When the condition (4-8) is written in differential form, it becomes

$$(ds)^2 = \sum_\mu (dx_\mu)^2 = \sum_\mu (dx_\mu')^2 \qquad (4\text{-}20)$$

In this case the quantity $(ds)^2$ is called an *interval*. The interval is always real, but in contrast to the distance between points in three-dimensional space it need not be positive and, in fact, we can have

$$(ds)^2 \gtreqless 0 \qquad (4\text{-}21)$$

If $(ds)^2 > 0$, the interval is called *spacelike*; if $(ds)^2 < 0$, it is called *timelike*.

4-2 4-vectors and tensors

DEFINITION. An *invariant* is a quantity whose value does not change in a Lorentz transformation. Examples are s^2 of (4-6) and the proper time $d\tau$ of (3-34).

DEFINITION. A *4-vector* A_μ is a set of four quantities (A_1, A_2, A_3, A_4) whose *transformation properties* are the same as those of the coordinates. That is, if the Lorentz transformation is described by (4-9), the components A_μ and A_μ' are related by

$$A_\mu' = \sum_\nu a_{\mu\nu} A_\nu \qquad (\mu = 1, 2, 3, 4) \qquad (4\text{-}22)$$

and the coefficients $a_{\mu\nu}$ are exactly the same as those in (4-9).

It follows from this definition that the first three components (A_1, A_2, A_3) must be the components of an ordinary three-dimensional vector $\mathbf{A}$. The sum of two 4-vectors must be a 4-vector so that

$$C_\mu = (A + B)_\mu = A_\mu + B_\mu \qquad (4\text{-}23)$$

We can define a scalar product of two 4-vectors by generalizing the result obtained for the dot product $\mathbf{A} \cdot \mathbf{B}$ as given by (I: 1-11); thus

$$\text{Scalar product} = \sum_\mu A_\mu B_\mu \qquad (4\text{-}24)$$

THEOREM. The scalar product is an invariant. In order to prove this, we use (4-22) and (4-11):

$$\sum_{\mu} A_{\mu}{}' B_{\mu}{}' = \sum_{\mu} \Big(\sum_{\nu} a_{\mu\nu} A_{\nu} \Big) \Big(\sum_{\lambda} a_{\mu\lambda} B_{\lambda} \Big) = \sum_{\nu\lambda} A_{\nu} B_{\lambda} \sum_{\mu} a_{\mu\nu} a_{\mu\lambda}$$
$$= \sum_{\nu\lambda} A_{\nu} B_{\lambda} \, \delta_{\nu\lambda} = \sum_{\nu} A_{\nu} B_{\nu} \qquad \text{q.e.d.} \tag{4-25}$$

The square of the "length" of a 4-vector is defined as the scalar product of the 4-vector with itself; thus

$$(\text{"length"})^2 = \sum_{\mu} A_{\mu}{}^2 \tag{4-26}$$

Besides the coordinates, we have already met an example of a 4-vector; it is the *4-velocity* U_{μ} whose components are obtained from (3-36) and (4-7) as

$$U_1 = \frac{dx_1}{d\tau} = \frac{u_x}{\sqrt{1 - u^2/c^2}} \tag{4-27a}$$

$$U_2 = \frac{dx_2}{d\tau} = \frac{u_y}{\sqrt{1 - u^2/c^2}} \tag{4-27b}$$

$$U_3 = \frac{dx_3}{d\tau} = \frac{u_z}{\sqrt{1 - u^2/c^2}} \tag{4-27c}$$

$$U_4 = \frac{dx_4}{d\tau} = \frac{ic}{\sqrt{1 - u^2/c^2}} \tag{4-27d}$$

where

$$u^2 = u_x{}^2 + u_y{}^2 + u_z{}^2 \tag{4-28}$$

We know that these four quantities constitute a 4-vector because we showed in (3-37) and (3-38) that their transformation properties are the same as those of the coordinates.

We find from (4-26), (4-27), and (4-28) that the length of the 4-velocity is given by

$$(\text{length})^2 = \sum_{\mu} U_{\mu}{}^2 = \frac{u_x{}^2 + u_y{}^2 + u_z{}^2 - c^2}{1 - (u^2/c^2)} = -c^2 \tag{4-29}$$

and is negative.

DEFINITION. A *second rank tensor* $T_{\mu\nu}$ is a set of sixteen quantities such that each index transforms in the same way as do the coordinate indices; thus, if (4-9) holds, then

$$T_{\mu\nu}{}' = \sum_{\lambda} \sum_{\rho} a_{\mu\lambda} a_{\nu\rho} T_{\lambda\rho} \tag{4-30}$$

Two indices are needed to specify each component; hence the term "second rank." Similarly, a 4-vector with its single index is a tensor of the first rank, while an invariant scalar is a tensor of zero rank. One can define tensors of higher rank by a straightforward generalization of (4-30), but we shall not need them.

A tensor is *symmetric* if $T_{\mu\nu} = T_{\nu\mu}$; hence a symmetric tensor has only ten independent components. A tensor is *antisymmetric* if $T_{\nu\mu} = -T_{\mu\nu}$ and therefore has only six independent components since the diagonal elements must be zero; that is, $T_{\mu\mu} = 0$. A tensor does *not* have to be symmetric or antisymmetric, but we now want to show that, if it is one or the other, this symmetry property is not changed by an arbitrary Lorentz transformation; that is, if $T_{\mu\nu}$ is symmetric (or antisymmetric), $T_{\mu\nu}{}'$ is also symmetric (or antisymmetric). In order to prove this let us write

$$T_{\mu\nu} = \pm T_{\nu\mu} \tag{4-31}$$

and choose the upper sign for the symmetric case and the lower for the antisymmetric case. We find from (4-30) and (4-31) that

$$T_{\mu\nu}{}' = \sum_{\lambda\rho} a_{\mu\lambda} a_{\nu\rho} T_{\lambda\rho} = \pm \sum_{\lambda\rho} a_{\mu\lambda} a_{\nu\rho} T_{\rho\lambda} \tag{4-32}$$

If we now interchange μ and ν in (4-30), and then interchange ρ and λ, we obtain

$$T_{\nu\mu}{}' = \sum_{\lambda\rho} a_{\nu\lambda} a_{\mu\rho} T_{\lambda\rho} = \sum_{\lambda\rho} a_{\nu\rho} a_{\mu\lambda} T_{\rho\lambda} \tag{4-33}$$

On comparing (4-32) and (4-33) we see that $T_{\mu\nu}{}' = \pm T_{\nu\mu}{}'$ with the choice of signs the same as that used in the original system as given by (4-31), and thus we have shown that the symmetry property is unchanged.

An important example is

$$F_{\mu\nu} = A_\mu B_\nu - A_\nu B_\mu \tag{4-34}$$

Although we have written this set of sixteen numbers as $F_{\mu\nu}$, we have *not* yet shown that $F_{\mu\nu}$ is really a tensor, although, if it is, it will be antisymmetric. We now want to show that $F_{\mu\nu}$ defined in (4-34) actually has the transformation properties of a second rank tensor. Substituting from (4-22) into (4-34), we find that

$$
\begin{aligned}
F_{\mu\nu}{}' = A_\mu' B_\nu' - A_\nu' B_\mu' &= \sum_{\lambda\rho} a_{\mu\lambda} a_{\nu\rho} A_\lambda B_\rho - \sum_{\lambda\rho} a_{\nu\rho} a_{\mu\lambda} A_\rho B_\lambda \\
&= \sum_{\lambda\rho} a_{\mu\lambda} a_{\nu\rho} (A_\lambda B_\rho - A_\rho B_\lambda) = \sum_{\lambda\rho} a_{\mu\lambda} a_{\nu\rho} F_{\lambda\rho}
\end{aligned}
\tag{4-35}
$$

which, on comparison with (4-30), is seen to complete the proof. We also note that, if $\mu, \nu = 1, 2, 3$, the components of $F_{\mu\nu}$ are precisely those of the ordinary three-dimensional cross product **A × B**, which is accordingly seen as actually being a tensor rather than a vector.

By using the same methods, it can be shown that the following quantities are 4-vectors:

$$B_\mu = \sum_\nu A_\nu T_{\nu\mu} \quad \text{and} \quad C_\mu = \sum_\nu T_{\mu\nu} A_\nu \qquad (4\text{-}36)$$

4-3 Differential operators

According to the rule for differentiating a function of given variables (unprimed) with respect to different variables (primed), we have

$$\frac{\partial}{\partial x_\mu{}'} = \sum_\nu \frac{\partial x_\nu}{\partial x_\mu{}'} \frac{\partial}{\partial x_\nu} \qquad (4\text{-}37)$$

From (4-16), we see that $\partial x_\nu / \partial x_\mu{}' = a_{\mu\nu}$ so that (4-37) becomes

$$\frac{\partial}{\partial x_\mu{}'} = \sum_\nu a_{\mu\nu} \frac{\partial}{\partial x_\nu} \qquad (4\text{-}38)$$

On comparing (4-38) and (4-22), we see that the four operators $\partial/\partial x_\mu$ ($\mu = 1, 2, 3, 4$) transform exactly like a 4-vector. In fact, we can define a four-dimensional del operator $\square$ with these components:

$$\square = \left[\frac{\partial}{\partial x_1}, \frac{\partial}{\partial x_2}, \frac{\partial}{\partial x_3}, \frac{\partial}{\partial x_4} \right] \qquad (4\text{-}39)$$

and use it in a fashion analogous to the three-dimensional operator ∇.

If φ is an invariant, we can define a gradient $\square\varphi$ as the 4-vector whose components are $\partial\varphi/\partial x_\mu$. Similarly, we can define

Divergence:

$$\sum_\mu \frac{\partial A_\mu}{\partial x_\mu} \quad \text{(an invariant)} \qquad (4\text{-}40)$$

Four-dimensional Laplacian:

$$\square^2 = \sum_\mu \frac{\partial^2}{\partial x_\mu{}^2} = \nabla^2 - \frac{1}{c^2} \frac{\partial^2}{\partial t^2} \quad \text{(an invariant)} \qquad (4\text{-}41)$$

Curl:

$$\mathscr{C}_{\mu\nu} = \frac{\partial A_\nu}{\partial x_\mu} - \frac{\partial A_\mu}{\partial x_\nu} \quad \text{(an antisymmetric tensor)} \qquad (4\text{-}42)$$

Divergence of a tensor:

$$\sum_\nu \frac{\partial T_{\nu\mu}}{\partial x_\nu} = D_\mu \quad \text{(a 4-vector)} \qquad (4\text{-}43)$$

We note that, if μ, $\nu \neq 4$ in (4-42), the corresponding components of $\mathscr{C}_{\mu\nu}$ are the components of the three-dimensional vector, curl **A**.

Although this discussion can be carried much further, the amount of tensor analysis we have developed here will be sufficient for our purposes.

4-4 The use of 4-vectors and tensors in relativity

It is wise to pause at this point and remind ourselves of the purpose of what we have just been doing. If we look back at the first postulate, we see that it says, in effect, that there should be no way of making an absolute distinction between two systems moving with constant velocity with respect to each other. With the help of the second postulate, we found that observations made in the two systems must be correlated by means of the Lorentz transformation. Combining these two results, we shall see immediately that we can say that the two postulates taken together require that the laws of physics when properly formulated must have their form unchanged when subjected to a Lorentz transformation; that is, they must be *covariant* with respect to the Lorentz transformation. In order to see that this is correct, let us investigate what the consequences would be if the last statement were not correct in a very simple case. Suppose that a particular law we were considering had the general form $\mathscr{E} = \mathscr{F} + \mathscr{G}$. Let us suppose also that when we referred everything to the primed system by means of a Lorentz transformation, this law became $\mathscr{E}' = \mathscr{F}' + \mathscr{G}' + \epsilon'$, where ϵ' depended on the particular primed system involved. This equation is clearly not covariant, and, in fact, the very existence of the ϵ' term would enable us to distinguish among the various systems in an absolute way. As this would definitely violate the first postulate, we can see the reason for requiring covariance with respect to a Lorentz transformation.

We have seen in the last sections that, by their very definitions, 4-vectors and second rank tensors are covariant. Thus it is evident that, if we were to express all our physical laws in 4-vector or tensor form, they would be *automatically* covariant with respect to the Lorentz transformation and would satisfy both postulates of special relativity. With this in mind we can see, in essence, what our next considerations will be. We shall look at some physical laws and first of all determine if they can be written in terms of 4-vectors or tensors. If they already are or easily can be, we need do nothing more because we know they are already valid in special relativity. If the laws are not covariant, yet are correct in the non-relativistic case, then our task is to try to *generalize* these results so that they can be expressed in terms of 4-vectors or tensors and thus be compatible with special relativity. There are two points to remember in connection with the latter situation, however; first, our generalizations will always have to reduce to the known valid results in the non-relativistic limit; second, our generalizations will still need to be tested by *experiment* because the process of generalization to 4-vector and tensor form is not necessarily a unique process. In the next chapter, we shall begin this program by considering the cornerstone of physics.

Exercises

4-1. Discuss briefly what the consequences would be if the transformation equations (4-4) were not linear.

4-2. Show that the coefficients $a_{\mu\nu}$ given in (4-19) satisfy the conditions (4-11) and (4-17).

4-3. Show that, if the interval between two events is spacelike, there exists a frame of reference in which the two events occur simultaneously; similarly, if the interval is timelike, show that there is a reference frame in which they occur at the same point.

4-4. Show that, if $\Sigma_\mu A_\mu B_\mu$ is an invariant for any arbitrary 4-vector A_μ, then B_μ is also a 4-vector.

4-5. Show that the quantities defined in (4-36) are 4-vectors.

4-6. Use the transformation properties of the *4-acceleration* defined by $a_\mu = dU_\mu/d\tau = d^2x_\mu/d\tau^2$ to derive the transformation formulas for the ordinary acceleration **a** which were previously obtained in Exercise 3-5.

4-7. Derive the set of coefficients $a_{\mu\nu}$ which describes a general Lorentz transformation consisting of a 30° rotation about the y axis plus a translation along the rotated x' axis with a constant speed $v = \frac{1}{2}c$.

5 Particle mechanics

The basic equation of the non-relativistic mechanics of a mass point subject to the force **f** is

$$\mathbf{f} = \frac{d\mathbf{p}}{dt} \tag{5-1}$$

where

$$\mathbf{p} = m_0\mathbf{u} \tag{5-2}$$

is the linear momentum of the particle in terms of its velocity **u** and its inertial (or rest) mass m_0. Equation (5-1) is clearly not in 4-vector or tensor form because it has only three components, the velocity **u** is not a 4-vector, and the differentiation is with respect to the time which, we know, is not an invariant scalar. Therefore we have to generalize these equations to make them satisfy the requirements of special relativity.

5-1   4-momentum and 4-force

We begin with the momentum. Although **u** is not a 4-vector, it is closely related to the 4-vector $U_\mu = dx_\mu/d\tau$. Hence a plausible generalization of (5-2) is to use the invariant scalar m_0 and define the *4-momentum* P_μ as

$$P_\mu = m_0 U_\mu \qquad (5\text{-}3)$$

We can write (5-3) in component form by substituting from (4-27); we then obtain

$$P_i = \frac{m_0 u_i}{\sqrt{1 - u^2/c^2}} \qquad (i = 1, 2, 3)$$

$$P_4 = \frac{i m_0 c}{\sqrt{1 - u^2/c^2}} \qquad (5\text{-}4)$$

We see that, as $u/c \to 0$, $P_i \to m_0 u_i$ which is the non-relativistic momentum; thus (5-3) appears to be a reasonable choice. For the moment, we ignore the extra component P_4 which we have introduced by this process.

In order to get an equation of motion which is analogous to (5-1), we differentiate (5-3) with respect to the invariant $d\tau$ and define the *4-force* F_μ by

$$F_\mu = \frac{dP_\mu}{d\tau} = \frac{d}{d\tau}(m_0 U_\mu) = m_0 \frac{d^2 x_\mu}{d\tau^2} \qquad (5\text{-}5)$$

This result is our desired generalization of the Newtonian equation of motion; the 4-vector F_μ is also called the *Minkowski force*.

If we desire to relate (5-5) to the ordinary force components, we can substitute for $d\tau$ from (3-34) so that (5-5) becomes

$$F_\mu \sqrt{1 - \frac{u^2}{c^2}} = \frac{d}{dt}(m_0 U_\mu) \qquad (5\text{-}6)$$

and, if we use (4-27) to write out the first three components of (5-6), we find that

$$F_i \sqrt{1 - \frac{u^2}{c^2}} = \frac{d}{dt}\left(\frac{m_0 u_i}{\sqrt{1 - u^2/c^2}}\right) = f_i \qquad (5\text{-}7)$$

where the f_i must be the x, y, z components of the ordinary force **f** since (5-7) must reduce to (5-1) and (5-2) combined when $u/c \ll 1$. Thus we see that the first three components of the Minkowski force can be simply related to the ordinary force by means of the equations

$$F_i = \frac{f_i}{\sqrt{1 - u^2/c^2}} \qquad (i = 1, 2, 3) \tag{5-8}$$

In practical calculations, one often does not want to deal with the 4-force but prefers to use simply the three equations (5-7); thus it is common practice to write

$$\mathbf{f} = \frac{d}{dt}\left(\frac{m_0\mathbf{u}}{\sqrt{1 - u^2/c^2}}\right) \tag{5-9}$$

and to call this the *relativistic equation of motion*. Then, if one wants to continue to regard force as the rate of change of momentum, (5-9) can be written $\mathbf{f} = d\mathbf{p}/dt$, where

$$\mathbf{p} = m\mathbf{u} \tag{5-10}$$

and

$$m = \frac{m_0}{\sqrt{1 - u^2/c^2}} \tag{5-11}$$

The quantity m introduced in this way is then called the *mass* of the particle because of the analogy between (5-10) and the non-relativistic equation (5-2). If this procedure is followed, (5-11) is the basis for the statement that the mass of a particle is no longer a constant but increases as the speed increases.

On the other hand, it is not at all necessary to interpret our results in this way, and doing so follows only from a natural desire to write momentum always as the product of the mass and the *ordinary velocity* $\mathbf{u}$. In fact, such an approach actually contradicts the basic philosophy of the covariant approach of relativity because (5-10) is not in 4-vector form. It is much more in keeping with relativistic concepts to ascribe an invariant scalar property—the rest mass m_0—to the particle and then define the 4-vector momentum as the product of this scalar invariant with the 4-vector velocity, exactly as we did in (5-3).

5-2   Energy and the 4-momentum

It is now appropriate to take account of the fact that in our process of generalization we began with (5-2) which has only three components and ended up with (5-3) which has *four*. We have seen that the first three components of P_μ can be adequately interpreted, and now we want to look at the "extra" one. We shall find that it is really not so unfamiliar after all.

If we introduce a new quantity W by

$$P_4 = \frac{iW}{c} \tag{5-12}$$

we find from (5-4) that

$$W = \frac{m_0 c^2}{\sqrt{1 - u^2/c^2}} \tag{5-13}$$

In order to interpret (5-13), let us look at its approximate form when $u/c \ll 1$; expanding the denominator, we find that

$$W = m_0 c^2 \left(1 + \frac{u^2}{2c^2} + \frac{3u^4}{8c^4} + \cdots \right) = m_0 c^2 + \tfrac{1}{2} m_0 u^2 + \cdots \tag{5-14}$$

The second term can be recognized immediately, for it is simply the ordinary expression for the *kinetic energy* of the particle in Newtonian mechanics. Accordingly, it seems quite reasonable in this more general case to call W the *total energy* of the particle. We see that, if the particle is at rest so that $u = 0$, the value of W is $m_0 c^2$ which is called the *rest energy*. It is therefore customary to regard the total energy of a particle as being composed of two parts—an intrinsic part due to its rest mass (the rest energy) and the additional part which appears when the particle is moving (the kinetic energy). Thus, if we let T be the kinetic energy, we can write

$$W = m_0 c^2 + T \tag{5-15}$$

so that

$$T = m_0 c^2 \left(\frac{1}{\sqrt{1 - u^2/c^2}} - 1\right) \tag{5-16}$$

according to (5-13).

We see now that the fourth component of the 4-momentum is not completely mysterious but is directly proportional to the energy of the particle. We also see that the linear momentum and energy of a particle are not to be regarded as different entities, but simply as two aspects of the same attributes of the particle since they appear as separate components of the *same* 4-vector.

We can obtain the same result quantitatively in the following manner. The components of the 4-momentum are

$$P_1 = P_x, \quad P_2 = P_y, \quad P_3 = P_z, \quad P_4 = \frac{iW}{c} \tag{5-17}$$

and transform according to

$$P_\mu' = \sum_\nu a_{\mu\nu} P_\nu \tag{5-18}$$

because of (4-22). Substituting (5-17) into (5-18) and using as an example the particular Lorentz transformation described by (4-19), we find that the equations appropriate to this case are

$$P_x' = \gamma\left(P_x - \frac{\beta W}{c}\right), \quad P_y' = P_y \tag{5-19}$$

$$P_z' = P_z, \quad W' = \gamma(W - \beta c P_x)$$

Clearly, what appears as energy in one system appears as momentum in another, and, conversely, what appears to be momentum in one system is energy in another. As a simple illustration, let us consider the specific case in which the particle is at rest in S'. Then $\mathbf{u}' = 0$, so that $P_x' = P_y' = P_z' = 0$ and $W' = m_0 c^2$, according to (5-4) and (5-13). We then find from (5-19) (or its equivalent obtained by interchanging primed and unprimed symbols and changing the sign of β) that

$$P_x = \frac{\gamma \beta W'}{c}, \quad P_y = P_z = 0, \quad W = \gamma W'$$

and, therefore,

$$P_x = \frac{m_0 v}{\sqrt{1 - v^2/c^2}}, \quad W = \frac{m_0 c^2}{\sqrt{1 - v^2/c^2}}$$

These results, however, are exactly those we would expect to get, according to (5-4) and (5-13), since, from the point of view of the observer in the unprimed system S, the particle is moving along the x axis with speed v. In summary, then, the particle possesses only energy in S' but has both energy and momentum with respect to S.

We can now look at the fourth component of the Minkowski force. We find from (5-5), (5-12), and (3-34) that

$$F_4 = \frac{dP_4}{d\tau} = \frac{i}{c}\frac{dW}{d\tau} = \frac{i}{c\sqrt{1 - u^2/c^2}}\frac{dW}{dt} \tag{5-20}$$

and is therefore related to the time rate of change of the energy, or to the rate at which the force is doing work on the particle.

We can see this in quite another way and can further justify the interpretation of W as the energy by proceeding as follows: From (5-3) and (4-29), we find that

$$\sum_\mu P_\mu^2 = m_0^2 \sum_\mu U_\mu^2 = -m_0^2 c^2 \tag{5-21}$$

and, on differentiating with respect to τ and using (5-5), we obtain

$$\sum_\mu P_\mu \frac{dP_\mu}{d\tau} = \sum_\mu P_\mu F_\mu = 0 \tag{5-22}$$

(Since the scalar product of P_μ and F_μ is zero, we can say that the 4-momentum and the 4-force are always "perpendicular.") If we write out (5-22) in detail and use (5-4), (5-7), and (5-20), we find that

$$P_4F_4 = -\sum_{j=1}^{3} P_j F_j = -\mathbf{P} \cdot \mathbf{F}$$

$$= -\frac{m_0\mathbf{u} \cdot \mathbf{f}}{(1 - u^2/c^2)} = \left(\frac{im_0c}{\sqrt{1 - u^2/c^2}}\right)\left(\frac{i}{c\sqrt{1 - u^2/c^2}}\right)\frac{dW}{dt}$$

so that

$$\frac{dW}{dt} = \mathbf{u} \cdot \mathbf{f} \tag{5-23}$$

Therefore the time rate of change of W is equal to the rate at which the force does work on the particle, and, since this is the way in which increase of energy is defined (I: 4-16), the result (5-23) is further justification for our interpretation of W as the energy.

The energy can be expressed in terms of the linear momentum by writing out (5-21) and using (5-17); the result is that

$$W^2 = c^2\sum_{i=1}^{3} P_i{}^2 + (m_0c^2)^2 = (\mathbf{P}c)^2 + (m_0c^2)^2 \tag{5-24}$$

which is a convenient starting point for the development of the Hamiltonian formulation of relativistic mechanics.

Other important aspects of mechanics which we have not yet mentioned explicitly are the conservation laws of momentum and energy. Since we have seen that we can no longer consider energy and momentum separately, it would seem that the natural relativistic generalization would simply be the conservation of the 4-momentum. In fact, this is exactly what has been found to be correct experimentally, and, in addition, this generalized conservation law holds for a system of particles, even when the number of particles and their rest masses are different in the initial and final states. The concept of 4-momentum conservation is particularly useful in the discussion of collisions. In quantitative form, this conservation law can be written as the four equations

$$\sum_{i=1}^{N} P_\mu{}^b(i) = \sum_{j=1}^{N'} P_\mu{}^a(j) \tag{5-25}$$

where $P_\mu{}^b(i)$ is the μth component of the 4-momentum of the ith particle before the collision (or general interaction); similarly, the superscript a on the right labels the values after the collision. In (5-25) there is also provision for the number of particles to change from N to N'. The fact that the sum of P_4 is also conserved shows that the rest energies and kinetic energies need *not* be conserved individually, although their sum must be. In other words, rest mass and kinetic energy can be converted into each other. The conservation law (5-25) has been well verified experimentally, particularly in reactions involving atomic nuclei and in collisions of high-energy particles of various kinds. The excellent agreement of (5-25) with experiment provides additional strong evidence for the basic correctness of special relativity.

Exercises

5-1. Find the transformation laws for the components of the Minkowski force and of the ordinary force. Partial answer: $F_1' = \gamma(F_1 + i\beta F_4), f_y'(1 - u^2/c^2)^{1/2} = f_y(1 - u'^2/c^2)^{1/2}$.

5-2. For many purposes, electromagnetic radiation can be treated as composed of small, localized "clumps" of radiation called *photons*. Show that, if we regard a photon as a particle of zero rest mass and total energy $W = h\nu$, the Doppler and aberration formulas, (3-27) and (3-30), can be obtained from the transformation laws for the 4-momentum P_μ.

5-3. Two particles, each of mass $\frac{1}{2}M$, are connected by a compressed spring of negligible rest mass. The particles are tied together with a massless string, and the whole system is at rest in a coordinate frame S_0. The string is then cut, and the two particles fly off in opposite directions, each with speed u_0. What is the initial potential energy of the system in S_0? By explicitly transforming the velocities to another frame S, find the final energy and momentum, and thus the initial energy and momentum, in S. Then find the rest mass of the initial system in the frame S, and interpret the result.

6 Electrodynamics in vacuum

The theory of special relativity essentially assumes that Maxwell's equations are covariant with respect to Lorentz transformations, although we originally required only that the speed of light be an invariant. It is both instructive and useful to write Maxwell's equations in 4-vector and tensor form.

According to the results given in (I: Sec. 19-9), Maxwell's equations for a vacuum in mks units are

$$\text{div } \mathbf{E} = \frac{\rho}{\epsilon_0} \tag{6-1a}$$

$$\text{curl } \mathbf{E} = -\frac{\partial \mathbf{B}}{\partial t} \tag{6-1b}$$

$$\text{div } \mathbf{B} = 0 \tag{6-1c}$$

$$\text{curl } \mathbf{B} = \mu_0 \mathbf{J} + \frac{1}{c^2}\frac{\partial \mathbf{E}}{\partial t} \tag{6-1d}$$

where we have written them entirely in terms of **E** and **B** and have used $\mu_0 \epsilon_0 = c^{-2}$. We also have the equation

$$\mathbf{J} = \rho \mathbf{u} \tag{6-2}$$

which relates the current density to the charge density ρ of the moving charges which have velocity **u**. These equations imply the equation of continuity

$$\text{div } \mathbf{J} + \frac{\partial \rho}{\partial t} = 0 \tag{6-3}$$

which can be obtained from (6-1*a*), (6-1*d*), and the vector identity div curl **B** = 0.

We can use the results of Chapter 4 to transform the differential operators involved in these equations, but we would also like to know the transformation properties of ρ, **J**, **E**, and **B**.

6-1   The 4-current and the 4-potential

We recall the results of (I: Chapter 31), namely, that we can write Maxwell's equations in terms of a vector potential **A** and a scalar potential ϕ by the defining equations

$$\mathbf{B} = \text{curl } \mathbf{A}, \quad \mathbf{E} = -\text{grad } \phi - \frac{\partial \mathbf{A}}{\partial t} \tag{6-4}$$

and if we impose the Lorentz condition

$$\text{div } \mathbf{A} + \frac{1}{c^2} \frac{\partial \phi}{\partial t} = 0 \tag{6-5}$$

then the differential equations satisfied by the potentials are

$$\nabla^2 \mathbf{A} - \frac{1}{c^2} \frac{\partial^2 \mathbf{A}}{\partial t^2} = -\mu_0 \mathbf{J}$$
$$\nabla^2 \phi - \frac{1}{c^2} \frac{\partial^2 \phi}{\partial t^2} = -\frac{\rho}{\epsilon_0} \tag{6-6}$$

which can be compactly written

$$\Box^2 \mathbf{A} = -\mu_0 \mathbf{J}, \quad \Box^2 \phi = -\frac{\rho}{\epsilon_0} \tag{6-7}$$

if we use (4-41).

These equations, of course, still imply the equation of continuity, which we certainly want to be covariant; that is, we want

$$\text{div } \mathbf{J} + \frac{\partial \rho}{\partial t} = 0 \quad and \quad \text{div}' \mathbf{J}' + \frac{\partial \rho'}{\partial t'} = 0 \tag{6-8}$$

If we introduce four quantities J_μ by means of the respective equalities given by

$$(J_1, J_2, J_3, J_4) = (J_x, J_y, J_z, ic\rho) \tag{6-9}$$

then (6-8) can be written

$$\sum_\mu \frac{\partial J_\mu}{\partial x_\mu} = 0 \quad and \quad \sum_\mu \frac{\partial J_\mu{}'}{\partial x_\mu{}'} = 0 \tag{6-10}$$

with the use of (4-7).

Since (6-10) has the form of the divergence of a 4-vector, this result makes us strongly suspect that J_μ as defined in (6-9) is a 4-vector. We now show that it actually is a 4-vector. Let us consider an element of volume dV in a coordinate system S; the charges in dV have the velocity $\mathbf{u}$. The total charge contained in dV is $\rho\, dV$. We now consider another coordinate system S_0, the *rest system*, which is defined as that in which the charges are at rest so that $\mathbf{u}_0 = 0$. In the volume element dV_0 in S_0 which corresponds to dV of S, the total charge is $\rho_0\, dV_0$, where ρ_0 is the charge density in the rest system. We make the natural assumption that *total charge is an invariant*; that is, we cannot expect to change the total amount of charge involved in some phenomenon (such as the charge of an electron or proton) by merely observing it from a different coordinate system. Therefore, equating the charges, we obtain

$$\rho_0\, dV_0 = \rho\, dV \tag{6-11}$$

Now the relative velocity of the two coordinate systems is $\mathbf{u}$; since the dimensions along the relative velocity are connected by the Lorentz contraction formula (3-10) while the dimensions transverse to the relative motion are not affected, the two volumes are related by

$$dV = \sqrt{1 - \frac{u^2}{c^2}}\, dV_0 \tag{6-12}$$

When (6-11) and (6-12) are combined, we obtain for charge densities the transformation formula

$$\rho = \frac{\rho_0}{\sqrt{1 - u^2/c^2}} \tag{6-13}$$

Using (6-2), (6-13), and (4-27a), we find that

$$J_x = \rho u_x = \frac{\rho_0 u_x}{\sqrt{1 - u^2/c^2}} = \rho_0 U_1$$

Similarly, we find that

$$J_y = \rho_0 U_2, \quad J_z = \rho_0 U_3, \quad ic\rho = \rho_0 U_4$$

so that (6-9) can be written

$$J_\mu = \rho_0 U_\mu \qquad (6\text{-}14)$$

showing that J_μ is actually a 4-vector since it is the product of the 4-velocity and the scalar invariant ρ_0 (rest system charge density). The 4-vector given in (6-14) and related to the more usual quantities by (6-9) is called the *4-current*. The transformation properties of J_μ are, of course, given by (4-22), or, to put it another way, we see that J_x, J_y, J_z, ρ transform, respectively, like x, y, z, t. Therefore, for our particular Lorentz transformation (2-10), we can immediately say that

$$J_x' = \gamma(J_x - v\rho), \quad J_y' = J_y$$
$$J_z' = J_z, \qquad \rho' = \gamma\left(\rho - \frac{vJ_x}{c^2}\right) \qquad (6\text{-}15)$$

with the inverse equations

$$J_x = \gamma(J_x' + v\rho'), \quad \rho = \gamma\left(\rho' + \frac{vJ_x'}{c^2}\right) \qquad (6\text{-}16)$$

As an example of the use of these equations, let us consider the case in which S' is fixed within a material body which moves with constant speed u relative to S; then we can replace v by u in (6-15) and (6-16). If we consider the non-relativistic case for which $u/c \ll 1$, then $\gamma \simeq 1$ and (6-16) yields

$$J_x \simeq J_x' + u\rho', \quad \rho \simeq \rho' \qquad (6\text{-}17)$$

Thus, while an observer on the moving body measures a charge density ρ' and a current density J_x', his colleague on S finds the current J_x' to be augmented by the *convection current* $u\rho'$ which is due to the motion of the charge density ρ' with respect to S.

If we define the 4-vector A_μ by

$$(A_1, A_2, A_3, A_4) = \left(A_x, A_y, A_z, \frac{i\phi}{c}\right) \qquad (6\text{-}18)$$

then, with the use of (6-9), the four equations of (6-7) can be combined into

$$\Box^2 A_\mu = -\mu_0 J_\mu \qquad (6\text{-}19)$$

since

$$\Box^2(i\phi/c) = -i\rho/c\epsilon_0 = -J_4/c^2\epsilon_0 = -\mu_0 J_4$$

while (6-5) becomes simply

$$\sum_\mu \frac{\partial A_\mu}{\partial x_\mu} = 0 \qquad (6\text{-}20)$$

This 4-vector A_μ is called the *4-potential*.

Equations (6-19) and (6-20) are the covariant forms of Maxwell's equations as written in terms of the potentials; at this stage, the fields must be still found by the use of (6-4).

6-2   The electromagnetic field tensor

In order that Maxwell's equations be covariant, we want $\mathbf{B} = \text{curl } \mathbf{A}$ to hold in S, while in S' we have $\mathbf{B}' = \text{curl}' \mathbf{A}'$; thus, in principle at least, we know how the components of $\mathbf{B}$ transform. To find the transformation properties, we can begin by considering one of the components of the equation determining $\mathbf{B}$; thus we obtain

$$B_x = \frac{\partial A_z}{\partial y} - \frac{\partial A_y}{\partial z} = \frac{\partial A_3}{\partial x_2} - \frac{\partial A_2}{\partial x_3} = f_{23} = -f_{32} \tag{6-21}$$

with the use of (6-4), (4-7), and (6-18) and where we have introduced the antisymmetric tensor

$$f_{\mu\nu} = \frac{\partial A_\nu}{\partial x_\mu} - \frac{\partial A_\mu}{\partial x_\nu} \tag{6-22}$$

which is the four-dimensional curl of A_μ.

If we continue this procedure and calculate all the other components of $f_{\mu\nu}$ in the same way, we find that

$$f_{31} = -f_{13} = B_y, \qquad f_{12} = -f_{21} = B_z$$
$$f_{14} = -f_{41} = -\frac{iE_x}{c}, \quad f_{24} = -f_{42} = -\frac{iE_y}{c} \tag{6-23}$$
$$f_{34} = -f_{43} = -\frac{iE_z}{c}$$

Thus the field vectors $\mathbf{E}$ and $\mathbf{B}$ can be written as components of the second rank antisymmetric tensor $f_{\mu\nu}$ according to the matrix representation

$$f_{\mu\nu} = \begin{pmatrix} 0 & B_z & -B_y & \dfrac{-iE_x}{c} \\[2mm] -B_z & 0 & B_x & \dfrac{-iE_y}{c} \\[2mm] B_y & -B_x & 0 & \dfrac{-iE_z}{c} \\[2mm] \dfrac{iE_x}{c} & \dfrac{iE_y}{c} & \dfrac{iE_z}{c} & 0 \end{pmatrix} \tag{6-24}$$

This tensor is known as the *electromagnetic field tensor*. Since we know how the components of a tensor transform, we are able to find the transformation properties of the field components; we shall do this in the next section.

It can also be shown that all of Maxwell's equations as written in terms of the fields are contained in the following system of equations:

$$\frac{\partial f_{\lambda\rho}}{\partial x_\nu} + \frac{\partial f_{\rho\nu}}{\partial x_\lambda} + \frac{\partial f_{\nu\lambda}}{\partial x_\rho} = 0 \tag{6-25}$$

$$\sum_\nu \frac{\partial f_{\mu\nu}}{\partial x_\nu} = \mu_0 J_\mu \tag{6-26}$$

As an illustration, let us consider the first component of (6-25), that is, the form in which the index *one* is not used; with the help of (6-24), we find that

$$\frac{\partial f_{34}}{\partial x_2} + \frac{\partial f_{42}}{\partial x_3} + \frac{\partial f_{23}}{\partial x_4} = 0 = -\frac{i}{c}\frac{\partial E_z}{\partial y} + \frac{i}{c}\frac{\partial E_y}{\partial z} + \frac{1}{ic}\frac{\partial B_x}{\partial t}$$

which can be rearranged as

$$\frac{\partial E_z}{\partial y} - \frac{\partial E_y}{\partial z} = -\frac{\partial B_x}{\partial t}$$

and which is just the x component of (6-1*b*). Similarly, it can be shown that the remaining three components of (6-25) are the y and z components of (6-1*b*) and the single equation (6-1*c*).

If we set $\mu = 1$ in (6-26), and use (6-24) and (6-9), we obtain

$$\frac{\partial f_{11}}{\partial x_1} + \frac{\partial f_{12}}{\partial x_2} + \frac{\partial f_{13}}{\partial x_3} + \frac{\partial f_{14}}{\partial x_4} = \mu_0 J_1 = \frac{\partial B_z}{\partial y} - \frac{\partial B_y}{\partial z} - \left(\frac{1}{ic}\right)\frac{\partial(iE_x/c)}{\partial t}$$

which can be written

$$\frac{\partial B_z}{\partial y} - \frac{\partial B_y}{\partial z} = \mu_0 J_x + \frac{1}{c^2}\frac{\partial E_x}{\partial t}$$

and is seen to be the x component of (6-1*d*). Similarly, the values $\mu = 2$ and 3 give the remaining components of (6-1*d*), and when $\mu = 4$ is used in (6-26) we find that the result is (6-1*a*). Thus we see that (6-25) and (6-26) are actually Maxwell's equations (6-1) written in terms of the electromagnetic field tensor.

6-3 Transformation equations for the electromagnetic field

According to (4-30), the transformation law for the electromagnetic field tensor is

$$f_{\mu\nu}' = \sum_{\lambda\rho} a_{\mu\lambda} a_{\nu\rho} f_{\lambda\rho} \tag{6-27}$$

We shall consider only the particular Lorentz transformation for which the $a_{\mu\nu}$ are given by (4-19). As an example, let us consider the 14 component of (6-27); using (4-30), (6-24), and $f_{\lambda\rho} = -f_{\rho\lambda}$, we find from (6-27) that

$$
\begin{aligned}
f_{14}' &= -\frac{iE_x'}{c} = \sum_{\lambda\rho} a_{1\lambda} a_{4\rho} f_{\lambda\rho} = \sum_{\lambda} a_{1\lambda}(a_{41} f_{\lambda 1} + a_{44} f_{\lambda 4}) \\
&= a_{11}(a_{41} f_{11} + a_{44} f_{14}) + a_{14}(a_{41} f_{41} + a_{44} f_{44}) \\
&= (a_{11} a_{44} - a_{14} a_{41}) f_{14} = (\gamma^2 - \beta^2 \gamma^2) f_{14} \\
&= f_{14} = -\frac{iE_x}{c}
\end{aligned}
$$

and, therefore, $E_x' = E_x$. Similarly, for the 42 component of (6-27), we find

$$
\begin{aligned}
f_{42}' &= \frac{iE_y'}{c} = \sum_{\lambda\rho} a_{4\lambda} a_{2\rho} f_{\lambda\rho} = \sum_{\lambda} a_{4\lambda} a_{22} f_{\lambda 2} \\
&= a_{41} f_{12} + a_{44} f_{42} = (-i\beta\gamma)B_z + \gamma \frac{iE_y}{c}
\end{aligned}
$$

and, therefore, $E_y' = \gamma(E_y - vB_z)$. Proceeding in the same way, we can find the complete set of transformation formulas:

$$
\begin{array}{ll}
E_x' = E_x & B_x' = B_x \\[2mm]
E_y' = \gamma(E_y - vB_z) & B_y' = \gamma\left(B_y + \dfrac{vE_z}{c^2}\right) \\[2mm]
E_z' = \gamma(E_z + vB_y) & B_z' = \gamma\left(B_z - \dfrac{vE_y}{c^2}\right)
\end{array}
\tag{6-28}
$$

The inverse transformations are

$$
E_x = E_x', \quad E_y = \gamma(E_y' + vB_z'), \quad \text{etc.}
$$

We can actually discard as unnecessary the restriction that the relative velocity $\mathbf{v}$ of S' with respect to S be along the x axis. Since the orientation of the x axis is completely arbitrary, if we introduce the field components parallel ($\parallel$) and perpendicular ($\perp$) to the direction of translation, we can write (6-28) *in general* as

$$
\begin{array}{ll}
E_\parallel' = E_\parallel & B_\parallel' = B_\parallel \\[2mm]
\mathbf{E}_\perp' = \gamma(\mathbf{E}_\perp + \mathbf{v} \times \mathbf{B}_\perp) & \mathbf{B}_\perp' = \gamma\left(\mathbf{B}_\perp - \dfrac{\mathbf{v}}{c^2} \times \mathbf{E}_\perp\right) \\[2mm]
\quad = \gamma(\mathbf{E} + \mathbf{v} \times \mathbf{B})_\perp & \quad = \gamma\left(\mathbf{B} - \dfrac{\mathbf{v}}{c^2} \times \mathbf{E}\right)_\perp
\end{array}
\tag{6-29}
$$

Example.   Pure Electric Case in S.   Suppose $\mathbf{E} \neq 0$ in S, but $\mathbf{B} = 0$. Then we find from (6-29) that, in S', ,

$$B_{\parallel}' = 0, \quad \mathbf{B}_{\perp}' = -\frac{\gamma}{c^2} \mathbf{v} \times \mathbf{E}_{\perp}$$

$$E_{\parallel}' = E_{\parallel}, \quad \mathbf{E}_{\perp}' = \gamma \mathbf{E}_{\perp}$$

so that

$$\mathbf{B}' = \mathbf{B}_{\perp}' = -\frac{\mathbf{v} \times \mathbf{E}_{\perp}'}{c^2} = -\frac{\mathbf{v} \times \mathbf{E}'}{c^2} \tag{6-30}$$

Thus we see that what appeared to one observer as purely an electric field appears as both an electric and a magnetic field to a second observer moving with respect to the first one.

Example.   Pure Magnetic Case in S.   Suppose now $\mathbf{E} = 0$ but $\mathbf{B} \neq 0$. Then we find from (6-29) that, in S',

$$B_{\parallel}' = B_{\parallel}, \quad \mathbf{B}_{\perp}' = \gamma \mathbf{B}_{\perp}$$
$$E_{\parallel}' = 0, \quad \mathbf{E}_{\perp}' = \gamma \mathbf{v} \times \mathbf{B}_{\perp}$$

so that

$$\mathbf{E}' = \mathbf{E}_{\perp}' = \mathbf{v} \times \mathbf{B}_{\perp}' = \mathbf{v} \times \mathbf{B}' \tag{6-31}$$

Thus we see that what appeared to one observer as purely a magnetic field appears as both a magnetic and an electric field to a second observer moving with respect to the first one.

In the non-relativistic limit in which $v/c \ll 1$, $\gamma \simeq 1$ and the results of the last example show that $\mathbf{B}' \simeq \mathbf{B}$; hence

$$\mathbf{E}' \simeq \mathbf{v} \times \mathbf{B} \tag{6-32}$$

Thus in the case in which the moving observer is not going too fast, the electric field is given by (6-32) and is exactly what we gave in (1-2) as a first approximation to be used in discussing electromagnetic effects in moving media—justifying our previous result which was obtained in another way.

The results found in this section clearly show that the electric and magnetic fields $\mathbf{E}$ and $\mathbf{B}$ have no independent existence as separate entities. The fundamental complex is the field tensor $f_{\mu\nu}$, and the resolution into electric and magnetic components is wholly relative to the motion of the observer.

The transformation equations, (6-28) or (6-29), sometimes make the solution of certain problems easier by enabling one to choose an appropriate coordinate system in which the answer can be simply found and then to obtain the desired results by transforming back to the actual system of interest. Of course, one does not get any results this way that could not be obtained by directly solving Maxwell's equations, but it is generally faster. We shall illustrate this method with an instructive and important example.

6-4 Field of a uniformly moving point charge

We consider a point charge q moving with a constant velocity $\mathbf{u}$ with respect to the system S as illustrated in Fig. 6-1.

Let us choose S' to be the system for which q is at rest at the origin. The field in S' is then just the electrostatic Coulomb field of a point charge as given by (I: 19-6):

$$\mathbf{E}' = \frac{q\mathbf{r}'}{4\pi\epsilon_0 r'^3}, \quad \mathbf{B}' = 0 \tag{6-33}$$

where

$$r' = (x'^2 + y'^2 + z'^2)^{\frac{1}{2}} \tag{6-34}$$

is the distance to the point at which the field is evaluated. Inserting (6-33) into (6-28) and using (6-34) and (2-10), we find one of the field components in S to be

$$E_x = E_x' = \frac{qx'}{4\pi\epsilon_0 r'^3} = \frac{q\gamma(x - ut)}{4\pi\epsilon_0[\gamma^2(x - ut)^2 + y^2 + z^2]^{\frac{3}{2}}} \tag{6-35}$$

where

$$\gamma = \frac{1}{\sqrt{1 - u^2/c^2}} \tag{6-36}$$

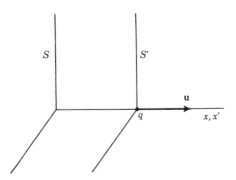

Fig. 6-1

If we let $X = ut$ be the position of q along the x axis so that the coordinates of q in S are $(X, 0, 0)$, then (6-35) can also be written

$$E_x = \frac{q\gamma(x - X)}{4\pi\epsilon_0[\gamma^2(x - X)^2 + y^2 + z^2]^{3/2}} \tag{6-37}$$

The other two components of $\mathbf{E}$ can be found from (6-28) in the same way; the results are that

$$E_y = \frac{q\gamma y}{4\pi\epsilon_0[\gamma^2(x - X)^2 + y^2 + z^2]^{3/2}} \tag{6-38}$$

$$E_z = \frac{q\gamma z}{4\pi\epsilon_0[\gamma^2(x - X)^2 + y^2 + z^2]^{3/2}} \tag{6-39}$$

The last three equations give the electric field at the point (x, y, z) in S when the point charge q is at $(X, 0, 0)$ in the same system.

The value of $\mathbf{B}$ could also be calculated from (6-28); however, we can simply use the result given for the pure electric case (6-30) by taking account of the interchange of S and S' so that we have

$$\mathbf{B} = \frac{\mathbf{u} \times \mathbf{E}}{c^2} \tag{6-40}$$

from which the components of $\mathbf{B}$ can be found explicitly by using (6-37) through (6-39). Thus we have found the exact solution of our problem in a comparatively simple manner.

Let us investigate the characteristics of this field by choosing the instant that the charge is at the origin, that is, $t = 0$. The basic structure of the field will be the same for all later times, and it can be obtained by simply translating the result for $t = 0$ with speed u along x, according to (6-37) through (6-40). Setting $X = 0$ in the equations for E_x, E_y, and E_z, we see that we can write

$$\mathbf{E} = \frac{q\gamma\mathbf{r}}{4\pi\epsilon_0(\gamma^2 x^2 + y^2 + z^2)^{3/2}} \tag{6-41}$$

which shows that $\mathbf{E}$ is directed radially outward, while $\mathbf{B}$ is perpendicular to the plane of $\mathbf{u}$ and $\mathbf{E}$, according to (6-40); this situation is illustrated in Fig. 6-2.

We also see from the figure that

$$x = r\cos\theta, \quad y^2 + z^2 = r^2\sin^2\theta$$

so that if we use (6-36) we find that

$$\gamma^2 x^2 + y^2 + z^2 = r^2\gamma^2(1 - \beta^2\sin^2\theta) \tag{6-42}$$

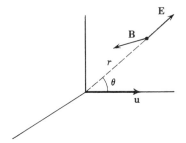

Fig. 6-2

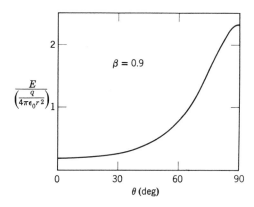

Fig. 6-3

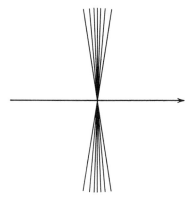

Fig. 6-4

where $\beta = u/c$. Substituting (6-42) into (6-41), we find

$$E = \frac{q(1 - \beta^2)\hat{\mathbf{r}}}{4\pi\epsilon_0 r^2 (1 - \beta^2 \sin^2 \theta)^{3/2}} \tag{6-43}$$

showing us that the field is inverse square in its dependence on radial distance r, but that its magnitude at a given distance depends on the direction. If we calculate the magnitude of the electric field from (6-43) for the two extreme cases, we find that:

(1) directly in front, $\theta = 0$,

$$E_{\parallel} = \frac{q}{4\pi\epsilon_0 r^2}(1 - \beta^2) \tag{6-44}$$

(2) at one side, $\theta = \pi/2$

$$E_{\perp} = \frac{q}{4\pi\epsilon_0 r^2}\frac{1}{\sqrt{1 - \beta^2}} \tag{6-45}$$

Therefore, for a very fast moving charge for which $\beta \simeq 1$, we see that at a given distance $E_{\parallel}$ is very small while $E_{\perp}$ is very large, whereas if $\beta \ll 1$ both of these components approach equality with the static Coulomb field.

These results are also illustrated in Fig. 6-3 which shows the magnitude of the field for a given distance plotted as a function of angle θ from the direction of motion for $\beta = 0.9$. We see from this figure that for a very rapidly moving charge practically the whole field is concentrated in a small angle around the equatorial plane, an effect which is illustrated very schematically in Fig. 6-4.

Exercises

6-1. Why are we justified in calling the quantities defined by (6-18) a 4-vector?

6-2. Verify the results of (6-23).

6-3. Show that (6-25) has only four different components, and show that (6-25) and (6-26) give all of Maxwell's equations.

6-4. Show that the quantities $\mathbf{E} \cdot \mathbf{B}$ and $\mathbf{B}^2 - \mathbf{E}^2/c^2$ are invariants. Apply these results to the case of a plane wave in vacuum.

6-5. Show that the equations of motion of a particle of charge q in an electromagnetic field where the force is given by

$$\mathbf{f} = q(\mathbf{E} + \mathbf{u} \times \mathbf{B}) \tag{6-46}$$

are given by

$$m_0 d^2 x_\mu / d\tau^2 = q \sum_\nu f_{\mu\nu} U_\nu \tag{6-47}$$

6-6. A charged particle enters a uniform electric field $\mathbf{E}$ which is perpendicular to the initial velocity $\mathbf{u}_0$. Find the subsequent trajectory of the particle, and show that it reduces to a parabola in the limit $u_0/c \rightarrow 0$.

6-7. Show that the correct relativistic Lagrangian and Hamiltonian functions for a charged particle moving in an electromagnetic field can be written as

$$L = -m_0 c^2 \sqrt{1 - u^2/c^2} + q\mathbf{A} \cdot \mathbf{u} - q\phi$$
$$H = [(\mathbf{p} - q\mathbf{A})^2 c^2 + m_0^2 c^4]^{1/2} + q\phi$$

Also write these quantities in 4-vector form and find the form of the corresponding Lagrangian and Hamiltonian 4-vector equations of motion.

Part Two

Thermodynamics

7 Mathematical introduction

We shall find in our discussion of thermodynamics that we will often have a fairly large selection of variables from which the independent variables can be chosen, and it is frequently convenient to transform from one set to another. Since partial derivatives are so extensively used in thermodynamics, it is desirable to have explicit formulas at hand which we can use to transform the derivatives. Therefore in this chapter we discuss a few aspects of functions of several variables which are particularly appropriate to thermodynamics.

7-1 Transformations of partial derivatives

Suppose we are given the function $z = z(x, y)$. By the usual rules of calculus, the *total differential* of z is given by

$$dz = \left(\frac{\partial z}{\partial x}\right)_y dx + \left(\frac{\partial z}{\partial y}\right)_x dy \qquad (7\text{-}1)$$

The notation for the partial derivatives which is shown in (7-1) is almost universal in thermodynamics and requires a few words of explanation, for it is a convenient way of showing what the independent variables are and which are being held constant in the process of partial differentiation. Thus, for example, $(\partial z/\partial x)_y$ tells us that the dependent variable z is a function of the independent variables x and y, and that the rate of change of z is being computed under the condition that y is held constant. Accordingly, we shall generally (but not necessarily always) have

$$\left(\frac{\partial z}{\partial x}\right)_y \neq \left(\frac{\partial z}{\partial x}\right)_u$$

since z is regarded as a function of different independent variables in the two cases.

This notation can easily be extended to more than two variables; if, for example, we have $z = z(x, y, a, b, c, \ldots)$, then $(\partial z/\partial x)_{y,a,b,c,\ldots}$, $(\partial z/\partial a)_{x,y,b,c,\ldots}$, etc., are possible partial derivatives.

Now suppose that, in addition, x and y are themselves functions of other variables u and v. Then their differentials would be given by

$$dx = \left(\frac{\partial x}{\partial u}\right)_v du + \left(\frac{\partial x}{\partial v}\right)_u dv \qquad (7\text{-}2)$$

$$dy = \left(\frac{\partial y}{\partial u}\right)_v du + \left(\frac{\partial y}{\partial v}\right)_u dv \qquad (7\text{-}3)$$

If we substitute (7-2) and (7-3) into (7-1), we find that

$$dz = \left[\left(\frac{\partial z}{\partial x}\right)_y \left(\frac{\partial x}{\partial u}\right)_v + \left(\frac{\partial z}{\partial y}\right)_x \left(\frac{\partial y}{\partial u}\right)_v\right] du$$

$$+ \left[\left(\frac{\partial z}{\partial x}\right)_y \left(\frac{\partial x}{\partial v}\right)_u + \left(\frac{\partial z}{\partial y}\right)_x \left(\frac{\partial y}{\partial v}\right)_u\right] dv \qquad (7\text{-}4)$$

Since we have $x = x(u, v)$ and $y = y(u, v)$, then z itself is actually a function of u and v, and we can also write

$$dz = \left(\frac{\partial z}{\partial u}\right)_v du + \left(\frac{\partial z}{\partial v}\right)_u dv \qquad (7\text{-}5)$$

and, on comparing (7-4) and (7-5), we see that

$$\left(\frac{\partial z}{\partial u}\right)_v = \left(\frac{\partial z}{\partial x}\right)_y \left(\frac{\partial x}{\partial u}\right)_v + \left(\frac{\partial z}{\partial y}\right)_x \left(\frac{\partial y}{\partial u}\right)_v \qquad (7\text{-}6a)$$

$$\left(\frac{\partial z}{\partial v}\right)_u = \left(\frac{\partial z}{\partial x}\right)_y \left(\frac{\partial x}{\partial v}\right)_u + \left(\frac{\partial z}{\partial y}\right)_x \left(\frac{\partial y}{\partial v}\right)_u \qquad (7\text{-}6b)$$

are the formulas which enable us to transform the derivatives to different sets of independent variables. We now want to consider two important special cases of these results.

Suppose that only one variable is being changed; that is, the new independent variables (u, y) replace the old set (x, y). Therefore, $v = y$ and $(\partial y/\partial u)_v = (\partial v/\partial u)_v = 0$ and (7-6a) becomes

$$\left(\frac{\partial z}{\partial u}\right)_y = \left(\frac{\partial z}{\partial x}\right)_y \left(\frac{\partial x}{\partial u}\right)_y = \frac{1}{\left(\frac{\partial u}{\partial z}\right)_y}$$

which can be written

$$\left(\frac{\partial z}{\partial x}\right)_y \left(\frac{\partial x}{\partial u}\right)_y \left(\frac{\partial u}{\partial z}\right)_y = 1 \qquad (7\text{-}7)$$

or

$$\left(\frac{\partial z}{\partial x}\right)_y = \frac{\left(\dfrac{\partial u}{\partial x}\right)_y}{\left(\dfrac{\partial u}{\partial z}\right)_y} \tag{7-8}$$

This result is called the *chain relation*, and we note that the same variable y is held constant in all of the differentiating.

Now we shall let $u = y$ and $v = z$; the net result is to change the dependent variable from z to x. In this case, then,

$$\left(\frac{\partial z}{\partial u}\right)_v = 0, \quad \left(\frac{\partial y}{\partial u}\right)_v = 1$$

so that (7-6a) becomes

$$0 = \left(\frac{\partial z}{\partial x}\right)_y \left(\frac{\partial x}{\partial y}\right)_z + \left(\frac{\partial z}{\partial y}\right)_x$$

which can be written

$$\left(\frac{\partial x}{\partial y}\right)_z = -\frac{\left(\dfrac{\partial z}{\partial y}\right)_x}{\left(\dfrac{\partial z}{\partial x}\right)_y} \tag{7-9}$$

or

$$\left(\frac{\partial x}{\partial y}\right)_z \left(\frac{\partial y}{\partial z}\right)_x \left(\frac{\partial z}{\partial x}\right)_y = -1 \tag{7-10}$$

This result is called the *cyclic relation*. We note that the effect of (7-9) is to make the variable which is held constant on the left side become the dependent variable on the right side.

7-2   Legendre transformations

Suppose we have a quantity z which is a function of t variables, x_i, so that we can write $z = z(x_1, x_2, \ldots, x_t)$. If we define

$$p_j = \left(\frac{\partial z}{\partial x_j}\right)_{x_1, \ldots, x_{j-1}, x_{j+1}, \ldots} \tag{7-11}$$

we can write the generalization of (7-1) as

$$dz = \sum_{j=1}^{t} p_j \, dx_j \tag{7-12}$$

It is often desirable to obtain a function related to z in which some of the variables x_j are replaced by the corresponding p_j as the independent variables. Such a transformation is known as a *Legendre transformation*.

Suppose we want the variables $x_1, \ldots, x_l (l \leqslant t)$ replaced as independent variables by the derivatives $p_1, \ldots, p_l$. We designate the transformed function by $z[p_1, \ldots, p_l]$, and we shall demonstrate the *rule*: Subtract the product of the two variables whose role you wish to interchange from the original function. Therefore

$$z[p_1, \ldots, p_l] = z - \sum_{j=1}^{l} p_j x_j \qquad (l \leqslant t) \tag{7-13}$$

In order to verify the correctness of this rule, we calculate the differential of the transformed function and use (7-12):

$$dz[p_1, \ldots, p_l] = dz - \sum_{j=1}^{l} (p_j \, dx_j + x_j \, dp_j)$$

$$= - \sum_{j=1}^{l} x_j \, dp_j + \sum_{j=l+1}^{t} p_j \, dx_j \tag{7-14}$$

We see from (7-14) that the independent variables are now $(p_1, \ldots, p_l, x_{l+1}, \ldots, x_t)$ as was desired. In addition, the previously independent x's are now derivable by differentiation from the transformed function; that is,

$$-x_j = \frac{\partial z[p_1, \ldots, p_l]}{\partial p_j} \qquad (j = 1, \ldots, l) \tag{7-15}$$

while

$$p_k = \frac{\partial z[p_1, \ldots, p_l]}{\partial x_k} \qquad (k = l + 1, \ldots, t) \tag{7-16}$$

One of the best-known examples of a Legendre transformation is found in mechanics, namely, the transformation from the Lagrangian to the Hamiltonian formulation. In fact, we see from (I: 10-3) that the definition

$$H(p_1, \ldots, p_n, q_1, \ldots, q_n) = \sum_j p_j \dot{q}_j - L(\dot{q}_1, \ldots, \dot{q}_n, q_1, \ldots, q_n)$$

shows that, except for a minus sign, the Hamiltonian function is the Legendre transformation of the Lagrangian which replaces the $\dot{q}_j$ by the $p_j = \partial L / \partial \dot{q}_j$ as the independent variables.

7-3   Exact and inexact differentials

Suppose we consider a general expression for a differential quantity dz of the form

$$dz = X(x, y) \, dx + Y(x, y) \, dy \tag{7-17}$$

where X and Y are given functions of x and y. When we come to calculate the total change by integrating (7-17) between the initial point

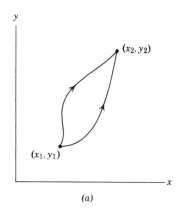
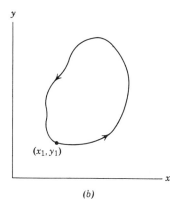

Fig. 7-1

$(x_1,\ y_1)$ and the final point $(x_2,\ y_2)$, we find that this change depends, in general, on the specific path in the xy plane which is used to go between the two points. The reason is that only for a specific path can y and dy be expressed as functions of x and dx, so that X, Y, and dz of (7-17) can be integrated in terms of the single variable x. Two such paths are illustrated in Fig. 7-1a.

However, if there should actually exist a definite *function* $z(x, y)$ whose differential is given by (7-17), the value of z would depend only on the coordinates (x, y) of a given point and not on how the point was reached. In this case the integral of (7-17) must have the same value independent of the path of integration, namely,

$$\int_1^2 dz = z(x_2,\ y_2) - z(x_1,\ y_1) \tag{7-18}$$

Under these circumstances, the quantity z is then called a *point function* or *state function* and its differential dz is known as an *exact differential*. In other words, an exact differential is the differential of an actual function of position whose value depends only on the coordinates of the point.

If the integral is taken over a closed path, such as that of Fig. 7-1b, the initial and final points coincide and we see from (7-18) that the integral over a closed path of an exact differential vanishes; that is,

$$\oint dz = 0 \tag{7-19}$$

Examples of exact differentials are those of mechanical potential energy dV and the scalar potential $d\phi$ of electromagnetism.

The fact that dz is an exact differential can be stated somewhat differently since, if $z = z(x, y)$, then (7-17) can also be written

$$dz = X(x, y)\, dx + Y(x, y)\, dy = \left(\frac{\partial z}{\partial x}\right)_y dx + \left(\frac{\partial z}{\partial y}\right)_x dy \quad (7\text{-}20)$$

so that

$$X(x, y) = \left(\frac{\partial z}{\partial x}\right)_y, \quad Y(x, y) = \left(\frac{\partial z}{\partial y}\right)_x \quad (7\text{-}21)$$

Because of the equality of mixed second partial derivatives, $\partial^2 z/\partial x\, \partial y = \partial^2 z/\partial y\, \partial x$, we see from (7-21) that we must have

$$\left(\frac{\partial X}{\partial y}\right)_x = \left(\frac{\partial Y}{\partial x}\right)_y \quad (7\text{-}22)$$

as a necessary condition that dz as given by (7-17) be exact. It can also be shown that (7-22) is a sufficient condition that dz be exact and, therefore, that there exists an actual function of position $z(x, y)$ whose differential is given by (7-17).

If the differential is not exact, it is called an *inexact differential* and is very often written in the notation dW. The most common example of an inexact differential is the increment of work since forces can be non-conservative, such as frictional forces or dissipative forces of any type.

Exercises

7-1. Verify that (7-7) and (7-10) are correct for the following examples: $z = ax^2 + by$, $z^2 = xy$, $z = cx^2/y^3$, where a, b, c are constants.

7-2. Which of the following are exact differentials: $dz = x\, dx \pm y\, dy$, $dz = y\, dx \pm x\, dy$, $dz = (dx/y) \pm (x/y^2)\, dy$? For those which are not exact, find the integral of dz counterclockwise around the closed path formed by the square whose corners (x, y) are at $(0, 1)$, $(1, 1)$, $(1, 2)$, $(0, 2)$.

7-3. What relation does (7-22) have to the vector identity curl grad $A = 0$ and to the condition that a mechanical force be derivable from a potential energy?

7-4. Show that $dz = y\, dx + (x + 2y)\, dy$ is exact. Find $z(1, 2) - z(0, 0)$ by integrating dz along the two paths: (*a*) the line segment $y = 0$ to $x = 1$ and the line segment $x = 1$ to $y = 2$; (*b*) the line segment $x = 0$ to $y = 2$ and the line segment $y = 2$ to $x = 1$; and thus show directly that the same result is obtained in both cases. Do the same for any other two paths of your own choosing.

8 Temperature, heat, and related concepts

Thermodynamics is basically an empirical subject which deals with the macroscopic properties of matter. The principal results of thermodynamics are in the form of relations among experimentally determined quantities. The theoretical prediction of the absolute magnitudes of these quantities is regarded as being outside the scope of thermodynamics, being left to theories, such as kinetic theory and statistical mechanics, which deal with the atomic and molecular structure of matter. The development and application of thermodynamics depend very strongly on the ideas of *equilibrium* and the *thermodynamic state* of a system; we shall develop and clarify these in more detail as we go along.

8-1 Temperature

A completely new concept which is introduced by thermodynamics is that of *temperature*. Everyone has a qualitative feeling for hotness or coldness, and this can be used initially as a sort of crude thermometer. From long experience, one concludes that, when a system (pail of water, table, room, etc.) is observed to be in thermodynamic equilibrium, that is, when no gross variations are noted in its macroscopic properties over a period of time, the system has the same temperature everywhere. Similarly, when two systems have been in thermal contact for a long time, that is, they have been able to affect each other's temperature, and it is finally decided that they are in mutual equilibrium, it is found that they have the same temperature. Hence it is concluded that equality of temperatures is a necessary condition for equilibrium between two systems.

One can also conclude from these observations that temperature is a property of a thermodynamic state or is a *state variable*; that is, temperature is one of the parameters whose numerical values are needed to specify the state of a system. These conclusions are often summarized in the following two-part statement, called a *law*, for historical reasons, although we shall state it in the form of a *postulate*:

ZEROTH LAW OF THERMODYNAMICS. There exists a scalar state variable called *temperature*. Equality of the temperature is a necessary condition for thermodynamic equilibrium between two systems or between two parts of a single system.

We shall generally represent the temperature by T although we will occasionally use t or θ; since it is characteristic *only* of the state, we know that its differential is exact and hence we can write dT as the temperature difference between two closely similar states.

By using the zeroth law, we can devise a method of measuring the temperature, that is, of being able to assign a numerical value to it. In order to do this, we need only choose any property of a system which clearly changes with temperature—such as the length of a metal rod or the pressure of a gas in a container—and assign numbers to the temperature according to the magnitude of the chosen property. This has been generally done by first assigning arbitrary numerical values to two convenient calibration points and then subdividing the interval between them in a uniform way. Two common calibration points are the freezing and boiling points of water under atmospheric pressure; these are assigned the respective values of 0 degrees and 100 degrees to obtain the *Celsius* scale of temperature (previously called centigrade), or 32 degrees and 212 degrees to obtain the *Fahrenheit* scale.

If one carries out this procedure for two different materials, for example, and assigns the same numbers to the calibration points, one generally finds that at intermediate temperatures these two thermometers will give *different* numerical values for the temperature of the same body. In other words, temperature scales defined by the use of different materials or properties or both will agree only at the calibrating points. One could, of course, simply arbitrarily choose one material and one property to define a standard temperature scale, but, fortunately, there is a more satisfactory solution for this difficulty. We can get almost exact agreement over a considerable temperature range if the material used is a confined gas which is as far as possible from its boiling point. Helium or hydrogen is generally chosen for this purpose, and the pressure at constant volume is what is usually measured. We shall discuss this temperature scale in more detail later, and we shall find that this particular choice helps us to define a natural zero for our temperature scale.

8-2   Thermodynamic systems

A terminology which we shall constantly use is that of a *thermodynamic system*, which means that in order to specify completely the state of the system it is necessary to give its temperature as well as the other mechanical, electrical, magnetic, etc., variables which may be required. The simplest example of a thermodynamic system, and one which we shall frequently discuss, is a *homogeneous fluid*. The fluid has one mechanical degree of freedom, the volume V; it also has a thermal degree of freedom, the temperature T. In addition, one generally gives the pressure p exerted by the fluid, so that the three variables p, V, T are deemed sufficient to specify completely the state of the system. However, it is found by experiment that only two of these three variables are independent so that, for example, we can regard p as a function of T and V and write

$$p = p(T, V) \tag{8-1}$$

Such an equation as this is usually called the *equation of state*, and it must be determined by experiment for each system of interest as it is, of course, not given by thermodynamics.

For a given system, the number of variables needed to specify the thermodynamic state depends somewhat on the information desired and on the particular system. For example, if our system were a tank filled with oxygen gas, p, V, T would be sufficient to answer most questions about the state of the gas. However, if we wanted to know the total magnetic moment of this paramagnetic gas, these three would be insufficient to specify the state and we would have to introduce the magnetization M and the induction B as well, leaving it to experiment to determine which of the variables p, V, T, B are significant in determining the value of M. Thus this example shows that the number of variables for a given system can change as requirements change, and, in a sense, one depends on experiment to determine how many are really needed to answer a given type of question.

Many quantities of interest which can be determined experimentally with comparative ease are the various rates of change of one variable with respect to another. We can define three important ones as follows:

$$\alpha = \frac{1}{V}\left(\frac{\partial V}{\partial T}\right)_p, \quad \kappa_T = -\frac{1}{V}\left(\frac{\partial V}{\partial p}\right)_T, \quad \beta = \frac{1}{p}\left(\frac{\partial p}{\partial T}\right)_V \tag{8-2}$$

α is called the *coefficient of thermal expansion*, and κ_T is the *isothermal compressibility*; β does not have a commonly used name. We see that these coefficients could be calculated if the exact form of (8-1) were known; conversely, measurements of these quantities would aid us in determining the equation of state.

These three coefficients are not independent, for we see that we can write (7-10) as

$$\left(\frac{\partial p}{\partial T}\right)_V \left(\frac{\partial T}{\partial V}\right)_p \left(\frac{\partial V}{\partial p}\right)_T = -1 \tag{8-3}$$

so that when the derivatives given by (8-2) are inserted into (8-3) we find that

$$\beta = \frac{\alpha}{p\kappa_T} \tag{8-4}$$

Thus one of these coefficients can always be found from measurements of the other two. However, the principal importance of (8-4) is that it is an excellent example of the type of result which thermodynamic methods yield, that is, a relation among macroscopic, empirical quantities without any information about their absolute values. The fact that the value of a particular quantity can be obtained indirectly and exactly in this way is clearly of great help if it is difficult to measure directly.

8-3 Work

If we recall the definition of work used in mechanics, which is

$$W = \int \mathbf{F} \cdot d\mathbf{s} \tag{8-5}$$

as given by (I: 4-11), it is clear that work cannot be a state variable of a system since it is a characteristic of the *process* as well as the states involved. In other words, we cannot say that a given system possesses a definite amount of work for a given condition; we can only tell how much work is done when the state of a system is changed. In order to see this in another way, let us consider the possibility that we can subject our system to a *cyclic* process; that is, we begin with the system in a certain state, change it to one or more other states, and finally return it to the initial state. In general, the net amount of work done in such a cycle will be different from zero if for no other reason than the existence of frictional or other non-conservative forces; however, if W were a state variable ΔW would be zero because the initial and final states are identical. Therefore the work W is not a state variable, and its differential dW is not exact.

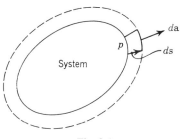

Fig. 8-1

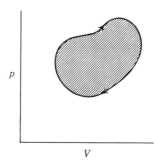

Fig. 8-2

We shall adopt the sign convention that work done *on* the system is *positive*, and work done by it is negative.

We can easily relate the work done dW to changes in the state variables for the important case in which our system is a fluid. From the definition of pressure as force per unit area and with the help of (8-5) and Fig. 8-1, we find that the work done in a change in volume dV is

$$dW = -\int \mathbf{F} \cdot d\mathbf{s} = -\int p \, d\mathbf{a} \cdot d\mathbf{s} = -p \int d\mathbf{a} \cdot d\mathbf{s} = -p \, dV \quad (8\text{-}6)$$

In spite of its appearance, $dW = -p \, dV$ is *not* an exact differential, as can be seen by considering a cyclic process such as that represented in the pV plane in Fig. 8-2. Since the area enclosed by the loop is different from zero, and since this represents the net work performed during the process, we have

$$\oint dW = -\oint p \, dV \neq 0$$

so that from (7-19) we see again that dW is inexact.

8-4 Heat

Another important concept which we shall have frequent occasion to use is that of *heat*. The general idea of heat is familiar to us from such observations as are involved in putting a pan of water over a flame and finding that it warms up. A natural interpretation of the observed rise in temperature of the water is that a definite quantity of something, which we call heat, has been transferred from the hot stove to the cold water. If we then pour the hot water into cold water, we find that when the final equilibrium state is reached it has an intermediate temperature. This process can be similarly interpreted as a transfer of heat from the warmer system to the cooler system with the result that the warmer system cools off while the cooler one warms up.

It is possible to reduce the measurement of heat to that of the measurement of temperature by an appropriate definition of the unit. The unit of heat is called a *kilocalorie* (or kilogram calorie) and is usually defined as the heat required at atmospheric pressure to raise the temperature of one kilogram of water the one degree from 14.5 to 15.5 degrees Celsius. Experimental results then show that the amount of heat required to change the temperature of a system through a given range depends on the system; for instance, on its mass or on the material of which it is composed. This leads to the idea of a *heat capacity* C of a system which, for the moment, we define somewhat crudely as the ratio of the heat added to the system ΔQ divided by the subsequent change in temperature ΔT; thus

$$C = \frac{\Delta Q}{\Delta T} \qquad (8\text{-}7)$$

One finds experimentally that the heat capacity is proportional to the amount of material involved; hence it is convenient to define:

Specific heat = heat capacity per unit mass

$$= c_m = \frac{C}{M} \qquad (8\text{-}8)$$

where M is the total mass of the system, and

$$\text{Molar heat capacity} = c = \frac{C}{v} \qquad (8\text{-}9)$$

where v is the number of kilomoles of the material. A kilomole (or kilogram mole) of material is defined as a quantity whose mass in kilograms equals its *molecular weight* μ or, equivalently, as the mass of a number of molecules equal to *Avogadro's number* L (6.025 × 10^{26} molecules /kilomole). For example, a kilomole of oxygen (O_2) contains 32 kilograms, while a kilomole of H_2O contains 18 kilograms; both samples contain the same number of molecules. Thus we have

$$v = \frac{M}{\mu} = \frac{N}{L} \qquad (8\text{-}10)$$

where N is the total number of molecules. As in (8-9), we shall let the value of a quantity which is evaluated for a kilomole be called the molar value.

Since the quantity of heat ΔQ involved in changing the state depends on the process as well as on the initial and final states, it is clear from (8-7) that the heat capacity of a system is not a unique attribute of a system; one must distinguish among the heat capacities associated with the different processes which may be used to transfer heat to and from the system. The two most important examples are the heat capacity at constant volume, C_v, and that at constant pressure, C_p, which are defined by

$$C_v = \left(\frac{\Delta Q}{\Delta T}\right)_V \tag{8-11}$$

$$C_p = \left(\frac{\Delta Q}{\Delta T}\right)_p \tag{8-12}$$

Whether these distinctions are quantitatively important depends on the system involved and must be determined from experiment.

Heat can be added to a system by mechanical means as well, as is illustrated by the rise in temperature due to frictional forces such as in the proverbial rubbing together of two sticks to start a fire. In all these processes involving friction, it is found that the amount of work done ΔW has a definite relation to the quantity of heat produced ΔQ, regardless of the conditions of the experiment. The best early experiments on this effect were done by Joule, and his and later results can be summarized by

$$\Delta W = J \Delta Q \tag{8-13}$$

where $J = 4.186 \times 10^3$ joules/kilocalorie and is called the *mechanical equivalent of heat* or the *heat equivalent of work*. We need not carry the symbol J along in all our equations, for when work and heat appear in the same equation we need only give them both in the same unit, joules or kilocalories as may be convenient.

We can conclude from the preceding discussion that the heat supplied to a system is not a unique function of the state since it depends on the process as well, as illustrated by the inequality $C_p \neq C_v$ and by the fact that the heat need not be added as *heat* but, for example, can be added by mechanical means involving friction or electrically by a current in a resistance. Thus a small quantity of heat added to a system is not an exact differential and must be written dQ. This, of course, means that a heat function or state variable Q, which is a definite function of the state of the system, does *not* exist. This result is analogous to the recognition that the question of how much rain there is in a lake is a meaningless one, although in principle one could always measure the amount of water which was added to the lake *as rain* during a given interval.

8-5   Equation of state of an ideal gas

As an example of a particular thermodynamic system, we shall consider the important system called an ideal gas. As the name implies, no real gas can be exactly treated as ideal, but, instead, an ideal gas represents a limiting behavior which is more closely approached by all real gases the less dense and the farther from their boiling points they are. For the usual conditions, helium is the nearest approximation to an ideal gas which we have.

The form of the equation of state can be deduced from a series of famous experimental results.

Boyle's law

For a given mass of gas and constant temperature,

$$pV = \text{const.} \tag{8-14}$$

We can conclude from this result that the constant in (8-14) may be a function of the mass and the temperature.

Charles' law

For a given mass of gas, and a suitable choice of temperature scale, the constant in (8-14) is proportional to the temperature; hence we can write

$$pV = KT \tag{8-15}$$

where K is another constant which is the same for all gases. In order to see how this result can be related to experiment, we use (8-15) in (8-2) and find that

$$\alpha = \beta = \frac{1}{T} \tag{8-16}$$

which shows that (8-15) implies that these coefficients are independent of the gas and depend only on the temperature. These conclusions are verified by experiment. We can use the results (8-16) to *define* the temperature scale T, known as the *gas thermometer scale*, by the equation $T = 1/\alpha$. If we choose the unit of this scale to be the same as the Celsius degree, we shall have the relation

$$T = t + T_0 = \frac{1}{\alpha} \qquad (8\text{-}17)$$

where t is the Celsius temperature. We see from (8-17) that the additive constant T_0 relating the two scales can be found from experiment as

$$T_0 = \frac{1}{(\alpha)_{t=0}} = 273.15 \text{ degrees} \qquad (8\text{-}18)$$

In order to evaluate K, we turn to a third result.

Avogadro's law

Although this law can be stated in various ways, it will be sufficient for our purposes to say that, under identical conditions, all gases have equal molar volumes; that is, the volume of a kilomole, v, is independent of the gas. Referring (8-15) to one kilomole, we have

$$pv = K_{\text{mole}}T = RT \qquad (8\text{-}19)$$

where $R = K_{\text{mole}}$ is called the *universal gas constant*. We can evaluate R by measuring the rest of the quantities in (8-19) for any arbitrary state; the results are generally quoted for *standard conditions*:

$p_0 = 1$ atmosphere = pressure of a column of mercury
      0.76 meter high

    $= 1.013 \times 10^5$ newtons/(meter)^2

$T_0 = 273.15$ degrees (i.e., 0°C)

$v_0 = 22.4$ liters $= 0.0224$ (meter)^3

so we can find from (8-19) that

$R = 8.31 \times 10^3$ joules/kilomole-degree $= 1.99$ kilocalories/kilomole-degree $\qquad (8\text{-}20)$

Since $v = V/v$ we can write (8-19) as $p(V/v) = RT$ or

$$pV = vRT \qquad (8\text{-}21)$$

which is the *ideal gas equation of state* and, when written as $p = vRT/V$, is in the general form originally given in (8-1).

As a simple application of this equation of state, we can use (8-21) to verify the empirical result known as *Dalton's law of partial pressures*: the pressure exerted by a mixture of ideal gases is the sum of the pressures which each gas would exert if it occupied the total volume. If ν_i is the mole number of the ith gas, $\nu = \nu_1 + \nu_2 + \cdots$ and (8-21) becomes

$$pV = (\nu_1 + \nu_2 + \cdots)RT = \nu_1 RT + \nu_2 RT + \cdots = p_1 V + p_2 V + \cdots$$

where p_i is the pressure which would be exerted by the ith gas if it alone were present; therefore

$$p = p_1 + p_2 + \cdots \tag{8-22}$$

which agrees with experiment. We also see that we can write

$$p_i = p\left(\frac{\nu_i}{\nu}\right) = \frac{p\nu_i}{\nu_1 + \nu_2 + \cdots} = px_i \tag{8-23}$$

where x_i is called the *mole fraction* of the ith gas.

Exercises

8-1. Verify that (8-4) is correct for the example of an ideal gas.

8-2. Show that $(\partial\alpha/\partial p)_T + (\partial\kappa_T/\partial T)_p = 0$.

8-3. It is found for a certain system that α and κ_T can be written in the forms

$$\alpha = \nu R/pV + \nu a/VT^2, \quad \kappa_T = (\nu T/V)f(p)$$

where a and R are constants and $f(p)$ is some function of the pressure. What sort of experimental conditions would result in an expression like that for κ_T which involves an undetermined function? Find $f(p)$ and $V = V(p, T)$. [*Hint:* Use (7-22) and (8-2).]

9 *The first law of thermodynamics*

The first law represents a generalization of the results of wide and varied experience. We shall state it in the form of a postulate consisting of essentially two parts, a definition and a characteristic property.

FIRST LAW OF THERMODYNAMICS. Every thermodynamic system possesses a state variable called the *energy* U whose increase dU equals the heat dQ added to the system plus the external work dW performed on it. The energy of an isolated system is constant.

Since U is a state variable, its differential is exact, as indicated above. The first law when stated in quantitative differential form is

$$dU = dQ + dW \tag{9-1}$$

and, therefore, in a cyclic process,

$$\oint dU = 0 \tag{9-2}$$

The first law combines the recognition of the fact that heat is a form of energy with the principle of the conservation of energy. This principle is thereby generalized from its previous form which was limited to mechanical and electromagnetic energy.

Historically, the first law usually was stated in a negative way: It is impossible to construct a machine which operates in a cycle and does a net amount of work on the surroundings without obtaining energy from an external source. In this form the first law assures us that it is impossible to build a perpetual motion machine of the first kind, that is, one which violates the energy conservation principle. However, it is important to realize that the first law is *more* than simply a restatement of the conservation of energy because of its assertion that the energy U is a well-defined function of the variables used to describe the state of the system. In fact, U must be a single-valued function, for, if it were not, we could use the multiple-valued property to construct a machine to create energy by operating it in an appropriate cycle.

If we consider a fluid system of fixed mass whose variables are p, V, T, and of which only two are independent because they are related by the equation of state (8-1), we see that U is therefore a function of only two variables and we could choose any pair; that is, we could write $U(T, V)$ or $U(T, p)$ or $U(p, V)$. The first law then tells us that, for example,

$$dU = \left(\frac{\partial U}{\partial T}\right)_V dT + \left(\frac{\partial U}{\partial V}\right)_T dV \tag{9-3}$$

is exact. For a fluid system we can substitute (8-6) into (9-1); then we have

$$dQ = dU + p\,dV \tag{9-4}$$

9-1 Heat capacities

As an example of the application of the first law, we shall see what it can tell us about the heat capacities we previously introduced as essentially the amount of heat required to change the temperature of the system of interest by one degree. The two most important cases correspond to processes at constant volume or at constant pressure; in the first, no external work is done, whereas work is involved in the second.

From (8-7) and (9-4), we see that the general heat capacity can be written

$$C = \frac{dU + p\,dV}{dT} \qquad (9\text{-}5)$$

It is convenient to regard $U = U(T, V)$ so that, for a constant volume process for which $dV = 0$, we find from (9-3) that $dU = (\partial U/\partial T)_V\,dT$ and then (9-5) yields

$$C_v = \left(\frac{dQ}{dT}\right)_V = \left(\frac{\partial U}{\partial T}\right)_V \qquad (9\text{-}6)$$

which we can use to calculate C_v if we know the dependence of U on T and V; conversely, if we measure C_v we learn about the temperature dependence of the energy.

The comparable calculation for the constant pressure process $(dp = 0)$ is more involved because we need to use both terms of (9-3). Thus we find from (9-4) that we can write, in general,

$$dQ = \left(\frac{\partial U}{\partial T}\right)_V dT + \left[\left(\frac{\partial U}{\partial V}\right)_T + p\right] dV$$

$$= C_v\,dT + \left[\left(\frac{\partial U}{\partial V}\right)_T + p\right] dV \qquad (9\text{-}7)$$

Since this is not directly applicable to our constant pressure case in this form, it is convenient to write the equation of state in the form $V = V(T, p)$ so that

$$dV = \left(\frac{\partial V}{\partial T}\right)_p dT + \left(\frac{\partial V}{\partial p}\right)_T dp \qquad (9\text{-}8)$$

If we now set $dp = 0$ in (9-8) and substitute the result into (9-7), we can identify the coefficient of dT as C_p; that is,

$$C_p = \left(\frac{dQ}{dT}\right)_p = C_v + \left[\left(\frac{\partial U}{\partial V}\right)_T + p\right]\left(\frac{\partial V}{\partial T}\right)_p \qquad (9\text{-}9)$$

Since it is generally more convenient to keep the system at constant pressure in the laboratory than to keep it at constant volume, C_p is easier to measure than is C_v. As we shall find later, however, C_v is easier to calculate theoretically; thus the important result (9-9) is very useful in the comparison of theory and experiment.

Example. Ideal Gas. From the equation of state (8-21), we find that

$$\left(\frac{\partial V}{\partial T}\right)_p = \frac{\nu R}{p} \qquad (9\text{-}10)$$

In order to evaluate the term in (9-9) which comes from the volume dependence of the energy, we must turn to direct experiment at this stage, although we shall see later that there is another way of evaluating $(\partial U/\partial V)_T$. For now, we shall simply state the experimental fact: The energy of an ideal gas is a function of the temperature *only*, that is, $U = U(T)$ (we shall justify this result in several ways, both in this chapter and later). If such is the case,

$$\left(\frac{\partial U}{\partial V}\right)_T = 0 \quad \text{(ideal gas)} \tag{9-11}$$

and, if we substitute (9-10) and (9-11) into (9-9), we can obtain the important result

$$C_p - C_v = p \cdot \frac{\nu R}{p} = \nu R \tag{9-12}$$

or, for one kilomole,

$$c_p - c_v = R \tag{9-13}$$

(Unless we state otherwise we shall always use lower-case letters to represent the kilomolar values of quantities which are proportional to the amount of material; such general quantities are called extensive.) The relation (9-12) is quite well confirmed by experiment.

Since $U = U(T)$ for the ideal gas,

$$C_v = \left(\frac{\partial U}{\partial T}\right)_V = \frac{dU}{dT} = C_v(T) \tag{9-14}$$

so that the heat capacity is also a function only of the temperature. If we integrate (9-14), we can therefore say that

$$U(T) = \int_0^T C_v(T') \, dT' + U_0 \tag{9-15}$$

which generally cannot be evaluated until the dependence of C_v on T has been determined. The constant of integration U_0 is called the *zero point energy*; from the point of view of our thermodynamic theory we cannot evaluate it further and, since only energy *changes* are of real importance, it is often customary to ignore U_0 by setting it equal to zero.

9-2 Enthalpy

We define a new state variable H called *enthalpy* by

$$H = U + pV \tag{9-16}$$

We shall see later why it is defined in this particular way. Since H is a state variable, its exact differential is given by

$$dH = dU + p \, dV + V \, dp = dQ + V \, dp \qquad (9\text{-}17)$$

with the use of (9-4).

In a constant pressure process, $dp = 0$, and we see from (9-17) that

$$dH = (dQ)_p \qquad (9\text{-}18)$$

Thus dH is the quantity of heat transferred to the system of interest from an external source during a process at constant pressure; for this reason enthalpy is often called the *heat function* because of the practical importance of constant pressure changes. If we write $H = H(T, p)$ so that

$$dH = \left(\frac{\partial H}{\partial T}\right)_p dT + \left(\frac{\partial H}{\partial p}\right)_T dp \qquad (9\text{-}19)$$

then, when $dp = 0$,

$$dH = \left(\frac{\partial H}{\partial T}\right)_p dT = (dQ)_p \qquad (9\text{-}20)$$

and we find from (8-12) that

$$C_p = \left(\frac{\partial H}{\partial T}\right)_p \qquad (9\text{-}21)$$

which is a result similar to (9-6) and in principle provides us with a method of calculating C_p by differentiation of a single function.

For an ideal gas, $pV = \nu RT$ and therefore

$$H = U + \nu RT = H(T) \quad \text{(ideal gas)} \qquad (9\text{-}22)$$

because of (9-11).

We shall have much use for enthalpy in other connections later, but for the present we shall simply indicate very briefly its importance in engineering. It is directly related to the energy flow involved in steady state processes where work is performed, as, for example, in turbines. We shall refer our considerations to one kilomole of the material which is passing through such a mechanism, as illustrated schematically in Fig. 9-1. The inlet pipe has a cross section A_1; when a kilomole of volume v_1 enters, the fluid will have been displaced a distance (v_1/A_1). Since the pressure is p_1, the force on this fluid is $p_1 A_1$ and the total work done on the fluid was $(v_1/A_1) \times (p_1 A_1) = p_1 v_1$. In addition, the entering fluid had an energy u_1 so that the total energy flux into the machine per kilomole is $u_1 + p_1 v_1 = h_1$. Similarly, the molar energy flux out is $u_2 + p_2 v_2 = h_2$. If the work done per kilomole by the machine on its surroundings is $-w$ while the heat q is consumed, then because the total energy *in* must equal the total energy *out*, since the machine is operating under steady state conditions, we must have $h_1 + q = h_2 - w$, or

$$-w = q + h_1 - h_2 \qquad (9\text{-}23)$$

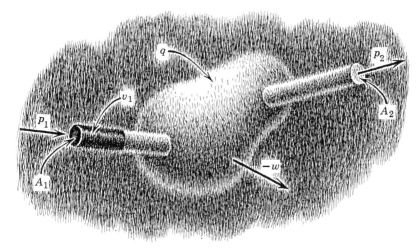

Fig. 9-1

Thus the relation between the input and the output of the machine has a very simple connection with the initial and final states of the fluid and does *not* refer to whatever specific processes may be occurring inside the apparatus.

9-3 Reversible and irreversible processes

Before we discuss particular processes in more detail, it is necessary to emphasize the important general distinction between reversible and irreversible processes. By a *reversible* process we mean one which, at any stage, can be reversed and the system of interest brought back to its initial state without producing any lasting changes of any sort in the system itself, or in its surroundings. In practice, one generally means that this idealization is a *quasi-static* process which is defined as a sequence of equilibrium states or, more accurately, as a sequence of states in which at any time the system is only infinitesimally away from a true equilibrium state.

The reason for the term "quasi-static" is that most imaginable processes of this type require that all velocities involved approach zero; hence all changes are produced infinitely slowly. For example, if our system is a gas which is allowed to expand by our decreasing the external pressure, this can be done quasi-statically and reversibly by our keeping the external pressure only infinitesimally lower than the gas pressure. The movable piston which confines the gas in the container will then move with only an infinitesimal speed, so that the friction between it and the walls will be negligible; also, no turbulence will be produced in the gas as a result of portions of the gas receiving finite velocities and thus there will be no dissipative viscous effects. As an over-all result, the gas will always be arbitrarily close to equilibrium during the whole expansion. We see that we can also describe this particular reversible process as one which may be made to reverse and proceed in the opposite direction by making an infinitesimal change in the parameters (in this case, by altering the pressure); if this is done, it will go through the same intermediate equilibrium states, but in the reverse order. Although a reversible process generally requires that everything be done infinitely slowly, this is not a sufficient condition; for example, the discharge of a condenser through a very large resistance will occur very slowly, yet the energy is dissipated as heat in the resistance, thus making the process irreversible, as we shall see in detail in the next chapter.

The principal importance of reversible processes in thermodynamics is that we can write definite *equations* to describe every part of the reversible process; the reason, of course, is that our thermodynamic equations apply only to equilibrium states and the system is always arbitrarily close to equilibrium in the sequence of intermediate stages between the initial and final states of the system.

On the other hand, natural processes encountered in practice are always *irreversible* and represent processes in which disturbed equilibria are being equalized by the flow of heat across finite temperature differences or by work being done across finite pressure differences; these dissipative effects are generally described macroscopically as friction, viscosity, hysteresis, resistance, etc. Since an irreversible process does not include equilibrium states during its intermediate stages we cannot describe such processes by equations, although we shall see that some aspects of irreversible processes can be described by inequalities. Of course, the initial and final states of an irreversible process *are* equilibrium states and we can write appropriate equations for each of them.

9-4   Reversible adiabatic and isothermal processes

The only specific processes we have considered up to this point are those for which p or V is held constant, although there are other possible processes for which other quantities are kept fixed. An important example is an *adiabatic* process which is defined as one in which no heat is added to or taken from the system, so that $dQ = 0$; we shall see in the next chapter precisely what variable remains constant in this process. An adiabatic process can be fairly well approximated in practice by enclosing the system in a good heat insulator.

Setting $dQ = 0$ in (9-4), we find that, for a fluid,

$$dU + p \, dV = 0 \qquad (9\text{-}24)$$

and, if we were to write $U = U(p, V)$ and substitute the resulting dU into (9-24), this equation would describe a family of curves, called *adiabatics*, in the pV plane.

Example. Ideal Gas. From (9-14), we find that $dU = C_v \, dT$; hence (9-24) can be written

$$C_v \, dT + p \, dV = 0 \qquad (9\text{-}25)$$

In order to put (9-25) into the form in which p and V are the only variables, we use the equation of state (8-21); from it we find that

$$dT = \frac{p \, dV + V \, dp}{\nu R} \qquad (9\text{-}26)$$

If we substitute (9-26) into (9-25) and use (9-12), we obtain

$$C_p p \, dV + C_v V \, dp = 0 \qquad (9\text{-}27)$$

If we define

$$\gamma = \frac{C_p}{C_v} = \frac{c_p}{c_v} \qquad (9\text{-}28)$$

and divide (9-27) through by pVC_v, we find that the adiabatic condition $dQ = 0$ can also be written for an ideal gas as

$$\frac{dp}{p} + \gamma \left(\frac{dV}{V} \right) = 0 \qquad (9\text{-}29)$$

If we assume for simplicity that $\gamma = \text{const.}$, we can integrate (9-29) to find that $\ln p + \gamma \ln V = \text{const.} = \ln (pV^\gamma)$, or

$$pV^\gamma = \text{const.} \qquad (9\text{-}30)$$

which is the equation describing an adiabatic process for an ideal gas. By using (8-21), we can also write (9-30) in terms of the other two pairs of variables; the results are that

$$TV^{\gamma-1} = \text{const.} \quad and \quad Tp^{(1-\gamma)/\gamma} = \text{const.} \qquad (9\text{-}30')$$

Another important example is an *isothermal* process for which the temperature is kept constant and thus $dT = 0$. For an ideal gas the equation of the curve is simply obtained by setting T equal to a constant

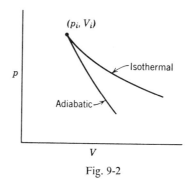

Fig. 9-2

in the equation of state (8-21); thus

$$pV = \text{const.} \tag{9-31}$$

The slope of an adiabatic can be obtained from (9-29) as

$$\frac{dp}{dV} = -\gamma \frac{p}{V} \tag{9-32}$$

while from (9-31) we find that $p\,dV + V\,dp = 0$ and thus the slope of an isothermal is found to be

$$\frac{dp}{dV} = -\frac{p}{V} \tag{9-33}$$

Since $\gamma > 1$ because of (9-12), the magnitude of the slope of an adiabatic must be greater than the magnitude of the slope of an isothermal, so that the adiabatics are steeper curves than are the isothermals. This is illustrated by Fig. 9-2 which shows the course of two expansions beginning at the same initial state (p_i, V_i); we are able to illustrate these processes as specific curves because the processes are reversible. We cannot, of course, plot intermediate stages of an irreversible process.

9-5 Free expansion

A free expansion is an example of an irreversible adiabatic process. Let us consider the experiment illustrated in Fig. 9-3 for which the apparatus consists of a well-insulated container which is divided into two parts. One portion is filled with a compressed gas, and the other portion is a vacuum. If we now quickly remove the partition, the gas will rush into the evacuated part, and eventually the gas will settle down to a new equilibrium state in which it fills the whole container. The temperature of the gas is measured both before and after the expansion.

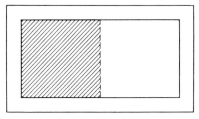

Fig. 9-3

The initial and final states are equilibrium states (although the inter-mediate ones obviously are not); hence we can write (9-1) as

$$\Delta U = \Delta Q + \Delta W \qquad (9\text{-}34)$$

Since the box is well insulated, the process is adiabatic and $\Delta Q = 0$; the gas expands against no external pressure, hence it does no work and $-\Delta W = 0$. Therefore

$$\Delta U = 0 \qquad (9\text{-}35)$$

showing that the internal energy of a gas remains constant in a free expansion. This experiment enables us to learn something about the dependence of the energy on the volume, for, if $U = U(T, V)$, then

$$\Delta U = \left(\frac{\partial U}{\partial T}\right)_V \Delta T + \left(\frac{\partial U}{\partial V}\right)_T \Delta V = 0 \qquad (9\text{-}36)$$

because of (9-35). Because of the conditions of the experiment, $\Delta V \neq 0$; therefore, if it is found that $\Delta T \neq 0$, we see from (9-36) that both the partial derivatives must be different from zero and of opposite sign in order to satisfy $\Delta U = 0$. Thus, if a difference of temperature is found for the gas, we must conclude that the energy depends on *both* the temperature and the volume.

It was found, however, that $\Delta T = 0$ for an ideal gas; therefore (9-36) becomes $(\partial U/\partial V)_T \Delta V = 0$ so that $(\partial U/\partial V)_T = 0$, which is exactly the condition (9-11). Thus this free expansion experiment shows that the energy of an ideal gas is independent of the volume; one can similarly conclude that the energy is independent of the pressure as well, so that $U = U(T)$ as was previously stated in (9-15).

9-6   Porous plug experiment

In the free expansion the gas was allowed to gain kinetic energy of mass motion. In the porous plug experiment, illustrated schematically in Fig. 9-4, the gas is made to pass slowly through the plug from compartment 1

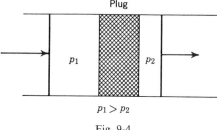

$$p_1 > p_2$$

Fig. 9-4

to compartment 2 by simultaneous motion of the two pistons. The primary purpose of the porous plug is to allow the gas to be slowed down without having it do any work on the surroundings *once the steady state has been attained.* Then one can measure the temperature change resulting from passage from one state to the other in order to get an idea of the energy change without the necessity of considering the effect of the gas having temporarily obtained kinetic energy of mass motion. Because the whole apparatus is kept well insulated, this is also an adiabatic process.

Such an arrangement is of exactly the type of steady state situation illustrated in Fig. 9-1 and described by (9-23). In this case, $q = 0$ since the process is adiabatic, and $-w = 0$ since the gas does no external work; thus (9-23) becomes

$$h_1 = h_2 \qquad (9\text{-}37)$$

Therefore the porous plug experiment is a process in which the enthalpy of the gas remains constant.

For the time being, we consider only the application of this result to an ideal gas for which the molar enthalpy is obtained from (9-22) as $h = u + RT$. Inserting this expression into (9-37), we quickly find that

$$u_2 - u_1 = -R(T_2 - T_1) = -R\,\Delta T \qquad (9\text{-}38)$$

It is found experimentally that ΔT is very small and is more nearly equal to zero the more nearly the gas is ideal; hence we conclude that, for the limiting case of an ideal gas, $\Delta T = 0$ and $u_2 = u_1$ by (9-38). Therefore u is independent of the volume, and we have again found that the energy of an ideal gas depends only on the temperature.

9-7   Another state variable for the ideal gas

We can use all this information about an ideal gas to obtain an important result which suggests the content of the next chapter. Using (8-21) and

(9-14), we can write (9-4) as

$$dQ = C_v(T)\, dT + \frac{\nu R T}{V}\, dV \qquad (9\text{-}39)$$

Now dQ is not an exact differential, but if we divide both sides of (9-39) by T we obtain

$$\frac{dQ}{T} = \frac{C_v(T)\, dT}{T} + \frac{\nu R\, dV}{V} \qquad (9\text{-}40)$$

which *is* an exact differential because the right side is integrable. Therefore, if we set

$$dS = \frac{dQ}{T} \qquad (9\text{-}41)$$

we can integrate (9-40) between the states (T_0, V_0) and (T, V) and we find that

$$S - S_0 = \int_{T_0}^{T} \frac{C_v(T')\, dT'}{T'} + \nu R \ln\left(\frac{V}{V_0}\right) \qquad (9\text{-}42)$$

and, if we assume for simplicity that $C_v = \text{const.}$, (9-42) becomes

$$S - S_0 = C_v \ln\left(\frac{T}{T_0}\right) + \nu R \ln\left(\frac{V}{V_0}\right) \qquad (9\text{-}43)$$

Thus we have found another state variable for an ideal gas since (9-43) depends only on the initial and final states and is independent of the path of integration. The function S is called the *entropy*. We can now rewrite the first law for an ideal gas in terms of entropy, for, from (9-41), $dQ = T\, dS$, and if we substitute this into (9-4) we have

$$dU = T\, dS - p\, dV \qquad (9\text{-}44)$$

which shows that T is conjugate to S in the same sense that $-p$ is to V; that is, if we write $U = U(S, V)$, then

$$T = \left(\frac{\partial U}{\partial S}\right)_V, \quad -p = \left(\frac{\partial U}{\partial V}\right)_S \qquad (9\text{-}45)$$

The variables V and S are both *extensive* variables; that is, they are proportional to the quantity of matter in the system. The variables p and T, however, are *intensive* variables; that is, their values are independent of the quantity of material. Reversible adiabatic processes are also called *isentropic* since, if $dQ = 0$, then $dS = 0$.

In the next chapter, we shall proceed with a generalization of this result and show that every system possesses the entropy as a state variable, so that this property is not restricted to an ideal gas.

Exercises

9-1. Eight liters of an ideal gas are initially at a pressure of 4 atmospheres and 200°C. The gas is allowed to expand until the pressure is reduced to 1 atmosphere. Find the final volume and temperature, the work done, and the heat absorbed under each of the following conditions: (*a*) isothermal expansion; (*b*) adiabatic expansion ($\gamma = \frac{5}{3}$); (*c*) the expansion is into a vacuum.

9-2. A certain system has the equation of state $V = AT + (p/B)$ and its energy is given by $U = CT - \frac{1}{2}BV^2$ where A, B, and C are constants. Find the enthalpy, C_v, and C_p.

9-3. Discuss in detail how you could perform a reversible expansion of a gas in a cylinder closed off by a movable piston. How would you store the work done by the expanding gas as potential energy of the surroundings so that if the process were reversed the work could be retrieved without permanently altering the surroundings?

10 *The second law of thermodynamics*

We shall proceed as before by stating the second law as a postulate which has two parts: a definition and a characteristic property.

SECOND LAW OF THERMODYNAMICS. Every thermodynamic system possesses a state variable called the *entropy S* whose increase dS equals the heat absorbed in an infinitesimal reversible change dQ_{rev} divided by the simultaneously defined "absolute temperature" T. The entropy of an isolated system in equilibrium is a maximum.

Historically, the beginnings of the second law can be found in the work of Carnot, who was interested in the study of the possible efficiencies of machines, such as steam engines, for converting heat into work. Even before the second law was clearly formulated, it was known that mechanical energy could be completely converted into heat at will, by means of friction for example, but that a given amount of heat could only be partially converted into work even in machines from which friction had been eliminated as much as possible. Accordingly, the early statements of the second law were phrased in terms of the impossibility of certain machines. One form due to *Clausius* says: It is impossible to construct a device which, operating in a cycle, will produce no effect other than the transfer of heat from a cooler to a hotter body. (This form reflects the experience that work is always required to transfer heat from a cold to a hot reservoir since the natural direction of heat flow is from hot to cold.)

Another form is due to *Kelvin* and *Planck*: It is impossible to construct an engine which operates in a cycle and produces no effect other than the extraction of heat from a reservoir and the performance of an equal amount of work. (We note first of all that such a machine would not violate the law of conservation of energy. This form reflects the experience that as yet no one has built an engine which operates without rejecting some heat at a lower temperature than the temperature at which heat is taken in.) Our approach will be to show that our statement of the second law is equivalent to these older statements; it is interesting to note their negative aspect in contrast to our more positive postulation form.

It is clear that it would be of great practical importance if the second law were not correct because there are tremendous stores of thermal energy available in the oceans and the earth, and all that one would need to do would be to cool them off by extracting heat from them. However, this cannot be done because it has been found by experience that we always require something of still lower temperature to which we can reject some heat. It should also be noted that these older formulations emphasize the cyclic nature of the process. A little thought, however, quickly shows that this is the only feasible way of constructing a machine which could continue working indefinitely. For example, if one obtained work by using the expansion of a gas to operate a piston, the gas pressure would decrease during the expansion until it eventually reached atmospheric pressure and then the whole process would cease. In order to continue getting work, the gas would have to be compressed again, thus producing a cycle. A machine which would operate in violation of the second law is called a perpetual motion machine of the second kind.

We shall not show the precise equivalence of the Clausius and Kelvin-Planck statements of the second law, although it is reasonably clear that they refer to essentially the same sort of thing. Instead we shall proceed directly to the rather lengthy and indirect process of showing their equivalence to our statement about the existence of entropy; we begin with the consideration of a special engine devised by Carnot.

10-1 The Carnot cycle

Let us assume that the working part of our engine is an arbitrary but homogeneous fluid. Thus we can define its state completely by giving only the two mechanical variables p and V; the temperature θ, as measured on some convenient, arbitrary empirical scale, can then be determined from the equation of state. The Carnot cycle through which we imagine our fluid taken is illustrated in the pV plane of Fig. 10-1 and consists of the

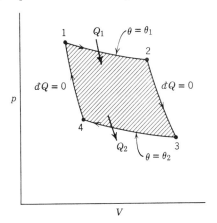

Fig. 10-1

two isothermal processes ($1 \to 2$ and $3 \to 4$) and the two adiabatic processes ($2 \to 3$ and $4 \to 1$) so that the system is finally brought back to the initial state 1. All processes are assumed to be reversible. As the system traverses the isothermal $1 \to 2$, it is necessary to add the heat Q_1 to the system from an external heat reservoir (like the boiler of a locomotive) at the constant temperature θ_1, while, on the other isothermal $3 \to 4$, an amount of heat Q_2 is rejected by the system to a cooler reservoir (such as the atmosphere) at the temperature θ_2. The net amount of heat added is

$$\Delta Q = Q_1 - Q_2 \qquad (10\text{-}1)$$

The total work W_e done *by* the system on the surroundings is

$$W_e = -W = \oint p \, dV \qquad (10\text{-}2)$$

which equals the area enclosed by the cycle on the pV plane. Since the system returns to its initial state, the change in energy is zero according to (9-2); hence $\Delta Q + W = \Delta Q - W_e = 0$, or

$$W_e = Q_1 - Q_2 \qquad (10\text{-}3)$$

We define the *efficiency* η of the cycle as the ratio of the work done by the system to the heat input, so that

$$\eta = \frac{W_e}{Q_1} = 1 - \frac{Q_2}{Q_1} \qquad (10\text{-}4)$$

with the help of (10-3).

We now want to show that the efficiency of this engine is independent of the properties of the particular fluid which is being used. Let us consider two engines E and E' which use different fluids but which operate between the same heat reservoirs of temperatures θ_1 and θ_2 and which do the same work W_e. The quantities of heat corresponding to E' are Q_1' and Q_2' and its efficiency is η'. Suppose we assume that

$$\eta' > \eta \qquad (10\text{-}5)$$

Let us arrange the engine so that E (which is reversible) operates as a refrigerator on the cycle 1 4 3 2 1 of Fig. 10-1 and is driven by E' so that E' adds the work $|W_e'| = |W_e|$ to E; this situation is illustrated very schematically in Fig. 10-2. From (10-4) we have $\eta' = |W_e|/Q_1'$ and $\eta = |W_e|/Q_1$, so that we find from (10-5) that $Q_1 > Q_1'$; in other words, the hotter reservoir gets more heat from E than it gives to E'. Since the two engines are being operated simultaneously, the net effect of one cycle is that this quantity of heat, $Q_1 - Q_1'$, is transferred from the lower temperature θ_2 to the higher temperature θ_1 without performing work and without making any permanent changes in the two engines or their surroundings. However, this violates the Clausius statement of the second law, and we must conclude that (10-5) is impossible. Similarly, by interchanging the roles of E and E', we can show that $\eta > \eta'$ is equally impossible; hence a consequence of the second law is that

$$\eta = \eta' \qquad (10\text{-}6)$$

This says that all reversible Carnot engines which exchange heat only at the two temperatures θ_1 and θ_2 have equal efficiencies. Therefore η can

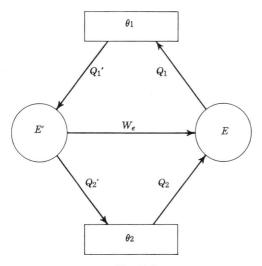

Fig. 10-2

depend only on these two temperatures, and we see from (10-4) that

$$\frac{Q_1}{Q_2} = f(\theta_1, \theta_2) \tag{10-7}$$

where f is a universal function of the temperatures and is independent of the nature of the working fluid.

We also see now that this conclusion is not restricted to fluid systems but applies to any material, because we used only the fact that the Carnot cycle involves adiabatics and isothermals. We now want to determine the properties of this function f defined in (10-7).

10-2 Absolute temperature

Let us consider two reversible Carnot engines (E and E') operating between the two temperatures θ_1 and θ_2 as well as using a reservoir of arbitrary, but intermediate, temperature θ_0, so that θ_0 acts as the cool reservoir for one cycle, absorbing the heat Q_0 and rejecting this same amount to the other engine for which it serves as the hot reservoir. This process is illustrated in Fig. 10-3. It is clear that this arrangement is, in effect, a single engine operating between the temperatures θ_1 and θ_2, absorbing the heat Q_1 and rejecting the heat Q_2; thus (10-7) applies to the over-all system. If we apply (10-7) to the engines separately, we can also write

$$\frac{Q_1}{Q_0} = f(\theta_1, \theta_0), \quad \frac{Q_0}{Q_2} = f(\theta_0, \theta_2) \tag{10-8}$$

Multiplying together the two equations of (10-8) and using (10-7), we find that

$$f(\theta_1, \theta_2) = f(\theta_1, \theta_0)f(\theta_0, \theta_2) \tag{10-9}$$

If we consider the special case $\theta_1 = \theta_2$, then $Q_1 = Q_2$, so that $f(\theta_2, \theta_2) = 1$ by (10-7) and (10-9) becomes $1 = f(\theta_2, \theta_0)f(\theta_0, \theta_2)$ and therefore

$$f(\theta_0, \theta_2) = \frac{1}{f(\theta_2, \theta_0)} \tag{10-10}$$

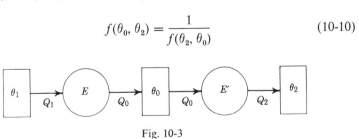

Fig. 10-3

As a result, (10-9) can now be written

$$f(\theta_1, \theta_2) = \frac{f(\theta_1, \theta_0)}{f(\theta_2, \theta_0)} \tag{10-11}$$

which has the appearance of θ_0 having "cancelled out" in order to make the left side independent of θ_0. Therefore we conclude that it is possible to satisfy (10-11) in general by writing f in the form

$$f(\theta_1, \theta_2) = \frac{\phi(\theta_1)}{\phi(\theta_2)} \tag{10-12}$$

where $\phi(\theta)$ is another universal function, but now only of a single temperature. With the substitution of (10-12) into (10-7), we find that

$$\frac{Q_1}{Q_2} = \frac{\phi(\theta_1)}{\phi(\theta_2)} \tag{10-13}$$

Since ϕ is a universal function of the empirical temperature θ, we can use the existence of this function to define a new temperature scale, which we shall call the *absolute temperature* T, by means of the equation

$$T = \phi(\theta) \tag{10-14}$$

putting off until later the question of exactly how this can be done in practice. Combining (10-14) and (10-13), we find that

$$\frac{Q_1}{Q_2} = \frac{T_1}{T_2} \tag{10-15}$$

so that the efficiency as obtained from (10-4) is

$$\eta = 1 - \frac{T_2}{T_1} = \frac{T_1 - T_2}{T_1} \tag{10-16}$$

If we want to compare the absolute temperatures of the two reservoirs, we see now that in principle all we have to do is to operate a reversible Carnot engine between these reservoirs and measure the engine's efficiency. The efficiency will be unity only when $T_2 = 0$; since this would represent the complete conversion of heat into work, it is reasonable to call this temperature *absolute zero*.

Before we go on to apply these results to an arbitrary reversible cycle, we shall first show that the absolute temperature scale T defined by (10-14) is identical with the ideal gas temperature scale (which we temporarily write as T_g) and which is defined by the ideal gas equation of state $pV = \nu R T_g$. In order to do this, let us assume that we are using ν kilomoles of an ideal gas as the working fluid in the Carnot cycle of Fig.

10-1, in which we now label the isothermal portions with the temperatures T_{g1} and T_{g2}.

For the isothermal processes, $dT = 0$, so that $dU = 0$ by (9-14) and therefore $dQ = p \, dV$ by (9-4). Integrating along the isothermal $1 \rightarrow 2$ and using (8-21), we find

$$Q_1 = \int_1^2 p \, dV = \int_1^2 \frac{\nu R T_{g1} \, dV}{V} = \nu R T_{g1} \ln \frac{V_2}{V_1} \qquad (10\text{-}17)$$

Similarly,

$$Q_2 = \int_4^3 p \, dV = \nu R T_{g2} \ln \frac{V_3}{V_4} \qquad (10\text{-}18)$$

and then

$$\frac{Q_1}{Q_2} = \left(\frac{T_{g1}}{T_{g2}}\right) \frac{\ln (V_2/V_1)}{\ln (V_3/V_4)} \qquad (10\text{-}19)$$

Equation (9-30′) applies to the adiabatic processes, so that for the expansion $2 \rightarrow 3$ we have

$$T_{g1} V_2^{\gamma-1} = T_{g2} V_3^{\gamma-1} \qquad (10\text{-}20)$$

while for $4 \rightarrow 1$ we have

$$T_{g2} V_4^{\gamma-1} = T_{g1} V_1^{\gamma-1} \qquad (10\text{-}21)$$

Multiplying (10-20) and (10-21) together, we find that

$$T_{g1} T_{g2} (V_2 V_4)^{\gamma-1} = T_{g1} T_{g2} (V_3 V_1)^{\gamma-1}$$

and therefore $V_2 V_4 = V_3 V_1$; this can also be written as $V_2/V_1 = V_3/V_4$, which leads to

$$\ln \frac{V_2}{V_1} = \ln \frac{V_3}{V_4} \qquad (10\text{-}22)$$

When we insert (10-22) into (10-19) and use (10-15), we find that

$$\frac{Q_1}{Q_2} = \frac{T_{g1}}{T_{g2}} = \frac{T_1}{T_2} \qquad (10\text{-}23)$$

where T_1 and T_2 are the absolute temperatures. We can conclude from this that

$$T_{\text{gas}} = T_{\text{absolute}} \qquad (10\text{-}24)$$

provided that the degree is chosen to be the same for each scale. Accordingly, we no longer need to decide whether the temperature scale we are using is based on (8-21) or on (10-15), and we can simply continue writing T for the temperature, which we shall always measure on the absolute scale, unless we specifically say otherwise.

10-3 Arbitrary reversible cycles and the existence of entropy

It will be convenient to revert to our normal sign convention for heat for which the rejected heat is considered to be negative, so that (10-15) becomes $Q_1/T_1 = -Q_2/T_2$. If we now apply this basic result to a Carnot cycle whose isothermal portions represent infinitesimal changes of state, the quantities of heat transferred will also be infinitesimal and we shall have $dQ_1/T_1 = -dQ_2/T_2$ or

$$\frac{dQ_1}{T_1} + \frac{dQ_2}{T_2} = 0 \qquad (10\text{-}25)$$

Let us now consider an arbitrary, reversible cycle involving an arbitrary fluid which can be represented by the closed curve in the pV plane as shown in Fig. 10-4. As shown by the heavy saw-tooth line on the figure, we can approximate the closed curve representing this cycle as closely as we please by using the isothermals and portions of the adiabatics of properly chosen, neighboring infinitesimal Carnot cycles. Since (10-25) holds for each of the infinitesimal cycles, when we sum these expressions up for all the exchanges of heat for the whole reversible cycle, we obtain in the limit

$$\oint \frac{dQ_{\text{rev}}}{T} = 0 \qquad (10\text{-}26)$$

where we have added the subscript to dQ to emphasize the reversible nature of the cycle. According to (7-19) the vanishing of this integral over the closed path means that the integrand is an exact differential of some

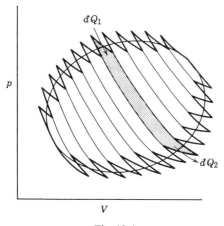

Fig. 10-4

function which we call *entropy* and write as S, so that

$$dS = \frac{dQ_{\text{rev}}}{T} \tag{10-27}$$

For a fluid, where we can use the first law in the form (9-4), we have

$$T\,dS = dU + p\,dV \tag{10-28}$$

The result (10-27) is the basis for sometimes defining the absolute temperature as the integrating factor for heat.

Although we have obtained this result only for the special system consisting of a homogeneous fluid, it can be shown without too much difficulty that (10-26) is also true for any reversible cycle of any system of interest and is equivalent to the first part of our statement of the second law, where it was asserted that every system possesses entropy as a state variable.

The difference in the entropy of two arbitrary states A and B can be calculated by integrating (10-27) to obtain

$$S_B - S_A = \int_A^B \frac{dQ_{\text{rev}}}{T} \tag{10-29}$$

It is important to remember that the path of integration used in (10-29) is completely arbitrary, as long as it is reversible, since the entropy depends only on the state; thus the path chosen to calculate $S_B - S_A$ can be chosen solely for convenience, and it need have no relation to the actual way in which the system changed its state from A to B. In particular, the process $A \rightarrow B$ may have been completely irreversible, yet (10-29) will, of course, give the correct entropy difference. Let us illustrate these remarks with a particular example.

Example. Ideal Gas in a Porous Plug Experiment.   Since the process is adiabatic, $dQ_{\text{actual}} = 0$ and for the *real* process

$$\int_A^B \frac{dQ_{\text{actual}}}{T} = 0 \tag{10-30}$$

but this is not the entropy change because the actual process is irreversible. According to (10-29), in order to calculate the entropy change we need a reversible process which will take the system from the same initial state to the same final state which, we recall, corresponds to no temperature change for an ideal gas; let us accordingly choose an *isothermal* reversible expansion from V_A to V_B as our process to be used for calculations.

Since we are considering an ideal gas and $T = $ const., $dU = 0$ and (9-4) becomes $dQ_{rev} = p\,dV$. We also have $pV = \nu RT = $ const., from (8-21), so that (10-29) becomes

$$S_B - S_A = \int_{V_A}^{V_B} \frac{p\,dV}{T} = \nu R \int_{V_A}^{V_B} \frac{dV}{V} = \nu R \ln \frac{V_B}{V_A} \tag{10-31}$$

It will be left as an exercise to show that the same result will be obtained by integrating along any other reversible path between these two states.

This example with its contrast between (10-30) and (10-31) clearly shows that the existence and value of the entropy of the final state depends only on the state and not on whether it was reached reversibly or irreversibly. We also note that (10-29) gives us only changes in the entropy, so that the actual value of S for a given state is determined only up to an additive constant; later, we shall find several ways of deciding the proper value for this constant.

10-4 Irreversible processes and the second part of the second law

Let us again consider the situation involving the two Carnot engines E and E' which is depicted in Fig. 10-2, but let us now assume that E' is *not* reversible. If we again assume that $\eta' > \eta$ and repeat all the considerations following (10-5), we shall again find at the end of one cycle that the net effect has been a transfer of heat from the cold reservoir to the hot one. Since this is impossible according to Clausius' statement of the second law, we conclude as before that it is impossible to have $\eta' > \eta$. We clearly cannot have equal efficiencies, $\eta' = \eta$, because E' is irreversible and has dissipative energy losses that E does not have. Thus the only possibility is that

$$\eta > \eta' \tag{10-32}$$

Hence a reversible Carnot engine has a greater efficiency than an irreversible Carnot engine which is operating between the same temperatures and producing the same work per cycle. Because of (10-32), we have $(1 - \eta) < (1 - \eta')$ and therefore (10-4) yields

$$\frac{Q_2}{Q_1} < \frac{Q_2'}{Q_1'} \tag{10-33}$$

If we use (10-15) to replace Q_2/Q_1 in (10-33), we find that $T_2/T_1 < Q_2'/Q_1'$, or that

$$\frac{Q_1'}{T_1} < \frac{Q_2'}{T_2} \tag{10-34}$$

holds for an irreversible Carnot engine. If the engine has infinitesimal isothermals in it, we can write (10-34) as $(dQ_1'/T_1) < (dQ_2'/T_2)$ which becomes

$$\frac{dQ_1'}{T_1} + \frac{dQ_2'}{T_2} < 0 \tag{10-35}$$

when we again regard rejected heat as negative.

If we now consider an arbitrary cycle that is completely or partially irreversible by subdividing it into a large number of infinitesimal cycles exactly as we did after (10-25), then because (10-35) is now applicable rather than (10-25) we obtain

$$\oint \frac{dQ}{T} < 0 \tag{10-36}$$

instead of (10-26). Combining (10-26) and (10-36), we can state the general result that

$$\oint \frac{dQ}{T} \leqslant 0 \tag{10-37}$$

with the equality holding only if the cycle is completely reversible.

Let us now consider two states A and B and construct a cycle in which we go from A to B by an irreversible process and from B to A by a reversible process. The inequality of (10-37) applies to the whole cycle, and since we can use (10-29) for the reversible part we obtain

$$\oint \frac{dQ}{T} = \int_A^B \frac{dQ_{\text{irrev}}}{T} + \int_B^A \frac{dQ_{\text{rev}}}{T} = \int_A^B \frac{dQ_{\text{irrev}}}{T} + S_A - S_B < 0$$

which can be written

$$S_B - S_A > \int_A^B \frac{dQ_{\text{irrev}}}{T} \tag{10-38}$$

and is applicable to any system. We have already seen an example of this result in our discussion of the porous plug experiment in the last section where we found the entropy change by (10-31) to be greater than the value of the integral given by (10-30).

In general, we can write

$$dQ_{\text{irrev}} = (dQ^e)_{\text{irrev}} + (dQ^i)_{\text{irrev}} \tag{10-39}$$

where the superscript e refers to heat transfer between the system of interest and its surroundings and i refers to internal transfers of heat within the system. For an *isolated* system, $(dQ^e)_{\text{irrev}} = 0$, and (10-38) becomes

$$S_B - S_A > \int_A^B \frac{(dQ^i)_{\text{irrev}}}{T} \tag{10-40}$$

If there are no internal transfers of heat in the system, the integral is zero and $S_B > S_A$. If there are internal transfers of heat within the system, the integral will be positive, as we can show by considering the typical situation in which a quantity of heat Q is transferred by the natural irreversible process of conduction from a portion of the system at temperature T_1 to another portion at temperature T_2; the contribution of this process to the integral of (10-40) is

$$-\frac{Q}{T_1} + \frac{Q}{T_2} > 0$$

since $T_1 > T_2$ because the heat flow is from the higher temperature region to that of lower temperature. Therefore $S_B > S_A$ also when there are internal transfers of heat.

Consequently, for an *isolated* system, we shall have

$$S_B > S_A \qquad (10\text{-}41)$$

in general, except for the case when the system is in internal equilibrium; then no irreversible processes can occur, the equality of (10-37) is applicable, there are no transfers of heat, and $S_B = S_A$. In other words, the entropy of an isolated system in equilibrium is a constant, and in fact it is a *maximum* since (10-41) shows us that any entropy changes which will occur in an isolated system will be increases. Thus we have demonstrated the validity of the second part of the second law. By using (10-41) as a way of stating the second law, we ascribe a definite sense or direction to natural processes; equation (10-41) is also sometimes helpful in deciding whether a certain process is spontaneously possible or not by determining whether or not the corresponding entropy change would satisfy (10-41).

10-5 Relation between the energy and the equation of state

Several times in our discussions we have needed the dependence of the energy on the other variables, particularly on the volume. We shall reconsider this problem as an illustration of one application of the second law.

Suppose we regard T and V as the independent variables so that we can write $S = S(T, V)$. If we calculate dS, equate the result to the combined first and second laws (10-28), and use (9-3) in order to express everything completely in terms of T and V, we find

$$dS = \left(\frac{\partial S}{\partial T}\right)_V dT + \left(\frac{\partial S}{\partial V}\right)_T dV = \frac{dU + p\,dV}{T}$$

$$= \frac{1}{T}\left[\left(\frac{\partial U}{\partial T}\right)_V dT + \left(\frac{\partial U}{\partial V}\right)_T dV + p\,dV\right]$$

and, therefore, on equating coefficients of corresponding differentials, we find that

$$\left(\frac{\partial S}{\partial T}\right)_V = \frac{1}{T}\left(\frac{\partial U}{\partial T}\right)_V \tag{10-42}$$

$$\left(\frac{\partial S}{\partial V}\right)_T = \frac{1}{T}\left[\left(\frac{\partial U}{\partial V}\right)_T + p\right] \tag{10-43}$$

From (9-6) and (10-42), we see that we can also write

$$C_v = T\left(\frac{\partial S}{\partial T}\right)_V \tag{10-44}$$

We also see from (10-43) that (9-9) can be written

$$C_p - C_v = T\left(\frac{\partial S}{\partial V}\right)_T\left(\frac{\partial V}{\partial T}\right)_p \tag{10-45}$$

However, it is possible to put $(C_p - C_v)$ into an even more useful form. We base our considerations on the equality of the mixed second partial derivatives as expressed by (7-22) which, for this case, becomes

$$\frac{\partial^2 S}{\partial V\,\partial T} = \frac{\partial^2 S}{\partial T\,\partial V}$$

so that, when (10-42) and (10-43) are used, we find that

$$\left\{\frac{\partial}{\partial V}\left[\frac{1}{T}\left(\frac{\partial U}{\partial T}\right)_V\right]\right\}_T = \frac{1}{T}\frac{\partial}{\partial V}\left(\frac{\partial U}{\partial T}\right)_V = \frac{1}{T}\frac{\partial}{\partial T}\left(\frac{\partial U}{\partial V}\right)_T = \frac{\partial}{\partial T}\left\{\frac{1}{T}\left[\left(\frac{\partial U}{\partial V}\right)_T + p\right]\right\}$$

$$= -\frac{1}{T^2}\left[\left(\frac{\partial U}{\partial V}\right)_T + p\right] + \frac{1}{T}\frac{\partial}{\partial T}\left[\left(\frac{\partial U}{\partial V}\right)_T + p\right]$$

which, when the third term is cancelled from the last term, leads to

$$\left(\frac{\partial U}{\partial V}\right)_T = T\left(\frac{\partial p}{\partial T}\right)_V - p \tag{10-46}$$

Then (9-9) can be written

$$C_p - C_v = T\left(\frac{\partial p}{\partial T}\right)_V\left(\frac{\partial V}{\partial T}\right)_p \tag{10-47}$$

We see that the last two equations are now in such a form that in order to evaluate the important quantities on the left we need only know the equation of state. On comparing (10-43) and (10-46), we also get the interesting result that

$$\left(\frac{\partial S}{\partial V}\right)_T = \left(\frac{\partial p}{\partial T}\right)_V \tag{10-48}$$

which enables us to learn something about the entropy of a system from its equation of state.

Example. Energy of an Ideal Gas. We find from $pV = vRT$ that $(\partial p/\partial T)_V = vR/V$, which when used in (10-46) gives $(\partial U/\partial V)_T = 0$ just as in (9-11). Again we find that the energy of an ideal gas is independent of the volume as we deduced from the free expansion and porous plug experiments, except that now we see that it follows rigorously from the known equation of state and the formula (10-46) which was derived from the second law.

Example. Relation between the Heat Capacities. The result (10-47) which also follows from the second law has been tested by experiment. It is usual to express it in terms of more directly determined experimental quantities. If we use (8-2) to evaluate the derivatives, we find that (10-47) can be written

$$C_p - C_v = \alpha \beta p V T \tag{10-49}$$

and, if we use (8-4) to eliminate β, we obtain

$$C_p - C_v = \frac{\alpha^2 V T}{\kappa_T} \tag{10-50}$$

which is a very general result and is especially useful for discussing solids.

In the case of an ideal gas we have $\alpha = \beta = 1/T$ by (8-16) and (10-49) becomes

$$C_p - C_v = \frac{pV}{T} = vR$$

exactly as we found before in (9-12), except that now we can regard it as having been obtained more accurately, since we required only the knowledge of the equation of state.

Exercises

10-1. Show that the Clausius and Kelvin-Planck statements of the second law are equivalent.

10-2. Show, by integrating over at least three different paths in the pV plane which have the same values of T at the beginning and end, that the value of the entropy difference for an ideal gas is always given by (10-31).

10-3. Verify that (10-47) is satisfied by the system of Exercise 9-2.

10-4. It is asserted that the equation of state of a certain system is given by $pV = DT + Bp$ and its energy is given by $U = CT - (A/V)$, where A, B, C, and D are constants. Show, with the help of (10-47), that this is impossible.

10-5. The energy of a system is given by $U = bVT^4$ and the equation of state is given by $pV = aU$, where a and b are constants. Show that $a = \frac{1}{3}$.

10-6. What is the shape of a Carnot cycle when it is drawn in the TS plane? What is the physical interpretation of the area? To what aspect of the figure is the efficiency related?

11 Thermodynamic potentials

The last few examples of the previous chapter illustrate the useful type of relation which can be obtained simply from the knowledge that dS, for example, is an exact differential. On the other hand, it is also evident that a certain amount of skill is required to be able to choose the appropriate independent variables as well as exactly how to proceed in differentiation. Fortunately, these methods can be systematized in such a way that the more significant and useful relations can be selected without too much difficulty from the extremely large number of possible ones.

11-1   The potentials and their natural variables

For a homogeneous system possessing one mechanical and one thermal degree of freedom, we have found that there are two pairs of conjugate variables (T, S) and $(-p, V)$; each pair consists of one extensive variable (S, V) and its conjugate intensive variable $(T, -p)$. The mechanical intensive variable is $-p$ because the first law has the form

$$dU = T\,dS - p\,dV \tag{11-1}$$

This differential form indicates that it is natural to regard the extensive variable U as a function of the other extensive variables so that $U = U(S, V)$. Since we would then have

$$dU = \left(\frac{\partial U}{\partial S}\right)_V dS + \left(\frac{\partial U}{\partial V}\right)_S dV \tag{11-2}$$

we see, on comparing with (11-1), that the intensive variables would be given as functions of the extensive variables by

$$T = \left(\frac{\partial U}{\partial S}\right)_V, \quad -p = \left(\frac{\partial U}{\partial V}\right)_S \tag{11-3}$$

which are the same results we found first for the ideal gas in (9-45).

The last equations show us that in a sense we can call U a "potential" by analogy with the mechanical case, because the variables conjugate to the independent variables can be simply obtained from the function U by differentiation with respect to the corresponding independent variable. However, the selection of the independent variables may actually be determined primarily by experimental convenience; if we want to use pairs of independent variables consisting of one thermal variable and one mechanical variable per pair, then for a system of constant composition there is a total of four possibilities from which to make our choice: (S, V); (S, p); (T, V); (T, p). We know that U is the potential for which (S, V) are the natural independent variables, and we want to find the potentials appropriate to the other pairs of variables. Since we want to replace an original variable by its conjugate as the new independent variable, the appropriate method is to form the necessary Legendre transformations of the energy according to the rule discussed in Sec. 7-2 and given by (7-13), that is, by subtracting the product of the two conjugate variables whose role we wish to interchange. Thus we can construct the following scheme for changing the variable pairs:

$$\text{from} \begin{bmatrix} S, V \\ S, V \\ S, V \end{bmatrix} \text{to} \begin{bmatrix} S, p \\ T, V \\ T, p \end{bmatrix}, \quad \text{subtract} \begin{bmatrix} -pV \\ TS \\ -pV + TS \end{bmatrix}$$

In this way, starting from $U(S, V)$, we can form three more potentials which are functions of the indicated variables:

$$H(S, p) = U + pV = \text{enthalpy} \tag{11-4a}$$

$$F(T, V) = U - TS = \text{Helmholtz function} \tag{11-4b}$$

$$G(T, p) = U + pV - TS = \text{Gibbs function} \tag{11-4c}$$

The function F is sometimes called the *free energy*; G is also known as the *Gibbs free energy*.

We can verify that the listed variables are actually the independent ones by calculating the differentials of (11-4) and using (11-1); the results are found to be

$$dH = T\,dS + V\,dp \tag{11-5a}$$

$$dF = -S\,dT - p\,dV \tag{11-5b}$$

$$dG = -S\,dT + V\,dp \tag{11-5c}$$

Using the same method we used to obtain (11-3) from (11-1), we find at once from (11-5) that

$$T = \left(\frac{\partial H}{\partial S}\right)_p, \qquad V = \left(\frac{\partial H}{\partial p}\right)_S \tag{11-6a}$$

$$-S = \left(\frac{\partial F}{\partial T}\right)_V, \qquad -p = \left(\frac{\partial F}{\partial V}\right)_T \tag{11-6b}$$

$$-S = \left(\frac{\partial G}{\partial T}\right)_p, \qquad V = \left(\frac{\partial G}{\partial p}\right)_T \tag{11-6c}$$

We also see that the right-hand equations of (11-6b) and (11-6c) are actually equations of state. These relations in which the conjugate variables are derived by differentiation, as in (11-3), are partial justification for also giving the name of potential to the functions of (11-4). We can now proceed further and obtain some remarkable and useful relations from these results.

11-2 Maxwell's reciprocal relations

These relations are simply expressions of the equality of mixed second partial derivatives. For example, from (11-3) and

$$\frac{\partial^2 U}{\partial S \, \partial V} = \frac{\partial^2 U}{\partial V \, \partial S}$$

we find that

$$\left(\frac{\partial T}{\partial V}\right)_S = -\left(\frac{\partial p}{\partial S}\right)_V \tag{11-7a}$$

Similarly, using the equations of (11-6) to form $\partial^2 H/\partial S \, \partial p$, $\partial^2 F/\partial T \, \partial V$, and $\partial^2 G/\partial T \, \partial p$, we find that

$$\left(\frac{\partial T}{\partial p}\right)_S = \left(\frac{\partial V}{\partial S}\right)_p \tag{11-7b}$$

$$\left(\frac{\partial S}{\partial V}\right)_T = \left(\frac{\partial p}{\partial T}\right)_V \tag{11-7c}$$

$$\left(\frac{\partial S}{\partial p}\right)_T = -\left(\frac{\partial V}{\partial T}\right)_p \tag{11-7d}$$

We recall that in (10-48) we had already given (11-7c), which we had obtained in a different manner.

The principal use of these reciprocal relations is to express certain derivatives in terms of more easily accessible quantities, as we shall see in examples to follow. The equations (11-7) are quite difficult to memorize and, when they are needed, it is generally much easier and more accurate to start afresh and derive them as needed from the definitions of the various potentials given by (11-4).

11-3 Use of the potentials to characterize thermodynamic equilibrium

In mechanics the condition of stable equilibrium can be characterized as corresponding to a minimum in the potential energy. Since we have been describing these new functions (11-4) as "potentials," it should not be too surprising to find that extreme values of them also correspond to equilibrium situations. We can begin this investigation by restating our basic result that the entropy of an isolated system never decreases. By definition, an isolated system cannot interchange heat or work with its surroundings; hence we know that U and V will both be constant. Since the system will be in equilibrium when no more changes occur, and since all changes in this isolated system will tend to increase its entropy, equilibrium will correspond to a maximum value of the entropy. Thus we can state our *fundamental condition for equilibrium* for an isolated system as

$$S_i = \text{maximum}, \quad U_i = \text{const.}, \quad V_i = \text{const.} \tag{11-8}$$

In practice, however, almost never are we interested in nor do we deal with a strictly isolated system, because the situations we want to discuss involve systems which are not isolated but which are free to interact with their surroundings, that is, with the rest of the laboratory, the city, the atmosphere, and in principle with the whole universe, although many of these interactions are really quite small. Therefore it is natural to ask whether it is possible to discuss the equilibrium of a general system, which is free to interact with its surroundings, solely in terms of a function or functions characteristic *only of the system itself* and properly chosen so as to take into account the behavior of the surroundings which generally are of an indeterminate and unspecifiable nature. However, we can obviously take the system of interest *plus* its surroundings as a large isolated system to which (11-8) applies. In order to accomplish this in a quantitative manner, it is customary in thermodynamics to replace the rather indefinite surroundings by the definite concept of a *heat reservoir*, which is defined as a very large system at the temperature T and whose heat capacity is assumed to be so large that its temperature remains constant no matter how much heat is added to or taken from it. Thus we take the system of interest plus the heat reservoir as our isolated system, as illustrated schematically in Fig. 11-1.

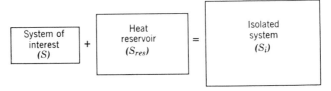

Fig. 11-1

Since $S_i = S + S_{res}$, the fundamental condition that the entropy of an isolated system can only increase becomes

$$dS + dS_{res} \geqslant 0 \qquad (11\text{-}9)$$

We can easily calculate the entropy change of the reservoir because the only heat gained by the reservoir is due to an equal heat loss from the system of interest, so that

$$dS_{res} = \frac{dQ_{res}}{T} = -\frac{dQ}{T} = -\frac{dU + p\,dV}{T} \qquad (11\text{-}10)$$

and therefore (11-9) can be written as $dS \geqslant (dU + p\,dV)/T$, or

$$T\,dS \geqslant dU + p\,dV \qquad (11\text{-}11)$$

which is actually the fundamental statement (11-9) but now involves only quantities referring to the system of interest because the effect of the reservoir has been taken into account. We now apply (11-11) to some more specialized processes.

Processes at constant entropy and volume

If $dS = 0$ and $dV = 0$, we see from (11-11) that

$$dU \leqslant 0 \qquad (11\text{-}12)$$

Thus the energy can only decrease in this kind of process, and the equilibrium state can be characterized by

$$U = \text{minimum}, \quad S = \text{const.}, \quad V = \text{const.} \qquad (11\text{-}13)$$

In this sense, we see that the energy U behaves somewhat like mechanical potential energy. Although this result (11-13) is of interest as an alternative way of stating (11-8), it is not of as practical importance as the results we shall obtain next.

Processes at constant temperature

If $T = $ const., we can use (11-4b) and (8-6) to write (11-11) as

$$0 \geqslant d(U - TS) + p\,dV = dF + p\,dV = dF - dW \qquad (11\text{-}14)$$

If we rewrite this inequality in the form

$$-dW \leqslant -dF \qquad (11\text{-}15)$$

we see that the decrease in the free energy is the *maximum* external work $-dW$ which can be done *by* the system during an isothermal process; this is the historical basis for the use of the name "free energy" for the function F.

Processes at constant temperature and volume

If $dT = 0$ and $dV = 0$, then (11-14) shows that

$$dF \leqslant 0 \qquad (11\text{-}16)$$

Since F can only decrease for these processes, equilibrium must correspond to the minimum value of F, or

$$F = \text{minimum}, \quad T = \text{const.}, \quad V = \text{const.} \qquad (11\text{-}17)$$

Processes at constant temperature and pressure

If $dT = 0$ and $dp = 0$, we can use (11-4c) to write (11-14) as

$$0 \geqslant d(U - TS + pV) = dG \qquad (11\text{-}18)$$

Since G can only decrease for these processes, equilibrium must correspond to the minimum value of G, or

$$G = \text{minimum}, \quad T = \text{const.}, \quad p = \text{const.} \qquad (11\text{-}19)$$

Hence, as has already been indicated several times, the functions we have defined in this chapter do have many of the properties we usually associate with the term "potential." Since most laboratory experiments are most easily performed under constant pressure conditions (such as that of the atmosphere), it seems clear that the Gibbs function G is of greatest practical importance. However, as we shall see in our discussion of statistical mechanics, it is the Helmholtz function F which is the most easily calculated.

Exercises

11-1. Use (9-21) and (11-5a) to show that

$$C_p = T(\partial S/\partial T)_p \tag{11-20}$$

11-2. Show that

$$
\begin{aligned}
T \, dS &= C_v \, dT + T(\partial p/\partial T)_V \, dV \\
&= C_p \, dT - T(\partial V/\partial T)_p \, dp \\
&= C_p (\partial T/\partial V)_p \, dV + C_v (\partial T/\partial p)_V \, dp
\end{aligned}
$$

11-3. If the adiabatic compressibility is defined by $\kappa_S = -V^{-1}(\partial V/\partial p)_S$, show that $\kappa_T/\kappa_S = C_p/C_v$.

11-4. Show that the enthalpy can only decrease for processes at constant entropy and pressure, and thereby find the corresponding equilibrium condition.

12 Real gases

Before we go on to consider more of the general aspects of thermodynamics, it is desirable to apply the results we have obtained so far to the discussion of the properties of a specific thermodynamic system—real gases. Up to now we have used only the ideal gas approximation, and we begin by considering another approximation to the equation of state of gases which is due to van der Waals. Although this historically important equation of state is not adequate to describe all real gases with complete accuracy, it is sufficiently accurate and simple enough to illustrate quite well many of the qualitative differences between real and ideal gases.

12-1 The van der Waals equation of state

Although the use of specific ideas associated with the molecular structure of gases is somewhat foreign to the macroscopic, empirical methods of thermodynamics, nevertheless we shall briefly recount the type of reasoning used by van der Waals in devising his famous equation. In principle, we cannot actually expect the equation of state (8-21) to hold for real gases because of the neglect of two factors: first, because the gas molecules presumably have a finite volume, the equation of state should reflect the fact that the actual volume available for the molecules to move around in should be less than the volume V of the container which appears in the equation of state; second, since there are undoubtedly forces of some sort between the molecules, the effective pressure within the system may be different from the observed pressure p which is also used in the equations.

Evidently we have to subtract the *effective* volume occupied by the molecules from the observed volume V. We can obtain an idea of this correction factor by considering a collision between two of the molecules which for simplicity are assumed to be spherical; the contact between them at collision is illustrated in Fig. 12-1. We see that, as far as the volume is concerned, the effect is the same as a collision between a point molecule and one of radius $2R$ and therefore involves a volume

$$\tfrac{4}{3}\pi(2R)^3 = 8(\tfrac{4}{3}\pi R^3) = 8 \times \text{(volume of one molecule)}$$

Taking an average over the pair, we can conclude that, as far as collisions are concerned, the effective volume per molecule is four times the actual volume of one molecule. Therefore, if we multiply this by the total number of molecules and subtract the result from the total volume, the effective volume available for the whole gas can be written as

$$V_{\text{eff}} = V - \nu b \qquad (12\text{-}1)$$

where b is a constant which we can interpret as four times the volume of a kilomole of molecules. We shall reconsider this problem in our later discussion of statistical mechanics and shall find that our interpretation of b is substantially correct, in spite of the crude way in which we evaluated it above.

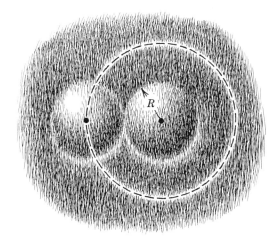

Fig. 12-1

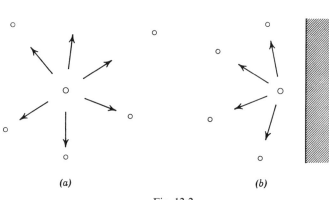

Fig. 12-2

The intermolecular attractive forces which act on a molecule in the interior of the gas will cancel out on the average because the forces are equal in all directions, as illustrated in Fig. 12-2a. However, this will not generally be true for a molecule near the wall, as shown in Fig. 12-2b, and the net effect will be a force tending to draw the molecule back into the interior. Hence we can expect that the observed pressure p exerted by the gas on the walls will be somewhat less than the effective pressure p_{eff} in the interior, so that we should write $p_{\text{eff}} = p + p'$. The force acting on a given molecule is proportional to the number of interactions it has with other molecules and hence is proportional to the number per unit volume and thus to v/V. The pressure correction is also proportional to the number of molecules colliding with the wall and thus to v/V; therefore the total correction to the pressure, p', is proportional to $(v/V)^2$, and we can write

$$p_{\text{eff}} = p + \frac{v^2 a}{V^2} \qquad (12\text{-}2)$$

where a is a proportionality constant characteristic of the gas.

Since Boyle's law (8-14) for ideal gases stated that $pV = \text{const.}$, we would now expect that in order to apply this basic result to real gases we should replace it by

$$p_{\text{eff}} \, V_{\text{eff}} = \text{const.} \qquad (12\text{-}3)$$

and therefore by

$$\left(p + \frac{v^2 a}{V^2} \right)(V - vb) = \text{const.} \qquad (12\text{-}4)$$

If we were now to follow the same line of reasoning we used in Sec. 8-5 to derive the ideal gas equation of state after obtaining Boyle's law, we would find from (12-4) that

$$\left(p + \frac{\nu^2 a}{V^2}\right)(V - \nu b) = \nu R' T \tag{12-5}$$

where R' is a constant which depends on the particular gas involved. For simplicity, we usually replace R' by the universal gas constant R and approximate (12-5) by

$$\left(p + \frac{\nu^2 a}{V^2}\right)(V - \nu b) = \nu R T \tag{12-6}$$

which is the van der Waals equation of state.

It is sometimes more convenient to write (12-6) in the form

$$p = \frac{\nu R T}{V - \nu b} - \frac{\nu^2 a}{V^2} \tag{12-7}$$

and we see from this form that, as $V \to \infty$, $p \to \nu R T / V$, showing that van der Waals' equation reduces to the ideal gas equation in this limit. [We can equally well obtain this result by setting $a = b = 0$ in (12-6) or (12-7).]

12-2 Some properties of a van der Waals gas

Now that we have the equation of state, we can go on to consider some of the ways in which a real gas differs from an ideal gas by using the van der Waals gas as a model. We begin by finding the coefficient of thermal expansion, α.

If we calculate dp from (12-7) and set it equal to zero, we find that

$$dp = 0 = \frac{\nu R\, dT}{V - \nu b} - \frac{\nu R T\, dV}{(V - \nu b)^2} + \frac{2\nu^2 a\, dV}{V^3}$$

and, since $dV = (\partial V / \partial T)_p\, dT$ in this case, we obtain

$$\alpha = \frac{1}{V}\left(\frac{\partial V}{\partial T}\right)_p = \frac{V - \nu b}{VT - [2\nu a(V - \nu b)^2 / RV^2]} \tag{12-8}$$

which becomes $\alpha_i = 1/T$ when $a = b = 0$ and is exactly the value for an ideal gas given by (8-16). Therefore the deviation of α from the ideal gas value is given by

$$\alpha - \alpha_i = \alpha - \frac{1}{T} = \frac{[2\nu a(V - \nu b)^2 / RTV^2] - \nu b}{VT - [2\nu a(V - \nu b)^2 / RV^2]} \tag{12-9}$$

If we assume that a and b are small enough that only their first powers need be included, we can approximate (12-9) by

$$\alpha - \alpha_i \simeq \frac{(2va/RT) - vb}{VT - (2va/R)} \simeq \frac{(2a/RT) - b}{T(V/v)} \tag{12-10}$$

where, in effect, we have assumed that $V/v \gg b$ and $RT(V/v) \gg 2a$.

It is found experimentally that $2a/RT > b$ for most gases in the ordinary temperature range so that $\alpha > \alpha_i$; the only exceptions are hydrogen and the rare gases, for which the attractive forces between the molecules are so small that $2a/RT < b$.

We see from (12-10) that, for any van der Waals gas, there will be a temperature

$$T_i = \frac{2a}{Rb} \tag{12-11}$$

called the *inversion temperature* for which $\alpha = \alpha_i$ so that the gas acts like an ideal gas, at least as far as its thermal expansion is concerned. If $T > T_i$, then $\alpha < \alpha_i$, and, if $T < T_i$, then $\alpha > \alpha_i$.

A convenient graphical way of representing some of the features of a van der Waals gas is to plot the isotherms on the pV plane as shown in Fig. 12-3; these curves are obtained by setting $T = $ const. in (12-7). We note first of all that, as $V \to vb$, $p \to \infty$ so that the dashed line $V = vb$ is one of the asymptotes and therefore $V < vb$ has no meaning for this

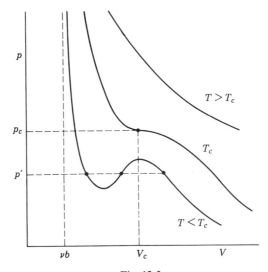

Fig. 12-3

equation of state. For large values of T, the curves are similar to the rectangular hyperbolas $pV = $ const., which are the isotherms of an ideal gas, but as T is made smaller the curves become quite different and eventually develop a maximum and a minimum. In this region, we see from the figure that an isobar $p' = $ const. intersects the isotherm at three different values of the volume; this can also be seen from (12-6) which is a cubic equation in V for constant p and T and therefore has three roots—one of which may be real or all three may be real. The isotherm which is the transition curve between these two types occurs for a temperature T_c called the *critical* temperature. The three points of intersection with an isobar coalesce into only one, and then the critical isotherm has a point of inflection and zero slope at this point, known as the *critical point*; the coordinates of this point on the pV plane are p_c and V_c and are called the *critical pressure* and *critical volume*, respectively.

By using the facts just given, we can find the coordinates of the critical point. First, van der Waals' equation (12-7) must be satisfied so that

$$p_c = \frac{\nu R T_c}{V_c - \nu b} - \frac{\nu^2 a}{V_c^2} \tag{12-12}$$

Since the curve has zero slope at the critical point, we must have

$$\left[\left(\frac{\partial p}{\partial V} \right)_T \right]_{\text{crit}} = 0 = - \frac{\nu R T_c}{(V_c - \nu b)^2} + \frac{2 \nu^2 a}{V_c^3} \tag{12-13}$$

The critical point is also a point of inflection, and we must have

$$\left[\left(\frac{\partial^2 p}{\partial V^2} \right)_T \right]_{\text{crit}} = 0 = \frac{2 \nu R T_c}{(V_c - \nu b)^3} - \frac{6 \nu^2 a}{V_c^4} \tag{12-14}$$

By eliminating T_c from (12-13) and (12-14), we find that

$$V_c = 3 \nu b \tag{12-15}$$

Substituting V_c into (12-13), we find

$$R T_c = \frac{8a}{27b} \tag{12-16}$$

and, finally, we find from (12-12) that

$$p_c = \frac{a}{27 b^2} \tag{12-17}$$

The last three results can be combined to give

$$\frac{p_c V_c}{\nu R T_c} = \frac{3}{8} \tag{12-18}$$

in contrast to the ideal gas value $pV/\nu RT = 1$.

One can also solve for the constants characterizing the gas in terms of the measurable critical coordinates; the results are that

$$b = \frac{1}{3}\left(\frac{V_c}{\nu}\right), \quad a = 3p_c\left(\frac{V_c}{\nu}\right)^2, \quad R = \frac{8p_cV_c}{3\nu T_c} \tag{12-19}$$

If these are substituted in (12-6), the van der Waals equation becomes

$$\left(p + \frac{3p_cV_c^2}{V^2}\right)\left(V - \frac{V_c}{3}\right) = \frac{8p_cV_cT}{3T_c} \tag{12-20}$$

If we now define the *reduced variables* by

$$\pi = \frac{p}{p_c}, \quad \omega = \frac{V}{V_c}, \quad \tau = \frac{T}{T_c} \tag{12-21}$$

then (12-20) can also be written

$$\left(\pi + \frac{3}{\omega^2}\right)\left(\omega - \frac{1}{3}\right) = \frac{8}{3}\tau \tag{12-22}$$

The last equation has no undetermined constants in it and thus says that, if the (p, V, T) values for *all gases* are expressed in terms of the reduced variables (12-21) as calculated from the critical coordinates for the given gas, the *same equation of state* (12-22) should hold for all real gases. In other words, van der Waals' equation implies that the equation of state for any gas should be an equation involving only three constants. The existence of such an equation of state, which was first indicated by van der Waals' equation, is known as the *theorem of corresponding states*. Accordingly, one can say that all gases which are in states described by the same values of π, ω, and τ are in corresponding states regardless of how different their actual states as given by p, V, and T might be. It seems clear that such a theorem can be only approximately true and cannot hold for all cases, but it nevertheless proves to be of practical importance, not only in the study of gases but also for any general class of system which we can describe by reduced variables, such as the magnetic systems we shall consider later.

12-3   State variables of a van der Waals gas

We would expect the energy of a real gas to depend on the volume, because there are forces between the molecules and work must be done against these forces whenever the gas expands. We can calculate this effect rigorously for the van der Waals gas since we have its equation of state. Using (10-46) and (12-7), we find that

$$\left(\frac{\partial U}{\partial V}\right)_T = T\left(\frac{\partial p}{\partial T}\right)_V - p = \frac{v^2 a}{V^2} \tag{12-23}$$

This result agrees with the basic ideas of our derivation of the equation of state, since we saw in (12-2) that the pressure at the wall which is ascribed to intermolecular forces was $-v^2 a/V^2$. The work done on the gas in a small isothermal expansion would then be $dW = (v^2 a/V^2)\,dV$, so that the energy change would be $dU = dW = (v^2 a/V^2)\,dV$, which leads at once to (12-23).

We can use (12-23) to obtain an interesting property of the heat capacity C_v. From (9-6) and (12-23), we see that

$$\left(\frac{\partial C_v}{\partial V}\right)_T = \frac{\partial}{\partial V}\left(\frac{\partial U}{\partial T}\right)_V = \frac{\partial}{\partial T}\left(\frac{\partial U}{\partial V}\right)_T$$

$$= \left[\frac{\partial}{\partial T}\left(\frac{v^2 a}{V^2}\right)\right]_V = 0 \tag{12-24}$$

Therefore C_v is independent of the volume, and $C_v = C_v(T)$ just as for an ideal gas. We can now write an explicit expression for the energy by using (9-3), (9-6), and (12-23) to obtain

$$dU = C_v(T)\,dT + \frac{v^2 a}{V^2}\,dV \tag{12-25}$$

so that

$$U = U(T, V) = \int_0^T C_v(T')\,dT' - \frac{v^2 a}{V} + U_0 \tag{12-26}$$

which, when $a = 0$, reduces to (9-15) as found for the ideal gas.

We can now evaluate the difference in the heat capacities by using (9-9), (12-8), and (12-23) with the result that

$$C_p - C_v = \frac{vR}{1 - [2va(V - vb)^2/RTV^3]} \tag{12-27}$$

which becomes approximately

$$C_p - C_v \simeq vR\left[1 + \frac{2va(V - vb)^2}{RTV^3}\right] \simeq vR\left(1 + \frac{2va}{RTV}\right) > vR \tag{12-28}$$

showing that for a real gas we can expect the difference in the heat capacities to be greater than that found for an ideal gas.

We can now calculate the entropy by using (10-28), (12-25), and (12-6) to find that

$$dS = \frac{C_v(T)\,dT}{T} + \frac{\nu R\,dV}{V - \nu b} \tag{12-29}$$

and, on integrating (12-29), we obtain

$$S - S_0 = \int_{T_0}^{T} \frac{C_v(T')\,dT'}{T'} + \nu R \ln \frac{V - \nu b}{V_0 - \nu b} \tag{12-30}$$

which reduces to the ideal gas value (9-42) when $b = 0$.

It is of interest to note that the constant a which describes the intermolecular forces appears in the energy expression (12-26) but not in that for the entropy (12-30), while the opposite occurs for the constant b related to the molecular volumes. The reasons for these facts will become clearer when we consider gases by the methods of statistical mechanics.

12-4   Joule-Thomson effect

Now that we have more powerful methods than were previously available to us, we want to go back and discuss in more detail the *Joule-Thomson effect* which is a name used to describe the results of the porous plug experiment which we first discussed in Sec. 9-6; this process is also called a *throttling process*.

We have seen in (9-37) that this process is *isenthalpic*, that is, it can be characterized as one of constant enthalpy; this was shown to hold in general, regardless of the type of fluid that may be used. It will be well to review the way in which the experiment is actually performed. The initial values of the pressure p_i and temperature θ_i (measured on some

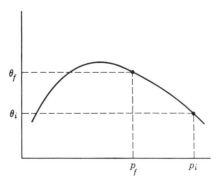

Fig. 12-4

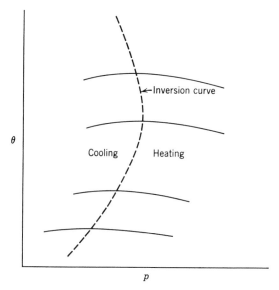

Fig. 12-5

convenient empirical scale) are arbitrarily chosen; then, as indicated in Fig. 9-4, the final pressure p_f is also chosen arbitrarily, the experiment is performed, and the final temperature θ_f is measured. The net result is that for each pair of initial values (p_i, θ_i), we can obtain a *set* of pairs of values (p_f, θ_f) *all of which correspond to the same enthalpy.* If these values are plotted on a θp diagram, the result is a curve like that shown in Fig. 12-4. Since all the points correspond to the same enthalpy of the gas, the curve is called *isenthalpic.* It does *not,* however, represent the actual throttling process which is irreversible and therefore cannot be represented as a sequence of equilibrium states.

If one now chooses a new initial set (p_i, θ_i), the whole process can be repeated and another isenthalpic curve corresponding to a different value of the enthalpy can be obtained. The set of isenthalpic curves obtained in this way has the general appearance shown in Fig. 12-5. Since the pressure is reduced in this process, the designations "cooling" and "heating" applied to the regions shown are quite appropriate. The numerical value of the slope of an isenthalpic curve is given by

$$\mu' = \left(\frac{\partial \theta}{\partial p}\right)_H = \text{Joule-Thomson coefficient} \qquad (12\text{-}31)$$

The locus of all points for which $\mu' = 0$ is called the *inversion curve* and is shown as the dashed line in Fig. 12-5. When the absolute temperature T is used, the Joule-Thomson coefficient is written as μ:

$$\mu = \left(\frac{\partial T}{\partial p}\right)_H \tag{12-32}$$

We now want to relate μ to other properties of the system. If we write $S = S(T, p)$ so that

$$dS = \left(\frac{\partial S}{\partial T}\right)_p dT + \left(\frac{\partial S}{\partial p}\right)_T dp = \frac{C_p \, dT}{T} - \left(\frac{\partial V}{\partial T}\right)_p dp \tag{12-33}$$

because of (11-20) and (11-7d), and then substitute (12-33) into (11-5a), we find that

$$dH = C_p \, dT + \left[V - T\left(\frac{\partial V}{\partial T}\right)_p\right] dp \tag{12-34}$$

which now involves the variables T and p needed to evaluate (12-32). In an isenthalpic process,

$$dH = 0, \quad dT = \left(\frac{\partial T}{\partial p}\right)_H dp \tag{12-35}$$

if we treat T as a function of p and H. If (12-35) is substituted into (12-34) and (12-32) is used, we find that

$$\mu = \left(\frac{\partial T}{\partial p}\right)_H = \frac{1}{C_p}\left[T\left(\frac{\partial V}{\partial T}\right)_p - V\right] \tag{12-36}$$

so that we have succeeded in relating the Joule-Thomson coefficient to the equation of state. We can also write (12-36) in terms of the coefficient of thermal expansion by using (8-2); the result is that

$$\mu = \frac{VT}{C_p}\left(\alpha - \frac{1}{T}\right) = \frac{VT(\alpha - \alpha_i)}{C_p} \tag{12-37}$$

if (8-16) is also used. We see at once that $\mu = 0$ for an ideal gas; this means that the temperature of an ideal gas does not change during a porous plug experiment. We have already discussed this result in Sec 9-6.

Example. van der Waals Gas. If we substitute (12-10) and (12-11) into (12-37), we find that

$$\mu \simeq \frac{v}{C_p}\left(\frac{2a}{RT} - b\right) = \frac{vb}{C_p}\left(\frac{T_i}{T} - 1\right) \tag{12-38}$$

in terms of the inversion temperature T_i. Therefore, if $T < T_i$, $\mu > 0$ and the gas will cool on expansion, whereas it will warm up if its initial temperature is greater than the inversion temperature. In the case of air, there is considerable cooling even at $0°C$, and this effect forms the basis of the Linde process of liquefying air by repeated expansions. Hydrogen, on the other hand, is above its inversion temperature even at 0°C, so that it will warm up when expanded; in order to liquefy hydrogen by repeated expansion, it is first necessary to cool it below its inversion temperature of about −80°C.

12-5 Measurement of the absolute temperature of the ice point

Another important practical result of the last considerations is the experimental determination of the quantitative relation between the absolute temperature and an empirical temperature. The initial basis we used for defining the absolute temperature was the equation of state of an ideal gas as given by (8-21). We also defined the absolute temperature T in terms of the heats absorbed and rejected by a reversible Carnot engine as given in (10-15). We then showed in (10-24) that the ideal gas temperature scale and the absolute temperature scale are identical.

However, we do not actually have ideal gases available for our use; consequently, what we really need to know is how the temperature θ as measured by a *real gas* thermometer can be related to the absolute temperature T. Since the Celsius scale and the absolute scale are chosen so as to have the same size unit, we see from the connection between them as given by (8-17) that the essential number for which an accurate measurement is needed is T_0 (the ice point), that is, the absolute temperature corresponding to 0°C. Although (10-15) could be used in principle, it would not be very satisfactory because calorimetric measurements are not sufficiently accurate. Since (10-14) and (10-15) form the basis for introducing T into the second law, any relation involving T which is obtained from the second law can equally well be used for this purpose, and it has been found that the Joule-Thomson effect is particularly suitable.

Our starting point will be (12-36), but, since all quantities used are measured in terms of the empirical scale θ, we must transform (12-36) to take this into account. From (10-14), (12-31), and (9-21), we find that

$$\mu = \left(\frac{\partial T}{\partial p}\right)_H = \left(\frac{dT}{d\theta}\right)\left(\frac{\partial \theta}{\partial p}\right)_H = \mu'\left(\frac{dT}{d\theta}\right) \tag{12-39}$$

$$C_p = \left(\frac{\partial H}{\partial T}\right)_p = \left(\frac{\partial H}{\partial \theta}\right)_p\left(\frac{d\theta}{dT}\right) = C_p'\left(\frac{d\theta}{dT}\right) \tag{12-40}$$

where C_p' is the experimentally determined heat capacity. We also have

$$\left(\frac{\partial V}{\partial T}\right)_p = \left(\frac{\partial V}{\partial \theta}\right)_p\left(\frac{d\theta}{dT}\right)$$

and, when these results are substituted into (12-36), we find that

$$T \left(\frac{\partial V}{\partial \theta}\right)_p \left(\frac{d\theta}{dT}\right) = V + \mu' C_p'$$

and therefore

$$\frac{dT}{T} = \frac{(\partial V/\partial \theta)_p \, d\theta}{V + \mu' C_p'} \tag{12-41}$$

which now has only measurable quantities on the right side. If we limit ourselves to values of μ' and V all at one definite pressure, $(\partial V/\partial \theta)_p \, d\theta = dV$ and (12-41) can be written

$$\frac{dT}{T} = \frac{dV}{V + \mu' C_p'} \tag{12-42}$$

If we integrate between the ice point (0°C) and the steam point (100°C) whose absolute temperatures are T_0 and $T_s = T_0 + 100$, respectively, we find that

$$\ln \frac{T_s}{T_0} = \ln \left(1 + \frac{100}{T_0}\right) = \int_{V_0}^{V_s} \frac{dV}{V + \mu' C_p'} \tag{12-43}$$

where V_0 and V_s are the measured *volumes* of the gas at the two temperatures. For an ideal gas, $\mu' = 0$ and (12-43) leads directly to $T_s/T_0 = V_s/V_0$, which is seen to be Charles' law (8-15) when we recall that all quantities involved correspond to the same pressure.

This result (12-43) expresses T_0 completely in terms of quantities measured by the use of *real* gases, and thus our problem is solved in principle. This is the way in which the accurate value $T_0 = 273.15$ degrees given by (8-18) was actually obtained.

Exercises

12-1. Assume that C_v for a van der Waals gas is constant and show that the equation of a reversible adiabatic process is $T(V - vb)^{vR/C_v} = \text{const.}$, while the temperature change in a free expansion is given by $T_f - T_i = v^2 a(V_i - V_f)/C_v V_i V_f$.

12-2. Show that $(\partial C_p/\partial p)_T = -T(\partial^2 V/\partial T^2)_p$ and apply to a van der Waals gas.

12-3. Find the critical variables p_c, T_c, and V_c for a gas which satisfies the Dieterici equation of state:

$$p(V - vb) = vRTe^{-va/RTV}$$

12-4. Calculate the Joule-Thomson coefficient μ for a gas obeying the Dieterici equation of state.

13 The third law of thermodynamics

The third law is different in character from the other three laws we have discussed because it does not postulate the existence of a particular state variable but, instead, makes a definite statement about the numerical values of functions we have already defined. We recall that in (10-27) the entropy was defined only in terms of its differential dS, so that S itself is defined only up to a constant S_c. As long as our applications of thermodynamics require only the use of entropy differences (as in evaluating derivatives), the unknown value of S_c does not present a problem; however, the potentials F and G involve a term TS in their definitions, so that there is also an undefined quantity TS_c involved in them, and there are situations where a knowledge of their absolute values is necessary. The third law enables us to make a definite statement about the absolute value of S; it was first proposed by Nernst, although we shall postulate it in a form which was given later by Planck.

THIRD LAW OF THERMODYNAMICS. The entropy of any system vanishes as the absolute temperature approaches zero; that is,

$$\lim_{T \to 0} S = 0 \qquad (13\text{-}1)$$

As Nernst initially formulated his statement, it related only to the change $\Delta S = S_f - S_i$ of the entropy of any system in an isothermal process connecting the initial and final states i and f, and he said that

$$\lim_{T \to 0} \Delta S = 0 \qquad (13\text{-}2)$$

This less general statement says only that the entropy of any system approaches a definite limiting value S_c which is completely independent of the nature of the state at $T = 0$. We can then say that, since this value S_c is universal and unobservable, then for all practical purposes it is zero and we can simply set $S_c = 0$ to obtain (13-1). We shall also see that we can obtain (13-1) by a simple extension of the reasoning leading to (13-2). In addition, the zero value for S as $T \to 0$ is the natural value indicated by statistical mechanics. We shall first indicate how Nernst was led to his result, and then we shall consider some of the experimental consequences of (13-1).

13-1   Derivation of Nernst's result

Nernst was led to postulate (13-2) by his attempts to account for the *principle of Thomsen and Berthelot*. This principle is an approximate empirical rule which is useful in chemistry for predicting the final equilibrium state of a chemical reaction. Basically, the rule says that, if we consider processes at constant T and p, the final state will be the one which corresponds to the release of the most *heat*. We can state this differently if we recall our result (9-18) in which we showed that the heat added to a system at constant pressure equals the increase in the enthalpy; therefore, in this case we have

$$\text{Heat given off} = H_i - H_f \qquad (13\text{-}3)$$

According to the principle of Thomsen and Berthelot, the final equilibrium corresponds to $(H_i - H_f)_{\max}$ or $(-H_f)_{\max}$ since the initial state is fixed or, finally, to

$$H_f = \text{minimum} \qquad (13\text{-}4)$$

In other words, the principle is equivalent to the rule that equilibrium at constant T and p corresponds to a minimum of the enthalpy. On the other hand, we know from (11-19) that the exact condition requires that the Gibbs function G be a minimum; the basic problem is therefore to determine how these two statements could be even approximately equivalent.

Experience also showed that the rule (13-4) is useful only if the temperature is not too high, and, in fact, the lower the temperature, the better the rule. By extrapolating this result, we are led to make the assumption that the rule (13-4) is *exact* at $T = 0$. Since $G = H - TS$, the changes occurring in the process are related by

$$\Delta G = \Delta H - T\,\Delta S \qquad (13\text{-}5)$$

which shows that if we assume

$$\lim_{T \to 0} \Delta H = \lim_{T \to 0} \Delta G \qquad (13\text{-}6)$$

we can conclude that ΔS is bounded at $T = 0$. If we try to determine the limiting value of ΔS by writing (13-5) as

$$\Delta S = \frac{\Delta H - \Delta G}{T} \qquad (13\text{-}7)$$

and letting $T \to 0$, we find that the expression approaches $0/0$ and hence is indeterminate because of (13-6). If we try to evaluate this indeterminate expression by the usual rule of separately differentiating the numerator and denominator and then going to the limit, we find from (13-7) that

$$\lim_{T \to 0} \Delta S = \left(\frac{d\,\Delta H}{dT}\right)_{T=0} - \left(\frac{d\,\Delta G}{dT}\right)_{T=0} \tag{13-8}$$

However, the approximate equality $\Delta H = \Delta G$ holds not only at $T = 0$ according to (13-6) but even when T is quite a bit different from zero; in other words, the two curves must almost coincide over a fairly large range of T; this is possible only if their slopes are equal as indicated in Fig. 13-1. Thus we have

$$\lim_{T \to 0} \left(\frac{\partial\,\Delta H}{\partial T}\right)_p = \lim_{T \to 0} \left(\frac{\partial\,\Delta G}{\partial T}\right)_p \tag{13-9}$$

so that we find from (13-8) that $\Delta S \to 0$ as $T \to 0$, exactly as given by (13-2).

Planck extended Nernst's postulates (13-6) and (13-9) to hold for the functions themselves as well as their differences; thus we can also write

$$\lim_{T \to 0} G = \lim_{T \to 0} H \tag{13-10}$$

$$\lim_{T \to 0} \left(\frac{\partial G}{\partial T}\right)_p = \lim_{T \to 0} \left(\frac{\partial H}{\partial T}\right)_p \tag{13-11}$$

If we use (11-4a), (11-4c), and (11-6c), we can write

$$G = H + T\left(\frac{\partial G}{\partial T}\right)_p \tag{13-12}$$

so that

$$\left(\frac{\partial G}{\partial T}\right)_p = \frac{G - H}{T} \tag{13-13}$$

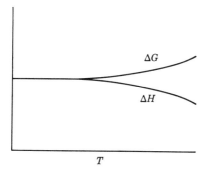

Fig. 13-1

If we look at the limit of this equation as $T \to 0$, we again get the indeterminate form $0/0$; if we then evaluate the limit as we did to obtain (13-8), we find from (13-13) and (13-11) that

$$\lim_{T \to 0} \left(\frac{\partial G}{\partial T}\right)_p = \lim_{T \to 0} \left(\frac{\partial G}{\partial T}\right)_p - \lim_{T \to 0} \left(\frac{\partial H}{\partial T}\right)_p = 0 \qquad (13\text{-}14)$$

and therefore, since $S = -(\partial G/\partial T)_p$ by (11-6c), we find that $S \to 0$ as $T \to 0$, showing that the Nernst-Planck postulates lead to the form of the third law we originally stated in (13-1). We also see from (13-14) and (13-9) that the initial slope of the ΔG (and ΔH) curve should be zero as shown in Fig. 13-1.

In connection with the third law, it should be emphasized that thermodynamics deals only with equilibrium situations and tells us nothing about the *time* required for equilibrium to be attained. Since atomic and molecular motions slow down considerably as the temperature is decreased and internal processes therefore generally proceed much more slowly, it may well take an extremely long time for the system to get into equilibrium in the state ·corresponding to zero entropy. Hence, for all practical purposes, this state may never be actually attained because one cannot wait that long and the net effect would be that one would be dealing with a real system at $T \simeq 0$ whose entropy is actually different from zero since the system is only in a quasi-equilibrium state.

13-2 Some consequences of the third law

In this section we want to consider some of the ways in which the third law can be checked experimentally because of the specific predictions it makes about certain properties of a system.

We begin with the reciprocal relation (11-7d):

$$\left(\frac{\partial S}{\partial p}\right)_T = -\left(\frac{\partial V}{\partial T}\right)_p \qquad (13\text{-}15)$$

Since S approaches a limit which is independent of p as $T \to 0$, then $(\partial S/\partial p)_T \to 0$ as $T \to 0$, so that

$$\lim_{T \to 0} \left(\frac{\partial V}{\partial T}\right)_p = 0 \qquad (13\text{-}16)$$

and therefore

$$\lim_{T \to 0} \alpha = 0 \qquad (13\text{-}17)$$

because of (8-2). In other words, the coefficient of thermal expansion of any system vanishes at absolute zero.

Similarly, by starting with $(\partial S/\partial V)_T = (\partial p/\partial T)_V$ as given by (11-7c), we can conclude that $(\partial p/\partial T)_V \to 0$ as $T \to 0$, and therefore that

$$\lim_{T \to 0} \beta = 0 \tag{13-18}$$

because of (8-2).

We have seen in (10-44) that $C_v = T(\partial S/\partial T)_V$ so that, if we calculate the entropy of a given state (T, V) by integrating with respect to temperature at constant volume and using (13-1), we obtain

$$S(T, V) = \int_0^T \frac{C_v(T') \, dT'}{T'} \tag{13-19}$$

In order that we get a finite value of the entropy, the integral must converge at the lower limit, and we must have

$$\lim_{T \to 0} C_v = 0 \tag{13-20}$$

Similarly, if we begin with (11-20), we find

$$\lim_{T \to 0} C_p = 0 \tag{13-21}$$

In the same way, we can conclude in general that *the heat capacities must vanish at absolute zero.* This important consequence of the third law led to a series of experiments which were done by Nernst and his students to measure heat capacities at low temperature. The relations (13-20) and (13-21) have been amply confirmed by experiment and therefore provide evidence for the basic correctness of (13-1).

One can carry out the same type of analysis for other quantities by using the Maxwell relations obtained from the various possible Legendre transformations of the energy. The general result is that *all* the temperature coefficients of the intensive and extensive parameters vanish at absolute zero, although we have seen only the examples (13-14), (13-17), (13-18), (13-20), and (13-21).

13-3 "Unattainability" of absolute zero

The third law can also be stated in a negative sense, just as the first and second laws could. The usual way of doing this is to say that absolute zero is a temperature which actually can never be attained but can only be approached asymptotically. One can show this to be a consequence of Nernst's postulate (13-2) by considering any general adiabatic process, but we shall do it in a specific way by discussing the only feasible way of

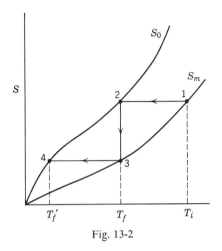

Fig. 13-2

reaching very low temperatures—the method of adiabatic demagnetization.

We shall discuss magnetic materials in detail in the next chapter, but for our present purposes we only need the general result that the entropy of an unmagnetized material, S_0, is greater than the entropy S_m when it is in the magnetized state. These entropies are shown qualitatively as functions of temperature in Fig. 13-2 which is drawn in accordance with (13-1). Suppose we were to start with the magnetized system at temperature T_i and demagnetize it adiabatically, for example, by simply switching off the external field. Since $dQ = 0$, the entropy will be constant according to (10-27) and the process will take place along the horizontal line $1 \to 2$ whose intersection with the curve S_0 determines the final temperature T_f, which is seen to be less than T_i. We can now magnetize the system isothermally along the path $2 \to 3$; the net result is that our magnetized system has been cooled from T_i to T_f. We can repeat the adiabatic demagnetization along $3 \to 4$ and lower the temperature to T_f'. We see from these considerations, however, that, no matter how many steps like this we may make, we can never actually attain $T = 0$, although we can get arbitrarily close to it in principle. The closeness of the approach to $T = 0$ is seen to be determined by the steepness of the curve for S_0.

Exercises

13-1. Is it possible for a system to be described by the ideal gas equation of state all the way down to $T = 0$? by the van der Waals equation?

13-2. Redraw Fig. 13-2 in a form which violates (13-1), and show that then it would be possible to reach absolute zero in a finite number of steps.

14 Magnetic systems

In this chapter we want to consider the thermodynamic properties of a system which requires variables in addition to the pressure and volume for the specification of its state. Although there are many possible types we could discuss, we shall confine ourselves to the important case of magnetic systems.

The first problem is to express the energy in terms of appropriate variables. In a previous discussion we found the energy density associated with a magnetic field to be given by (I: 26-16) as $u_m = B^2/2\mu$ for a linear, isotropic, homogeneous magnetic material of permeability μ. If we change the fields slightly, the increase in the energy density will be

$$du_m = \frac{B}{\mu} dB = H\, dB \tag{14-1}$$

since all the magnetic vectors are parallel in an isotropic material. We also know from (I: 19-59) that we can write $B = \mu_0(H + M)$, where M is the magnetization, that is, the magnetic dipole moment per unit volume; when this expression for B is inserted into (14-1) we find

$$du_m = \mu_0 H\, dH + \mu_0 H\, dM \tag{14-2}$$

In all the cases we shall consider, the magnetization of the material will be so small that H can be taken as approximately equal to the external field. The first term of (14-2) will always be present even in the absence of the material; hence it can be dropped from consideration since we are primarily interested in the thermodynamic properties of the matter. Accordingly, we can take our expression for the increment of magnetic energy density as simply

$$du_m = \mu_0 H\, dM \tag{14-3}$$

If we let $\mathscr{M}$ be the total magnetic moment of the system, where

$$\mathscr{M} = VM \tag{14-4}$$

we find from (14-3) that

$$dU_m = \mu_0 H\, d\mathscr{M} \tag{14-5}$$

If we now augment the expression for the conservation of energy (11-1) by (14-5), we obtain

$$dU = T\, dS - p\, dV + \mu_0 H\, d\mathscr{M} \tag{14-6}$$

so that

$$T\, dS = dU + p\, dV - \mu_0 H\, d\mathscr{M} \tag{14-7}$$

Since our aim is to concentrate on the magnetic effects, and since the volume change associated with a change in magnetization is negligible unless we consider magnetostrictive materials, we can neglect the $p\,dV$ term in (14-7) and simply use

$$T\,dS = dU - \mu_0 H\,d\mathcal{M} \tag{14-8}$$

as our basic equation. Although our derivation has been somewhat oversimplified, the final result is correct; we can see that it has the proper qualitative form since (14-5) is written as the product of the intensive variable (or "generalized force" $\mu_0 H$ acting *on* the system) and the differential of the extensive variable (or "generalized displacement" $d\mathcal{M}$). We also see that the signs in (14-8) agree with the curves of Fig. 13-2.

Now that we have (14-8), we are able to investigate the properties of magnetic systems in a manner similar to that previously used for fluid systems. For example, if we regard both S and U as functions of T and $\mathcal{M}$, (14-8) can be written

$$dS = \frac{1}{T}\left(\frac{\partial U}{\partial T}\right)_{\mathcal{M}} dT + \frac{1}{T}\left[\left(\frac{\partial U}{\partial \mathcal{M}}\right)_T - \mu_0 H\right] d\mathcal{M} \tag{14-9}$$

If we now apply our condition for an exact differential (7-22) to (14-9), we obtain

$$\frac{\partial}{\partial \mathcal{M}}\left[\frac{1}{T}\left(\frac{\partial U}{\partial T}\right)_{\mathcal{M}}\right] = \frac{\partial}{\partial T}\left\{\frac{1}{T}\left[\left(\frac{\partial U}{\partial \mathcal{M}}\right)_T - \mu_0 H\right]\right\}$$

from which we find that

$$\left(\frac{\partial U}{\partial \mathcal{M}}\right)_T = \mu_0\left[H - T\left(\frac{\partial H}{\partial T}\right)_{\mathcal{M}}\right] \tag{14-10}$$

which is similar to (10-46) and can be evaluated to give us the dependence of the energy on the magnetization once we know the *magnetic equation of state:* $\mathcal{M} = \mathcal{M}(T, H)$ or $H = H(T, \mathcal{M})$.

Just as we could have defined an ideal gas as one for which the energy was independent of the volume, that is, $(\partial U/\partial V)_T = 0$, so can we define an *ideal magnetic material* as one for which

$$\left(\frac{\partial U}{\partial \mathcal{M}}\right)_T = 0 \tag{14-11}$$

so that the energy depends only on the temperature. We see from (14-10) that this would require $T(\partial H/\partial T)_{\mathcal{M}} = H$, or

$$\left(\frac{\partial H}{\partial T}\right)_{\mathcal{M}} = \frac{H}{T} \tag{14-12}$$

We can satisfy (14-12) by writing $H = h(\mathcal{M})T$, where $h(\mathcal{M})$ is an arbitrary function of $\mathcal{M}$. If we solve the last expression for $\mathcal{M}$, we find (14-11) to be equivalent to

$$\mathcal{M} = m\left(\frac{\mathscr{C}H}{T}\right) \tag{14-13}$$

where $m(x)$ is some function of the variable x and $\mathscr{C}$ is an appropriate dimensional constant; in other words, the magnetic moment of an ideal magnetic material is a function only of the *ratio H/T*. The simplest form to assume is a linear one: $m(x) = x$; (14-13) then becomes

$$\mathcal{M} = \frac{\mathscr{C}H}{T} \tag{14-14}$$

This equation of state is known as *Curie's law* and is found experimentally to be applicable to many paramagnetic materials where $\mathscr{C}$ is a constant characteristic of the material. We shall find in a later chapter that ferromagnetic materials do not have a simple equation of state of the form (14-13) and therefore cannot be characterized as ideal magnetic materials.

We note too that an ideal magnetic material cannot exist as such all the way down to absolute zero, since we can find from (14-13) that

$$\left(\frac{\partial \mathcal{M}}{\partial T}\right)_H = \frac{dm(x)}{dx}\left[\frac{\partial}{\partial T}\left(\mathscr{C}\frac{H}{T}\right)\right]_H = -\frac{\mathscr{C}H}{T^2}\frac{dm}{dx} \tag{14-15}$$

which leads to $(\partial \mathcal{M}/\partial T)_H \to \infty$ as $T \to 0$ in contradiction to the third law. Thus, although (14-13) may be found to be an adequate description for a given material in a given temperature region, we know from the last result that, as the temperature is lowered, we shall eventually need another equation of state to describe the material properly.

If we now substitute (14-10) into (14-9), we obtain

$$T\,dS = \left(\frac{\partial U}{\partial T}\right)_{\mathcal{M}} dT - \mu_0 T\left(\frac{\partial H}{\partial T}\right)_{\mathcal{M}} d\mathcal{M} \tag{14-16}$$

We can define a heat capacity at constant magnetic moment $C_{\mathcal{M}}$ and we see from (10-27) and (14-16) that

$$C_{\mathcal{M}} = T\left(\frac{\partial S}{\partial T}\right)_{\mathcal{M}} = \left(\frac{\partial U}{\partial T}\right)_{\mathcal{M}} \tag{14-17}$$

In order to define a heat capacity at constant field C_H, we need to express (14-16) as a function of T and H. This can be done by writing the magnetic equation of state as $\mathcal{M} = \mathcal{M}(T, H)$ so that

$$d\mathcal{M} = \left(\frac{\partial \mathcal{M}}{\partial T}\right)_H dT + \left(\frac{\partial \mathcal{M}}{\partial H}\right)_T dH \tag{14-18}$$

which, when substituted into (14-16), leads to

$$T\,dS = \left[\left(\frac{\partial U}{\partial T}\right)_{\mathscr{M}} - \mu_0 T \left(\frac{\partial H}{\partial T}\right)_{\mathscr{M}} \left(\frac{\partial \mathscr{M}}{\partial T}\right)_{H} \right] dT$$

$$- \mu_0 T \left(\frac{\partial H}{\partial T}\right)_{\mathscr{M}} \left(\frac{\partial \mathscr{M}}{\partial H}\right)_{T} dH \qquad (14\text{-}19)$$

from which we find that

$$C_H = T\left(\frac{\partial S}{\partial T}\right)_{H} = \left(\frac{\partial U}{\partial T}\right)_{\mathscr{M}} - \mu_0 T \left(\frac{\partial H}{\partial T}\right)_{\mathscr{M}} \left(\frac{\partial \mathscr{M}}{\partial T}\right)_{H} \qquad (14\text{-}20)$$

and, if we use (14-17), we finally obtain

$$C_H - C_{\mathscr{M}} = -\mu_0 T \left(\frac{\partial H}{\partial T}\right)_{\mathscr{M}} \left(\frac{\partial \mathscr{M}}{\partial T}\right)_{H} \qquad (14\text{-}21)$$

As an example, let us consider a Curie law material described by (14-14) for which

$$\left(\frac{\partial H}{\partial T}\right)_{\mathscr{M}} = \frac{\mathscr{M}}{\mathscr{C}}, \quad \left(\frac{\partial \mathscr{M}}{\partial T}\right)_{H} = -\frac{\mathscr{C}H}{T^2} \qquad (14\text{-}22)$$

Therefore (14-21) becomes

$$C_H - C_{\mathscr{M}} = \frac{\mu_0 \mathscr{M} H}{T} = \mu_0 \mathscr{C} \left(\frac{H}{T}\right)^2 \qquad (14\text{-}23)$$

and shows that $C_H = C_{\mathscr{M}}$ when $H = \mathscr{M} = 0$, as would be expected since then the distinction between the two processes vanishes.

Another application of these results concerns the temperature changes accompanying changes in magnetization and field to which we referred near the end of the last chapter. If we substitute (14-20) into (14-19) and use (7-10), we obtain

$$dS = \frac{C_H\,dT}{T} + \mu_0 \left(\frac{\partial \mathscr{M}}{\partial T}\right)_{H} dH \qquad (14\text{-}24)$$

If we now consider an adiabatic process so that the entropy is constant, we find that the relation connecting the changes in temperature and field as obtained from (14-24) by setting $dS = 0$ is

$$\frac{dT}{T} = -\frac{\mu_0}{C_H} \left(\frac{\partial \mathscr{M}}{\partial T}\right)_{H} dH \qquad (14\text{-}25)$$

and it describes the *magneto-caloric effect*. For virtually all materials, $(\partial \mathscr{M}/\partial T)_H$ is negative and therefore dT has the same sign as dH. Thus a sudden increase in the field will result in a temperature rise, while a decrease in the field will produce a decrease in the temperature, exactly as we concluded from Fig. 13-2.

For the example of a Curie law material, if we substitute the second equation of (14-22) into (14-25), we find that

$$T \, dT = \left(\frac{\mu_0 \mathscr{C}}{C_H}\right) H \, dH \qquad (14\text{-}26)$$

If we integrate (14-26) for the case in which the field is decreased from H_0 to zero, we find

$$\int_{T_i}^{T_f} T \, dT = \frac{\mu_0 \mathscr{C}}{C_H} \int_{H_0}^{0} H \, dH = \tfrac{1}{2}(T_f^2 - T_i^2) = -\frac{\mu_0 \mathscr{C} H_0^2}{2C_H}$$

and therefore the final temperature obtained in this adiabatic demagnetization is given by

$$T_f = T_i \left[1 - \frac{\mu_0 \mathscr{C}}{C_H}\left(\frac{H_0}{T_i}\right)^2 \right]^{1/2} \qquad (14\text{-}27)$$

This result shows us that the lowest final temperature will generally correspond to a large initial field and a low initial temperature.

The magneto-caloric effect is the basis of the methods by which temperatures below $0.001°$K have been attained. The principal difficulty with this method is that the only way in which the temperature can be measured is by measuring the susceptibility ($\mathscr{M}/VH$) of the material, and this requires a knowledge of the true dependence of the magnetization on the temperature which, as we have already indicated, is generally not so simple as that given by (14-14).

Exercises

14-1. Show that for a Curie law material the entropy is given by

$$S = \int C_m \, dT/T - \mu_0 \mathscr{M}^2/2\mathscr{C} + \text{const.}$$

and that $(\partial C_H / \partial H)_T = 2\mu_0 \mathscr{C} H/T^2$.

14-2. By starting from (14-8), define the magnetic analogs of enthalpy, Helmholtz function, and Gibbs function and derive all the equations corresponding to (11-5), (11-6), and (11-7).

14-3. Show that the analog of (14-6) for an electric system is $dU = T \, dS - p \, dV + E \, d\mathscr{P}$, where E is the electric field and $\mathscr{P}$ is the total electric dipole moment of the system. Also find the analog of a Curie law material and of (14-25).

15 *Phase transitions*

Up to now we have assumed that our system has been completely homogeneous throughout. Such a situation is not always an equilibrium possibility, however, and then it is observed that the system breaks up into two or more homogeneous portions called *phases* which are in mutual equilibrium. A common example is the transition of liquid water to ice, and a possible equilibrium situation of water is one in which the liquid and solid phases are coexistent. In this chapter we are concerned with the transitions between phases and their equilibrium with each other.

Let us recall the behavior of a real gas below its critical temperature as predicted by the van der Waals equation and as illustrated by the isothermal depicted in Fig. 15-1*a*. Suppose we were to try to compress the gas along this isothermal by keeping its temperature constant at the value *T*. We see from the figure that, as one would expect, the pressure increases as the volume is decreased until the maximum point *M* is reached. If we were to decrease the volume even more, then, according to the van der Waals equation, the result would be a *decrease* in the pressure. A situation such as this one is physically unstable and cannot actually be a characteristic of the equilibrium states; hence the isothermal shown in the figure cannot be completely correct. What is found to happen instead is that at a certain stage, indicated by *v*, the gas begins to liquefy even before the volume corresponding to the point of maximum pressure *M* is reached.

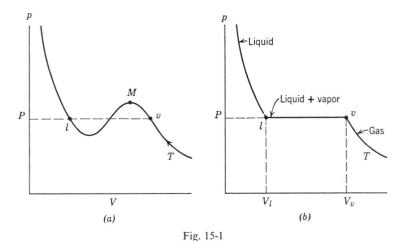

Fig. 15-1

If the volume is further decreased, the pressure remains constant at the value P as more liquid is condensed. This process continues until the point l is reached at which all the gas has been liquefied; from then on, it is necessary for the pressure to increase if the volume is to decrease further.

In other words, the *actual* isotherm observed for a gas is like that shown in Fig. 15-1b. If $V > V_v$, the system is all in the single gas phase, while, for $V < V_l$, it is all in the single liquid phase. At each point along the straight line at constant pressure P and $V_l < V < V_v$, the system exists in the two phases in equilibrium with each other (the gas when in equilibrium with the liquid is generally called a *vapor*). The pressure P corresponding to the two-phase portion of the isotherm is called the *vapor pressure*. It is fairly evident that, if a different isotherm is used, the vapor pressure will be different; in other words, P is a function of T and independent of the volume. It is of interest to determine this function $P(T)$ which is characteristic of the phase transition.

15-1 The equilibrium condition and the Clausius-Clapeyron equation

Since the equilibrium between the two phases corresponds to constant temperature and pressure, we recall from (11-19) that we must find the condition which minimizes the Gibbs function G. If there are a total of ν kilomoles of material in the system of which ν_1 kilomoles are in phase 1 and ν_2 kilomoles in phase 2 so that

$$\nu_1 + \nu_2 = \nu = \text{const.} \tag{15-1}$$

then we have

$$G = \nu_1 g_1 + \nu_2 g_2 = \nu_1 g_1 + (\nu - \nu_1)g_2 \tag{15-2}$$

in terms of the molar Gibbs functions g_1 and g_2 of the two phases. We also know from (11-5c) that g_1 and g_2 are functions only of T and P. We can minimize G by differentiating (15-2) with respect to the variable ν_1 and setting the derivative equal to zero:

$$\left(\frac{\partial G}{\partial \nu_1}\right)_{T,P} = g_1 - g_2 = 0$$

and therefore

$$g_1 = g_2 \tag{15-3}$$

is the condition for equilibrium between phases so that there is no transfer of matter between them.

Rather than trying at this time to describe the phase equilibrium by evaluating the molar Gibbs functions, we want to derive from (15-3) another useful and historically significant description in terms of the *vapor pressure curve* which is a plot of the function $P(T)$ as illustrated in Fig. 15-2a. The point C is the critical point, and it has the coordinates p_c and T_c of Sec. 12-2, as we can verify by comparing Figs. 12-3 and 15-1a and recalling how the vapor pressure curve is derived from the various isothermals.

To compare the equilibrium between phases 1 and 2 for two neighboring equilibrium states A and B, as illustrated in Fig. 15-2b, we apply (15-3) to both A and B and obtain

$$g_1{}^A = g_2{}^A \quad \text{and} \quad g_1{}^B = g_2{}^B \tag{15-4}$$

We can also write $g_i{}^B = g_i{}^A + dg_i$, and, when this is substituted into (15-4), we find that

$$dg_1 = dg_2 \tag{15-5}$$

which, with the use of (11-5c) becomes

$$-s_1 \, dT + v_1 \, dP = -s_2 \, dT + v_2 \, dP \tag{15-6}$$

If we solve (15-6) for dP/dT, we find that

$$\frac{dP}{dT} = \frac{s_2 - s_1}{v_2 - v_1} = \frac{\Delta s}{\Delta v} \tag{15-7}$$

This result (15-7) is known as the *Clausius-Clapeyron* equation, and it gives the slope of the equilibrium pressure vs. temperature curve in terms of the differences in the entropy and volume per kilomole of the two

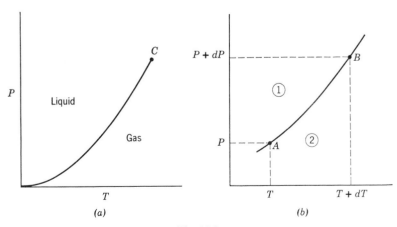

Fig. 15-2

phases. It bears an interesting resemblance to the Maxwell relation (11-7c).

It is often convenient to define the *latent heat* λ as the heat absorbed per kilomole during the transition from phase 1 to phase 2; because of (10-27), we can write

$$\lambda = T\,\Delta s = T(s_2 - s_1) \tag{15-8}$$

and (15-7) becomes

$$\frac{dP}{dT} = \frac{\lambda}{T\,\Delta v} \tag{15-9}$$

Although we have been constantly referring to the condensation of a vapor into a liquid and *vice versa* as a specific example of a phase transition, it is clear from our derivation that (15-3) and (15-7) apply to equilibrium between any two phases. Thus the term *vapor pressure* for P applies only when one is discussing the vapor-liquid or vapor-solid equilibrium; the corresponding latent heats are those of *vaporization* and *sublimation*, respectively.

If we apply (15-9) to the melting of a solid into a liquid, then λ is called the latent heat of *fusion*; if we invert (15-9), we obtain for this case

$$\frac{dT}{dP} = \frac{T\,\Delta v}{\lambda} = \frac{T(v_l - v_s)}{\lambda} \tag{15-10}$$

where v_l and v_s are the volumes of a kilomole of the liquid and the solid, respectively. This form of the Clausius-Clapeyron equation is appropriate for discussing how the freezing (melting) point changes with pressure. It turns out that $\lambda > 0$ so that, if $v_l > v_s$, that is, if the material expands on melting, then $dT/dP > 0$ and an increase in pressure produces an increase in the melting point. On the other hand, if $v_l < v_s$, the freezing point decreases as the pressure is increased; this is precisely the situation which applies to water, and it has many practical results. For example, it is used to account for the way in which glaciers can apparently "flow" over and around obstacles. The large pressure produced by the weight of the ice lowers the freezing point below the actual temperature so that the ice in contact with the obstacle melts, flows around the obstacle as liquid water, and then refreezes when it reaches a region where the pressure has decreased enough for the local temperature to be again below the freezing point.

15-2 The equation of the vapor pressure curve

Now let us consider the problem of determining the function $P = P(T)$ for the important case of the equilibrium between a liquid and its vapor.

We could do this by finding the molar Gibbs functions for the vapor and liquid, equating them according to (15-3), and solving the resultant equation involving only P and T for $P(T)$. An equivalent way, of course, is by direct integration of (15-9); we shall use this latter method first in a very approximate manner.

If v_v is the molar volume of the vapor, then generally there is so much expansion on evaporation that we can safely say that $v_v \gg v_l$ and therefore we can neglect the volume of the liquid and write

$$\Delta v = v_v - v_l \simeq v_v \qquad (15\text{-}11)$$

For simplicity and definiteness, let us assume that the pressure is low enough that the vapor can be treated as an ideal gas; therefore we find from (8-21) that

$$v_v = \frac{RT}{P} \qquad (15\text{-}12)$$

If we substitute (15-11) and (15-12) into (15-9), we obtain

$$\frac{dP}{P} = \frac{\lambda \, dT}{RT^2} \qquad (15\text{-}13)$$

and if we further assume that λ is independent of the temperature we can integrate (15-13) to obtain the equation of the vapor pressure curve in the form

$$\ln P = -\frac{\lambda R}{T} + B \qquad (15\text{-}14)$$

where B is a constant. In spite of the many assumptions we made to obtain (15-14), it is a surprisingly accurate representation of the dependence of the vapor pressure on temperature for many materials. In fact, it is common practice in many handbooks and other collections of data to write (15-14) as $\ln P = -A/T + B$ and simply tabulate the values of A and B for each material.

However, for our later purposes, we shall need a somewhat more accurate formula for the vapor pressure curve which we can obtain by a method originally due to Kirchhoff and which involves the use of (15-3) directly. If we continue to treat the vapor as an ideal gas, and assume that the temperature is high enough that the heat capacities can be treated as constant, we find from (11-4c), (9-15), (9-13), and (8-21) that

$$g_v = u + Pv - Ts = (c_v + R)T + u_{v0} - Ts = c_p T + u_{v0} - Ts \qquad (15\text{-}15)$$

We also find from (9-43) that we can write $s(T, v)$ for the vapor in the form

$$s = c_v \ln T + R \ln v + s_{v0} \qquad (15\text{-}16)$$

where s_{v0} is a constant needed so that (15-16) will give the absolute value of the entropy. If we write s as a function of T and P by using (9-13) and (8-21), we find that we obtain

$$s = c_p \ln T - R \ln P + s_{p0} \tag{15-17}$$

where

$$s_{p0} = s_{v0} + R \ln R \tag{15-18}$$

If we now substitute (15-17) into (15-15), we find the molar Gibbs function for the vapor to be given by

$$g_v = c_p T(1 - \ln T) + RT \ln P + u_{v0} - Ts_{p0} \tag{15-19}$$

By neglecting the small amount of work done in the change of volume of the liquid, we can also neglect the difference between c_p and c_v and simply write the molar heat capacity as c_l. Then we find from (9-5) that

$$u_l = u_{l0} + \int_0^T c_l \, dT' \tag{15-20}$$

and from (9-5) and (10-28) that

$$s_l = \int_0^T \frac{c_l \, dT'}{T'} \tag{15-21}$$

Neglecting the term Pv_l and substituting (15-20) and (15-21) into (11-4c), we find that

$$g_l = u_{l0} + \int_0^T c_l \, dT' - T \int_0^T \frac{c_l \, dT'}{T'} \tag{15-22}$$

If we now equate (15-19) and (15-22), according to the equilibrium condition (15-3), we can solve the resulting equation for $\ln P$ and we obtain

$$\ln P = -\frac{\lambda_0}{RT} + \frac{1}{R}\left(c_p \ln T - \int_0^T \frac{c_l \, dT'}{T'}\right)$$
$$-\frac{1}{R}\left(c_p - \frac{1}{T}\int_0^T c_l \, dT'\right) + \frac{s_{p0}}{R} \tag{15-23}$$

as the more general equation for the vapor pressure curve, where

$$\lambda_0 = u_{v0} - u_{l0} \tag{15-24}$$

is the molar energy difference between the liquid and vapor at absolute zero and therefore is the latent heat of vaporization at $T = 0$. Equation (15-23) could, of course, have been obtained in this form by integrating the Clausius-Clapeyron equation, and, conversely, if we were to differentiate (15-23) with respect to T and take account of all the approximations involved, we would eventually obtain (15-9).

The feature of (15-23) which will be of the most interest to us is the fact that it involves the absolute value of the entropy because of the appearance of the term s_{p0}. Thus in principle one can determine the quantity s_{p0} from measurements of the dependence of the vapor pressure on the temperature.

15-3   Higher order phase transitions

The phase transitions we have been discussing and which are described by (15-7) are called *first order phase transitions*. An essential feature of our derivation of (15-7) from (15-5) was the assumption that Δs and Δv were both different from zero, that is, that there was a *discontinuity* in the molar entropy and in the molar volume. However, we recall from (11-6c) that

$$-s = \left(\frac{\partial g}{\partial T}\right)_p, \quad v = \left(\frac{\partial g}{\partial p}\right)_T \tag{15-25}$$

so that we were actually assuming that the *first derivatives* of the molar Gibbs function were discontinuous. If they were not, we would need a more general treatment. The treatment we shall discuss was first considered by Ehrenfest and is commonly used as a basis of classification of observed phase transitions.

If we want to compare equilibrium at (T, P) with that at $(T + dT, P + dP)$, it follows again from (15-4) that we must equate

$$g(T + dT, P + dP) - g(T, P) = \left(\frac{\partial g}{\partial T}\right)_P dT + \left(\frac{\partial g}{\partial P}\right)_T dP$$

$$+ \frac{1}{2}\left[\left(\frac{\partial^2 g}{\partial T^2}\right)_P (dT)^2 + 2\frac{\partial^2 g}{\partial T\,\partial P}\,dT\,dP + \left(\frac{\partial^2 g}{\partial P^2}\right)_T (dP)^2\right] + \cdots \tag{15-26}$$

for the two phases, just as we did to obtain (15-5). The second derivatives can be written

$$\left(\frac{\partial^2 g}{\partial T^2}\right)_P = -\left(\frac{\partial s}{\partial T}\right)_P = -\frac{c_p}{T} \tag{15-27a}$$

$$\frac{\partial^2 g}{\partial T\,\partial P} = \left(\frac{\partial v}{\partial T}\right)_P = \alpha v \tag{15-27b}$$

$$\left(\frac{\partial^2 g}{\partial P^2}\right)_T = \left(\frac{\partial v}{\partial P}\right)_T = -v\kappa_T \tag{15-27c}$$

with the use of (15-25), (11-20), and (8-2), so that, if we equate (15-26) for both phases, use (15-25) and (15-27), and define

$$\Delta s = s_2 - s_1, \quad \Delta v = v_2 - v_1, \quad \Delta c_p = c_{p2} - c_{p1}, \quad \text{etc.} \quad (15\text{-}28)$$

we find the condition for equilibrium to be given by

$$-\Delta s \, dT + \Delta v \, dP + \frac{1}{2}\left[-\frac{\Delta c_p}{T}(dT)^2 + 2\Delta(\alpha v) \, dT \, dP \right.$$

$$\left. - \Delta(\kappa_T v)(dP)^2 \right] + \cdots = 0 \quad (15\text{-}29)$$

If $\Delta s \neq 0$ and $\Delta v \neq 0$, we can neglect the second and higher order terms in dT and dP so that (15-29) reduces to (15-6) and (15-7); thus we see again that the *first order transition* is characterized by discontinuities in the first derivatives of g which appear physically as a latent heat and a molar volume change.

To get a *second order transition*, we assume that $\Delta s = 0$ and $\Delta v = 0$ and that the *second derivatives of g are discontinuous*; then we can neglect the third and higher order terms in dT and dP in (15-29) so that the phase equilibrium condition becomes

$$-\frac{\Delta c_p}{T}(dT)^2 + 2\Delta(\alpha v) \, dT \, dP - \Delta(\kappa_T v) \, (dP)^2 = 0$$

from which we find the analog of the Clausius-Clapeyron equation to be

$$\frac{dP}{dT} = \frac{\Delta\alpha \pm [(\Delta\alpha)^2 - (\Delta\kappa_T \, \Delta c_p)/Tv]^{1/2}}{\Delta\kappa_T} \quad (15\text{-}30)$$

since $\Delta(\alpha v) = v \, \Delta\alpha$, etc., if $\Delta v = 0$. We also see from (15-27) that the physical characteristics of a second order phase transition are discontinuities in the molar heat capacity at constant pressure, the thermal expansion coefficient, and the isothermal compressibility.

One could now go on to define a phase transition of the *nth order* by assuming that the nth order derivatives of the molar Gibbs functions are discontinuous while all lower order derivatives are continuous. The characteristics of such a transition could be discussed by the same general method we used above for the first and second order transitions. In practice, however, one generally need not consider any possibilities other than first or second order. Distinguishing between the two possibilities is often quite difficult if one depends only on measurements of the heat capacity, since a sharp change and discontinuity in a heat capacity which occupies only a small temperature range is very hard to distinguish from a latent heat at a fixed temperature.

Exercises

15-1. Suppose a liquid in equilibrium with its vapor is used as the working substance in a reversible Carnot engine. Let the isothermal processes be those parts of the isothermals T and $T + dT$ which extend from the l and v points of Fig. 15-1b. If the corresponding pressures are P and $P + dP$, find the efficiency of this cycle and show that the result leads directly to the Clausius-Clapeyron equation.

15-2. Show that in a first order phase transition the molar energy change is given by

$$\Delta u = \lambda \left(1 - \frac{d \ln T}{d \ln P} \right)$$

15-3. Assuming that the conditions under which (15-14) was derived are applicable, find the equation of the condensation curve in the pV plane.

15-4. The vapor pressure, in atmospheres, of solid ammonia is given by $\ln P = 18.70 - (3754/T)$ while that of liquid ammonia is $\ln P = 15.16 - (3063/T)$. What are the temperature and pressure at the triple point, that is, the state for which all three phases are in mutual equilibrium? Find the latent heats of vaporization and sublimation. Find the latent heat of fusion at the triple point.

15-5. When a kilomole of gas is used in a porous plug experiment and changed from the initial state i to the final state f, it is found that the fraction x is liquefied. Show that

$$x = (h_{f \text{ vap}} - h_i)/(h_{f \text{ vap}} - h_{f \text{ liq}}).$$

15-6. Under what conditions are (15-14) and (15-23) equivalent?

Part Three

Kinetic Theory of Gases

16 Probability and the distribution function

As we have already mentioned several times, thermodynamics basically deals with relations among the experimentally determined macroscopic quantities which describe the bulk properties of matter. The absolute values of these quantities are also of interest, of course, and it would be desirable to be able to relate them to the individual characteristics and behavior of the atomic and molecular constituents of the material. In this way we can hope to develop a better understanding of the fundamental origins of the thermodynamic properties and laws, while at the same time we can obtain theoretical expressions which will enable us to make specific calculations.

The two principal methods which have been developed to discuss the relation between the macroscopic and microscopic characteristics of matter are called kinetic theory and statistical mechanics. As we shall find later, statistical mechanics is the more general in its concepts and methods and is correspondingly more difficult. Kinetic theory is much more detailed and graphic in its descriptions and therefore is somewhat more desirable as an introduction to the general ideas involved in a statistical approach; however, since kinetic theory is so very specific in its methods, it is easy to deal with only when one is discussing gases and we shall accordingly restrict ourselves to them.

Kinetic theory basically looks for its answers in terms of the motions of the individual atoms and molecules of which the system is comprised. Since the number of molecules in a kilomole of gas equals Avogadro's number, $L = 6.025 \times 10^{26}$ (kilomole)$^{-1}$, an enormous number of mechanical degrees of freedom are involved. On the other hand, we have seen that the needs of thermodynamics are adequately met with only a very few variables. These macroscopic variables are accordingly assumed to be obtainable as *averages* of appropriate molecular properties. Thus our approach can be statistical, and we therefore begin with a brief discussion of some of the concepts of probability.

16-1 Fundamentals of probability theory

If we let N_t be the total number of trials of some event, and N_s be the number of occurrences of a certain kind, then we define the *probability* of the occurrence as

$$P = \lim_{N_t \to \infty} \frac{N_s}{N_t} \qquad (16\text{-}1)$$

that is, as the limiting value of the ratio of occurrences to trials, and assuming that a limit exists. For example, the trials could be the tossing of a coin, and an occurrence of interest could be the appearance of the head or the tail; then, if the occurrences were due entirely to chance, heads and tails would appear equally often on the average so that $P = \frac{1}{2}$ for either case.

There are two fundamental laws or assumptions about the combining of probabilities. If we define $P_{1 \text{ or } 2}$ as the probability that one *or* the other of two *mutually exclusive* events 1 and 2 will occur, then

$$P_{1 \text{ or } 2} = P_1 + P_2 \qquad (16\text{-}2)$$

where P_1 and P_2 are the separate probabilities. If we define $P_{1 \text{ and } 2}$ as the probability that *both* of the *independent* events 1 and 2 will occur, then

$$P_{1 \text{ and } 2} = P_1 P_2 \qquad (16\text{-}3)$$

It will often be convenient for us to deal with variables which can assume continuous values and to which we want to apply probability concepts. For example, let us consider the probability that a point chosen at random along the length l of Fig. 16-1a will fall within the segment Δx. Since all points in l are equally likely, the desired probability is the ratio of the length of the segment Δx to the total length, or

$$P_{\Delta x} = \frac{\Delta x}{l} \qquad (16\text{-}4)$$

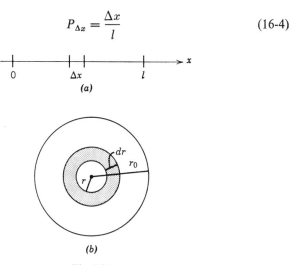

(a)

(b)

Fig. 16-1

We see that the sum of these probabilities is unity, as it should be since the point must lie somewhere on the segment by hypothesis; that is,

$$\sum P_{\Delta x} = \sum \frac{\Delta x}{l} = 1 \tag{16-5}$$

It is evident that this result is a general property of a probability, that is, the sum of the probability of each possibility over all the possibilities must be unity. If we choose Δx to be smaller and smaller, we can say that the probability of choosing a point in the segment dx is $P_{dx} = dx/l$.

If the probability that a variable x will have a value between x and $x + dx$ can be written in the form

$$P = w(x)\, dx \tag{16-6}$$

then the function $w(x)$ is defined as the *probability density*. In the example above, $w(x) = 1/l = $ const. As another example, let us consider the probability that a point picked at random in the circle of Fig. 16-1*b* will be in the ring shown shaded, that is, that the point will lie between the circles of radii r and $r + dr$. In this case the probability is the ratio of the area of the ring to the total area of the circle and thus is

$$P = \frac{2\pi r\, dr}{\pi r_0{}^2} = \frac{2r}{r_0{}^2}\, dr \tag{16-7}$$

When we compare (16-6) and (16-7), we see that the probability density in this case is

$$w(r) = \frac{2r}{r_0{}^2} \tag{16-8}$$

and is not a constant as it was for the first example.

If $M(x)$ is a given function of x, the *average value* of M is written as $\bar{M}$ and is defined by

$$\bar{M} = \int M(x)w(x)\, dx \tag{16-9}$$

where the integral is taken over all possible values of x. As an example, suppose that the speed u of a particle depends on the variable x. The average speed will then be given by

$$\bar{u} = \int u(x)w(x)\, dx$$

Similarly, the average of the square of the speed will be

$$\overline{u^2} = \int u^2(x)w(x)\, dx$$

It is clear from the last two expressions that, in general, $\overline{u^2} \neq (\bar{u})^2$.

We can extend these ideas to a situation where we have k variables $(x_1, x_2, \ldots, x_k)$ by defining a probability density w which is a function of all these variables so that $w(x_1, x_2, \ldots, x_k)\, dx_1\, dx_2 \cdots dx_k$ is the probability that the value of x_1 is between x_1 and $x_1 + dx_1$, that of x_2 is between x_2 and $x_2 + dx_2, \ldots$, and that of x_k is between x_k and $x_k + dx_k$.

It follows from our definitions that $0 \leqslant P_i \leqslant 1$, where P_i is the probability of a given value of a variable which only takes on discrete values, and that the relation $0 \leqslant w\, dx_1 \cdots dx_k \leqslant 1$ holds for continuous variables. Also, $\Sigma_i P_i = 1$ as previously remarked, and

$$\int \cdots \int w(x_1, \ldots, x_k)\, dx_1 \cdots dx_k = 1 \qquad (16\text{-}10)$$

The result (16-10) is sometimes called the *normalization* of w, and the k-fold integral is taken over all possible values of all the variables.

The definition of the average value of a function of several variables can be similarly generalized as

$$\bar{M} = \int \cdots \int M(x_1, \ldots, x_k) w(x_1, \ldots, x_k)\, dx_1 \cdots dx_k \qquad (16\text{-}11)$$

It follows at once from this definition that

$$\overline{M + N} = \bar{M} + \bar{N}, \quad \overline{CM} = C\bar{M} \qquad (16\text{-}12)$$

where C is a constant; we also see in general that $\overline{MN} \neq (\bar{M})(\bar{N})$.

Example. Isotropic Distribution of Velocities. Let us suppose that we have a situation in which the velocities of the molecules in a gas are isotropically distributed; by this we mean that there is as much chance that a molecule will be going in a given direction as in any other direction. In other words, there are exactly as many molecules traveling in one direction as in any other, on the average.

We let $P_\omega\, d\omega$ be the probability that the direction of the velocity vector $\mathbf{u}$ is in the element of solid angle $d\omega$. For an isotropic distribution in which all directions are equally likely, the probability cannot depend on the specific direction; hence

$$P_\omega\, d\omega = K\, d\omega, \quad K = \text{const.} \qquad (16\text{-}13)$$

We can determine K from the normalization condition (16-10):

$$\int_\omega P_\omega\, d\omega = 1 = K \int_\omega d\omega = 4\pi K$$

Therefore $K = 1/4\pi$ and

$$P_\omega\, d\omega = \frac{d\omega}{4\pi} \qquad (16\text{-}14)$$

As a simple application of this result, let us find the average of the component of the velocity along some fixed direction in space which we choose as the z axis. If we let θ be the angle between $\mathbf{u}$ and z, and, if we consider first only those molecules with speed u, we find from (16-11) and (16-14) that

$$\overline{u_z} = \overline{u \cos \theta} = \int_\omega u \cos \theta \left(\frac{d\omega}{4\pi} \right)$$

$$= \frac{u}{4\pi} \int_0^{2\pi} \int_0^\pi \cos \theta \sin \theta \, d\theta \, d\varphi = 0 \qquad (16\text{-}14')$$

Since this relation holds for any speed, we conclude that $\overline{u_z} = 0$ in general. This is not surprising, of course, and it must be true if the velocity distribution is isotropic for then there is no net transport of molecules from one place to another.

16-2 The molecular distribution function

We are able to apply statistical methods to a gas because of the very large number of molecules involved. In our description we shall assume that the positions of the molecules can be specified, at least in principle. We shall also assume for simplicity that any forces between the molecules can be neglected except when they are very close together as during a collision. The simple model of a gas which we shall adopt is that the molecules can be treated as small, smooth, perfectly elastic spheres; thus there will be forces of interaction only when the molecules are in actual contact, and since they are smooth they cannot transfer rotational energy and we need consider only their translational kinetic energy.

In order to calculate averages, we shall need to know the probabilities of the various molecular properties; that is, we shall need to know the *molecular distribution function* $f(\mathbf{r}, \mathbf{u}, t)$ which we shall define exactly below. The molecular velocity will be designated by $\mathbf{u}$, the components by u_x, u_y, u_z, and the speed by u. We shall let $d\tau$ be an element of physical volume, for example, $dx \, dy \, dz$ when rectangular coordinates are used. Then, by definition:

$f(\mathbf{r}, \mathbf{u}, t) \, d\tau \, du_x \, du_y \, du_z = $ *number of molecules* at the time t
which are in the volume $d\tau$ at the position $\mathbf{r}$, and whose
velocity components are in the range u_x to $u_x + du_x$, u_y to
$u_y + du_y$, and u_z to $u_z + du_z$ (16-15)

It will sometimes be convenient to refer to these molecules as having their velocities in the "volume" $du_x \, du_y \, du_z$ which is located at the point $\mathbf{u}$ in "velocity space."

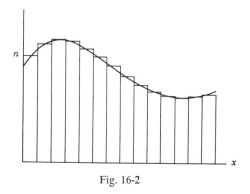

Fig. 16-2

It follows from (16-15) that

$$d\tau \iiint f(\mathbf{r}, \mathbf{u}, t)\, du_x\, du_y\, du_z = n\, d\tau$$

is the total number of molecules in the volume $d\tau$ regardless of their velocities; therefore n is the number of molecules per unit volume (the *number density*) and is given by

$$n(\mathbf{r}, t) = \int f(\mathbf{r}, \mathbf{u}, t)\, du_x\, du_y\, du_z \qquad (16\text{-}16)$$

It is clear that, if we took the volume element $d\tau$ to be extremely small, the density n as measured for the various $d\tau$ would have large fluctuations in it depending on whether there happened to be a molecule in $d\tau$ or not. Since we want to deal with continuous functions, what we shall always be doing is choosing our volume elements big enough to contain a large number of molecules, yet small enough that there is no appreciable variation of the properties of the gas within the volume element. We shall continue to choose $d\tau$ to be extremely small as far as macroscopic dimensions are concerned. This situation is illustrated schematically in Fig. 16-2, which shows the sort of step function we would obtain for n by measuring the number of molecules in adjacent volumes; the process we follow then is to define a smooth curve for n (and similar quantities) to replace this step function.

Although the time has been included in (16-15) and (16-16) for generality in the definition, we shall not be considering situations in which the probabilities and average properties are changing with time; that is, we shall discuss only "steady states."

We can see from our discussion so far that the problems in kinetic theory can be divided roughly into two classes, first, those of finding the appropriate distribution function, and, second, those of using the distribution function to calculate averages which can be compared with experimental values of the corresponding property.

16-3 Constant speed gas

Probably the simplest picture of a gas which can be visualized is one in which all molecules have the same speed u_0. Since many of our subsequent calculations would be greatly simplified if such were the case, we should investigate this possibility. In order for such a gas to exist, the molecules would have to have the same speeds *after a collision* as they did before. If we consider the particular type of collision illustrated in Fig. 16-3, we can show that the speeds do change.

We assume the rigid elastic spheres to have the same mass m. At the instant of collision, the line of centers is vertical as shown by the dashed line; both molecules have the same speed u_0 by hypothesis. After the collision, molecule 1 goes off, making an angle θ with its original direction of motion. Since no external forces are involved, the total momentum is conserved, according to (I: 6-10). The x and y components of the momentum conservation equation are, respectively,

$$mu_0 = mu_1' \cos \theta \qquad (16\text{-}17)$$

$$mu_0 = mu_1' \sin \theta - mu_2' \qquad (16\text{-}18)$$

The equation expressing conservation of energy is

$$\tfrac{1}{2}mu_0^2 + \tfrac{1}{2}mu_0^2 = \tfrac{1}{2}mu_1'^2 + \tfrac{1}{2}mu_2'^2 \qquad (16\text{-}19)$$

The speeds can be eliminated from these equations, and we find the

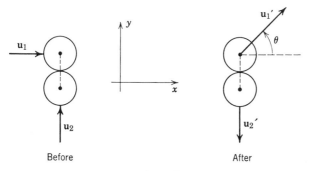

Before   After

Fig. 16-3

resulting condition on the angle θ to be

$$\sin \theta (\cos \theta - \sin \theta) = 0 \qquad (16\text{-}20)$$

The first possibility that $\sin \theta = 0$ and therefore $\theta = 0$ represents a complete miss and is of no further interest to us. The condition $\cos \theta = \sin \theta$ which follows from (16-20) tells us that $\theta = 45°$; when this value of θ is inserted into (16-17) and (16-18), we find that

$$u_1' = \sqrt{2}\, u_0, \quad u_2' = 0 \qquad (16\text{-}21)$$

which shows that the speeds of the molecules are definitely changed as a result of this particular collision. Since it is reasonable that this type of collision, as well as all other possible types, will frequently occur, we are forced to conclude that it will be impossible for a gas to consist of molecules which all have the same speed. In addition, we shall have to assume the possibility of all speeds from zero to infinity being found in the gas.

Exercises

16-1. By means of either a few examples or a general discussion based on counting of possibilities, verify the rules (16-2) and (16-3).

16-2. Show that the definition (16-9) is the same as the usual arithmetic definition of an average as the quotient of a sum divided by the number of terms.

16-3. Find the probability density which gives the chance that a point chosen at random within a sphere of radius r_0 will lie within the thin shell bounded by spheres of radii r and $r + dr$.

17 Pressure of an ideal gas and the equation of state

It is possible to obtain useful results simply from the knowledge that the distribution function f exists, without the necessity of knowing its specific form. We shall illustrate this fact for a particular example and postpone the detailed evaluation of f to the next chapter.

We want to calculate the pressure exerted on the walls of the container by an ideal gas, which we have defined for kinetic theory purposes as one in which the molecular forces can be neglected except at collision. For simplicity we shall assume that there is only one type of molecule. We shall consider a small portion of the bounding surface which we can treat as a plane surface of area ΔA, and we shall calculate the pressure p times the area ΔA as the time average of the force $F_\perp$ which is perpendicular to the wall and arises from the collisions of the molecules with the wall. If we write the time interval involved as Δt, then

$$p\,\Delta A = \overline{(F_\perp)}_{\text{gas on wall}} = \frac{1}{\Delta t}\int_{\Delta t} F_\perp\,dt \qquad (17\text{-}1)$$

Since the force exerted by the wall *on* the gas is the negative of $F_\perp$ as shown by (I: 3-10) and equals the time rate of change of the momentum $P_\perp$ *of the gas*, we have

$$F_\perp = -\frac{dP_\perp}{dt}$$

so that (17-1) becomes

$$p\,\Delta A\,\Delta t = \int_{\Delta t}\left(-\frac{dP_\perp}{dt}\right)dt = -\Delta P_\perp = (P_\perp)_i - (P_\perp)_f \qquad (17\text{-}2)$$

where $\Delta P_\perp = (P_\perp)_f - (P_\perp)_i$ is the net change of momentum of the gas as a result of the collisions.

In order to calculate $\Delta P_\perp$, let us consider first the group of molecules which are approaching the wall and whose velocity vectors equal **u** on the average and lie in the range $du_x\,du_y\,du_z$; the direction of **u** makes an angle θ with the normal to the wall where $0 \leqslant \theta \leqslant \pi/2$, as illustrated in Fig. 17-1. We construct a cylinder on ΔA whose cross section is shown and whose generators are parallel to **u** and of length $u\,\Delta t$; therefore all the molecules contained in this volume will strike the wall in the time Δt. Since the volume of the cylinder is $u\,\Delta t\cos\theta\,\Delta A$, the total number of molecules of

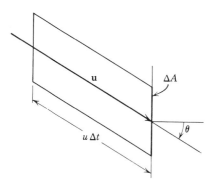

Fig. 17-1

this velocity type which collide with the wall in Δt is found from the definition (16-15) to be

$$f \cdot u \, \Delta t \cos \theta \, \Delta A \cdot du_x \, du_y \, du_z \qquad (17\text{-}3)$$

If m is the mass of each molecule, the perpendicular component of momentum of each molecule of this type is $mu \cos \theta$, and therefore the total momentum brought to the wall by molecules of this velocity group is found by multiplying the contribution of each by the total number given by (17-3) and is

$$mu \cos \theta \cdot f \cdot u \, \Delta t \cos \theta \, \Delta A \cdot du_x \, du_y \, du_z \qquad (17\text{-}4)$$

If we now integrate (17-4) over all velocities possible for the molecules incident upon the wall, we find the initial perpendicular momentum to be

$$(P_\perp)_i = m \, \Delta A \, \Delta t \int_{0 \leqslant \theta \leqslant \pi/2} u^2 \cos^2 \theta f \, du_x \, du_y \, du_z \qquad (17\text{-}5)$$

To calculate the momentum carried away from the wall we proceed in a similar manner and erect a volume on ΔA with generators of length $u \, \Delta t$ and parallel to $\mathbf{u}$ which is now directed away from the wall so that $\pi/2 \leqslant \theta \leqslant \pi$. The calculation is done exactly as above except that now the volume of the cylinder is

$$u \, \Delta t \, |\cos \theta| \, \Delta A = -u \, \Delta t \cos \theta \, \Delta A$$

since $\cos \theta$ is negative in this case. Therefore we find that

$$(P_\perp)_f = -m \, \Delta A \, \Delta t \int_{\pi/2 \leqslant \theta \leqslant \pi} u^2 \cos^2 \theta f \, du_x \, du_y \, du_z \qquad (17\text{-}6)$$

If we now insert (17-5) and (17-6) into (17-2), cancel out the common factor $\Delta A \, \Delta t$, note that the integrations over θ can be combined into a single one over the whole possible range of θ since the integrands are the same, and use the definitions (16-11), (16-15), and (16-16), we find that the pressure is given by

$$p = m \int (u \cos \theta)^2 f \, du_x \, du_y \, du_z$$

$$= nm \left[\frac{1}{n} \int (u \cos \theta)^2 f \, du_x \, du_y \, du_z \right] = nm \overline{(u \cos \theta)^2} \qquad (17\text{-}7)$$

If we let $u_\perp = u \cos \theta$ be the component of velocity perpendicular to the wall, we can write (17-7) as

$$p = nm \overline{u_\perp^2} \qquad (17\text{-}8)$$

We note again that we obtained this general result without knowing the specific form of the distribution function f.

If we now assume in addition that the velocities have an isotropic distribution so that all directions are equivalent, we have

$$\overline{u_\perp^2} = \overline{u_x^2} = \overline{u_y^2} = \overline{u_z^2} = \tfrac{1}{3}\overline{(u_x^2 + u_y^2 + u_z^2)} = \tfrac{1}{3}\overline{u^2} \qquad (17\text{-}9)$$

and (17-8) then becomes

$$p = \tfrac{1}{3}nm\overline{u^2} \qquad (17\text{-}10)$$

If we let $\overline{\varepsilon_t} = \tfrac{1}{2}m\overline{u^2}$ be the average translational kinetic energy of a molecule, we can also write (17-10) as

$$p = \tfrac{2}{3}n\overline{\varepsilon_t} \qquad (17\text{-}11)$$

Although our results so far have given us a kinetic definition of pressure, we can easily use them to obtain a kinetic theory definition of *temperature* as well. If N is the total number of molecules in the volume V, the number density n is

$$n = \frac{N}{V} \qquad (17\text{-}12)$$

and (17-11) can also be written as

$$pV = \tfrac{2}{3}N\overline{\varepsilon_t} \qquad (17\text{-}13)$$

We also have $N = \nu L$, however, where ν is the number of kilomoles and L is Avogadro's number, so that (17-13) becomes $pV = \nu \tfrac{2}{3}L\overline{\varepsilon_t}$ which is the same as the ideal gas equation of state, $pV = \nu RT$, provided that $\tfrac{2}{3}L\overline{\varepsilon_t} = RT$ or that

$$\overline{\varepsilon_t} = \frac{3}{2}\left(\frac{R}{L}\right)T = \frac{3}{2}kT \qquad (17\text{-}14)$$

The constant

$$k = \frac{R}{L} = 1.38 \times 10^{-23} \text{ joule/degree} \qquad (17\text{-}14')$$

is known as the *Boltzmann constant* or the gas constant per molecule. Thus we see from (17-14) that the average translational kinetic energy per molecule is $\tfrac{3}{2}kT$ which we can take as our kinetic definition of temperature. If (17-14) is substituted into (17-13), we obtain another useful form for the equation of state in terms of the total number of molecules:

$$pV = NkT \qquad (17\text{-}15)$$

We can also use this result to calculate some of the thermodynamic properties of a *monatomic* ideal gas, something we were not able to do before. Since the only energy is due to the translational energy, the energy per kilomole is

$$u = L\bar{\varepsilon}_t = \tfrac{3}{2}RT = u(T) \tag{17-16}$$

which is a function of the temperature only. We can use (9-14) and (9-13) to find the molar heat capacities; the results are

$$c_v = \frac{3}{2}R, \quad c_p = \frac{5}{2}R, \quad \frac{c_p}{c_v} = \frac{5}{3} = 1.67 \tag{17-17}$$

These numerical results agree very well with experiment.

If we solve for $\bar{u^2}$ from (17-10), (17-11), and (17-14), we find that

$$\bar{u^2} = \frac{3kT}{m} = \frac{3RT}{\mu} \tag{17-18}$$

where $\mu = Lm$ is the molecular weight. We can use this result to obtain an idea of the actual magnitude of molecular speeds. If we consider helium, for which $\mu = 4$ kilograms/kilomole, at a temperature $T = 273$ degrees, we find that the *root-mean-square* (rms) speed

$$u_{\mathrm{rms}} = (\bar{u^2})^{1/2} \tag{17-19}$$

is 1300 meters/second. We also see from (17-18) that the molecular speeds increase with temperature since $u_{\mathrm{rms}} \sim \sqrt{T}$, making the higher temperatures correspond to greater average energy of molecular motion.

Exercises

17-1. Extend the calculation of the pressure to the case in which more than one type of molecule is present, and thus obtain Dalton's law (8-22).

17-2. Find the temperature at which the average translational kinetic energy of an atom equals that of a singly charged ion of the same mass which has passed through a potential difference of one volt.

17-3. Show that the number of molecules per unit area per unit time which leak out through a small hole in the wall of the container is given by

$$\bar{\Gamma}_N = \tfrac{1}{4}n\bar{u} \tag{17-20}$$

17-4. Consider a two-dimensional gas in which the molecules are constrained to move in a plane. Show that the rate at which molecules strike the boundary per unit length is $n_a\bar{u}/\pi$, where n_a is the number of molecules per unit area.

18 Maxwell's velocity distribution function

In considering the distribution of molecular velocities apart from the question of the variation with position as described by the density n, we shall substantially be following the method used by Maxwell, who first obtained the correct answer to this problem.

We write f in the form of a product

$$f(\mathbf{r}, \mathbf{u}, t) = n(\mathbf{r}, t)F(\mathbf{u}, \mathbf{r}, t) \tag{18-1}$$

and we see that the meaning of F is that

$F(\mathbf{u}, \mathbf{r}, t)\, du_x\, du_y\, du_z$ = the *fraction* of the molecules at $\mathbf{r}$ whose velocity components are in the range $du_x\, du_y\, du_z$ about u_x, u_y, u_z. $\qquad(18\text{-}2)$

If we consider only gases at equilibrium, F will not depend on $\mathbf{r}$ or t, and it can be a function only of the components of $\mathbf{u}$; that is, $F = F(u_x, u_y, u_z)$.

We assume first of all that the velocity distribution is *isotropic* and therefore F can be a function only of the speed,

$$F = F(u) \tag{18-3a}$$

The second assumption we make is that the distribution of the x component is *independent* of the distributions of the y and z components, etc., so that we can write

$$F(u) = \mathscr{F}(u_x)\mathscr{F}(u_y)\mathscr{F}(u_z) \tag{18-3b}$$

These two assumptions are sufficient to determine the form of F and of $\mathscr{F}$ uniquely.

Taking the logarithm of (18-3b), we obtain

$$\ln F(u) = \ln \mathscr{F}(u_x) + \ln \mathscr{F}(u_y) + \ln \mathscr{F}(u_z) \tag{18-4}$$

and, if we differentiate this expression with respect to u_x, we obtain

$$\frac{\partial \ln F}{\partial u_x} = \frac{d \ln F}{du}\frac{\partial u}{\partial u_x} = \frac{u_x}{u}\frac{d \ln F}{du} = \frac{d \ln \mathscr{F}(u_x)}{du_x} \tag{18-5}$$

since $u = (u_x^2 + u_y^2 + u_z^2)^{1/2}$. Two more equations like (18-5) can be found by differentiating (18-4) with respect to u_y and u_z; by dividing them through by u_x, u_y, and u_z, respectively, we find that

$$\frac{d \ln F}{u\, du} = \frac{d \ln \mathscr{F}(u_x)}{u_x\, du_x} = \frac{d \ln \mathscr{F}(u_y)}{u_y\, du_y} = \frac{d \ln \mathscr{F}(u_z)}{u_z\, du_z} \tag{18-6}$$

These functions of different variables in (18-6) can be always equal to each other only if they equal the same *constant*. Letting this constant be written as -2γ, we find from (18-6) that

$$\frac{d \ln \mathscr{F}(u_x)}{u_x \, du_x} = -2\gamma$$

and therefore

$$\ln \mathscr{F}(u_x) = \ln a - \gamma u_x^2$$

where a is another constant; finally we obtain

$$\mathscr{F}(u_x) = a e^{-\gamma u_x^2} \tag{18-7}$$

with similar expressions for $\mathscr{F}(u_y)$ and $\mathscr{F}(u_z)$. Substituting these results into (18-3b), we find

$$F(u) = a^3 e^{-\gamma(u_x^2 + u_y^2 + u_z^2)} = a^3 e^{-\gamma u^2} \tag{18-8}$$

The constant a can be evaluated from the normalization condition since the speed must have some value; therefore, if we use (18-2) and (16-10) and the fact that the $\mathscr{F}$'s all have the same form, we obtain

$$\int F(u) \, du_x \, du_y \, du_z = 1 = \left(a \int_{-\infty}^{\infty} e^{-\gamma \xi^2} \, d\xi \right)^3 = \left(a \sqrt{\frac{\pi}{\gamma}} \right)^3$$

if we introduce ξ as a general variable of integration. We also used the general formula

$$\int_0^{\infty} \xi^n e^{-\alpha \xi^2} \, d\xi = \frac{\Gamma[\frac{1}{2}(n+1)]}{2\alpha^{\frac{1}{2}(n+1)}} \tag{18-9a}$$

involving the gamma function which also satisfies the relations

$$\Gamma(x) = (x-1)\Gamma(x-1), \quad \Gamma(\tfrac{1}{2}) = \sqrt{\pi} \tag{18-9b}$$

Therefore $a = \sqrt{\gamma/\pi}$ and (18-7) and (18-8) become

$$\mathscr{F}(u_x) = \left(\frac{\gamma}{\pi}\right)^{\frac{1}{2}} e^{-\gamma u_x^2}, \quad F(u) = \left(\frac{\gamma}{\pi}\right)^{\frac{3}{2}} e^{-\gamma u^2} \tag{18-10}$$

γ can be determined by calculating $\overline{u^2}$ and using (17-18); we find from (18-9) and (18-10) that

$$\overline{u^2} = \int_{-\infty}^{\infty} \int_{-\infty}^{\infty} \int_{-\infty}^{\infty} u^2 F(u) \, du_x \, du_y \, du_z$$

$$= \left(\frac{\gamma}{\pi}\right)^{\frac{3}{2}} \int_0^{2\pi} \int_0^{\pi} \int_0^{\infty} u^2 e^{-\gamma u^2} u^2 \sin\theta \, du \, d\theta \, d\varphi$$

$$= 4\pi \left(\frac{\gamma}{\pi}\right)^{\frac{3}{2}} \int_0^{\infty} u^4 e^{-\gamma u^2} \, du = \frac{3}{2\gamma} \tag{18-11}$$

where we introduced spherical coordinates in velocity space in order to perform the integration easily. Combining (18-11) and (17-18), we obtain

$$\overline{u^2} = \frac{3}{2\gamma} = \frac{3kT}{m}$$

so that

$$\gamma = \frac{m}{2kT} \tag{18-12}$$

and therefore

$$\mathscr{F}(u_x) = \left(\frac{m}{2\pi kT}\right)^{1/2} e^{-mu_x^2/2kT} \tag{18-13}$$

$$F(u) = \left(\frac{m}{2\pi kT}\right)^{3/2} e^{-mu^2/2kT} = \left(\frac{m}{2\pi kT}\right)^{3/2} e^{-\varepsilon_t/kT} \tag{18-14}$$

are the final forms of the functions which we have obtained by combining the experimental law for the pressure with a very general derived expression for the pressure. This result (18-14) is *Maxwell's velocity distribution function*. We shall be able to derive it in a more satisfactory way during our discussion of statistical mechanics, although a more precise derivation of (18-14) can be obtained by purely kinetic theory methods and concepts. The latter procedure was first carried out by Boltzmann, who studied the effect of molecular collisions on the distribution function and was able to show that the distribution (18-14) is, on the average, unchanged by collisions and therefore would be constant in time, as it should be in order that it represent an equilibrium distribution.

18-1 Distribution functions for the components and speed

Now let us try to find what fraction of the molecules have an x component of their velocity between u_x and $u_x + du_x$; we shall write this fraction as $h(u_x)\, du_x$. We can see from the $u_x u_y$ plane of velocity space shown in Fig. 18-1 that all vectors **u** whose end points lie in the slab of thickness du_x perpendicular to the u_x axis at u_x have the x component of interest. Thus we can use (16-2) and find our fraction $h(u_x)\, du_x$ by summing $F(u)\, du_x\, du_y\, du_z$ over all values of u_y and u_z while keeping u_x constant; with the use of (18-10) we then obtain

$$h(u_x)\, du_x = \left(\frac{\gamma}{\pi}\right)^{3/2} e^{-\gamma u_x^2}\, du_x \int_{-\infty}^{\infty} e^{-\gamma u_y^2}\, du_y \int_{-\infty}^{\infty} e^{-\gamma u_z^2}\, du_z$$

$$= \left(\frac{\gamma}{\pi}\right)^{1/2} e^{-\gamma u_x^2}\, du_x = \mathscr{F}(u_x)\, du_x \tag{18-15}$$

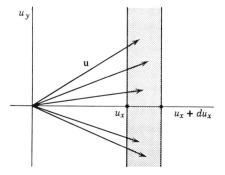

Fig. 18-1

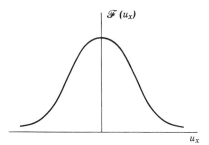

Fig. 18-2

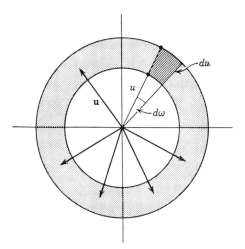

Fig. 18-3

Since there will be similar equations for the other components, we see that the functions $\mathscr{F}(u_i)$ which were introduced in (18-3b) have the physical significance that each is the distribution function for a single *component*.

The function $\mathscr{F}(u_x)$ has the familiar form of the Gaussian error curve and has the general appearance shown in Fig. 18-2. It is apparent from the figure that the most probable value of a component is zero; since the curve is an even function, the average value of a given component is also zero, that is, $\overline{u_x} = 0$. The physical reason for this, of course, is that it is a consequence of our initial assumption of an isotropic distribution for which all directions are equally probable.

Let the fraction of the molecules which have a speed between u and $u + du$ be $\phi(u)\, du$. We see from Fig. 18-3 that this distribution function can be obtained by finding the total fraction represented by all the vectors **u** whose end points in velocity space lie within the two spheres of radii u and $u + du$. Thus we want to sum $F(u)\, du_x\, du_y\, du_z$ over the complete solid angle while keeping the value of u constant; if we use (18-14) and write the volume element as $u^2\, du\, d\omega$ where $d\omega$ is an element of solid angle in velocity space, we obtain

$$\phi(u)\, du = \int_\omega F(u)u^2\, du\, d\omega = 4\pi\left(\frac{m}{2\pi kT}\right)^{3/2} u^2 e^{-mu^2/2kT}\, du \quad (18\text{-}16)$$

This distribution is no longer Gaussian and is not symmetric with respect to the most probable speed since u can have only positive values. The general dependence of $\phi(u)$ on u is shown in Fig. 18-4.

The most probable speed u_w is found by calculating $d\phi/du$ from (18-16) and then setting $d\phi/du = 0$ to find the value of u which corresponds to the maximum of ϕ. The result is

$$u_w = \left(\frac{2kT}{m}\right)^{1/2} \quad (18\text{-}17)$$

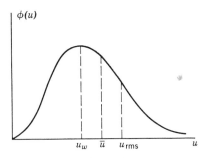

Fig. 18-4

The average speed $\bar{u}$ is different from this and is obtained from (18-16) and (18-9) as

$$\bar{u} = \int_0^\infty u\,\phi(u)\,du = \left(\frac{8kT}{\pi m}\right)^{1/2} \tag{18-18}$$

The rms speed is given by (17-18) and (17-19). One can easily show that

$$\bar{u} = \frac{2}{\sqrt{\pi}}\,u_w = 1.13\,u_w, \quad u_{\mathrm{rms}} = \sqrt{\frac{3}{2}}\,u_w = 1.22\,u_w \tag{18-19}$$

and therefore that $u_w < \bar{u} < u_{\mathrm{rms}}$ as illustrated in Fig. 18-4, although the relative location of these three quantities on the curve has been exaggerated in order to show them separated.

Exercises

18-1. Verify (18-17) and (18-18).

18-2. Find the value of $\overline{(1/u)}$ for a Maxwell distribution.

18-3. Calculate the total x component of momentum transported per unit area per unit time in the positive x direction across the yz plane within a gas in equilibrium, and interpret the result.

18-4. Gas leaks out slowly through a small hole in a container and into a vacuum. Find the rate per unit area at which energy is transported out the hole. With the help of (17-20), show that the average energy of an escaping molecule is $2kT$. How do you account for the fact that this energy is greater than the average energy of a molecule in the container?

18-5. Show that the normalized distribution function which gives the fraction of the molecules whose translational kinetic energy is between ε_t and $\varepsilon_t + d\varepsilon_t$ is

$$\frac{2\pi}{(\pi kT)^{3/2}}\,\sqrt{\varepsilon_t}\,e^{-\varepsilon_t/kT}\,d\varepsilon_t \tag{18-20}$$

Find the most probable energy and the average energy.

19 *Mean free path phenomena*

Because in our specific calculations so far we have neglected the finite size of the gas molecules, we have not explicitly needed to consider the collisions of the molecules with each other. To find what effect the mutual collisions of the molecules may have on the macroscopic properties of the gas, we begin with a concept introduced by Clausius which is extremely useful in characterizing the effect of collisions.

19-1 The mean free path

The *free path* of a molecule is defined as the distance traveled by it between two successive collisions; the *mean free path* l is similarly defined as the average distance traveled by a molecule between two collisions. In an ideal gas where the molecules are treated as points, the mean free path is infinite and we need only discuss collisions with the walls as we did when we calculated the pressure. We shall consider first a special case in order to illustrate the general approach which can be used in dealing with molecules of finite size.

Example. *Collisions with Fixed Molecules.* Suppose the gas molecules are colliding with other molecules which are located at fixed positions— as would be the case, for instance, for neutrons in paraffin or in a pile. If the radius of the moving molecule is R_1 and that of the fixed molecule is R_2, the distance between their centers at collision is

$$s = R_1 + R_2 \tag{19-1}$$

as illustrated in Fig. 19-1a. The problem is therefore the same as if the moving molecules had an "effective" radius s and were colliding with fixed point molecules. Thus a molecule of velocity $\mathbf{u}$ will have swept out a volume $\pi s^2 u \, \Delta t$ in a time Δt as seen from Fig. 19-1b. If the density of fixed molecules is n, the number contained in this volume will be $n\pi s^2 u \, \Delta t$. Since every fixed molecule in this volume will correspond to a collision with our representative moving molecule, we can say that

$$\text{Average number of collisions in } \Delta t = n\pi s^2 u \, \Delta t \tag{19-2}$$

On the other hand, the average number of collisions also equals the total distance traveled divided by the average distance between collisions (the mean free path l); hence we also have

$$\text{Average number of collisions in } \Delta t = \frac{u \, \Delta t}{l} \tag{19-3}$$

Equating (19-2) and (19-3), we find l to be given by

$$l = \frac{1}{n\pi s^2} = \frac{1}{n\sigma} \tag{19-4}$$

where $\sigma = \pi s^2$ is the effective area for a collision and is called the *cross section for collision*. We note that (19-4) is independent of u.

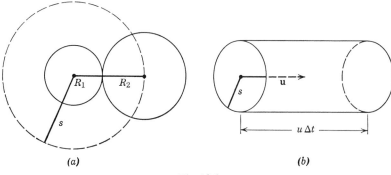

Fig. 19-1

Of even more interest to us is the mean free path for the mutual collisions of gas molecules having a Maxwell distribution of velocities. This is a much harder quantity to calculate, and we shall only quote the final result which is

$$l = \frac{1}{\sqrt{2}\,n\pi s^2} = \frac{0.707}{n\pi s^2} \tag{19-5}$$

Thus, if we are primarily interested in order of magnitude calculations we can use either (19-4) or (19-5) for our estimates.

Let us find the approximate value of l for a monatomic gas under reasonable conditions. We use $s \simeq 2 \times 10^{-10}$ meter, which is typical of atomic sizes; we also use the value of n at the standard conditions listed after (8-19)—called *Loschmidt's number* $n_0 = 2.69 \times 10^{25}$ (meter)$^{-3}$. Inserting these numbers into (19-5), we find that $l \simeq 2 \times 10^{-7}$ meter $\simeq 10^3 s$. We can compare this with the average distance between the molecules, l_0, which we can obtain by equating $l_0{}^3$ to the average volume per molecule so that $l_0{}^3 \simeq 1/n_0$. Thus $l_0 \simeq n_0{}^{-1/3} \simeq 3.3 \times 10^{-9}$ meter $\simeq 15s$ and $l \simeq 70 l_0$. If we use the value previously found for the average speed in helium, we find the average time between collisions to be about

$$\tau \simeq \frac{l}{\bar{u}} \simeq 1.5 \times 10^{-10} \text{ second}$$

so that the frequency of collisions is about $1/\tau \simeq 7 \times 10^9$ (second)$^{-1}$. These results show that the molecules of an ideal gas undergo collisions at an enormous rate and that the molecule travels with its very large average speed only for the short time between collisions; during this time it travels about one hundred times the average distance between molecules before a collision abruptly alters its direction of motion.

The utility of the mean free path will become evident from the following examples.

19-2 Viscosity

We shall consider first the situation in which the gas has a mass motion corresponding to a velocity in the x direction of speed v, which will be in addition to the velocity of thermal motion which is described by the Maxwell distribution; therefore $\overline{u_x} = v$ while $\overline{u_y}$ and $\overline{u_z}$ are still zero. We shall also assume that $v = v(y)$ so that the mass velocity changes in a direction perpendicular to the net flow as illustrated in Fig. 19-2. In Fig. 19-3, we see how a rectangular parallelepiped enclosing a definite portion of the gas will have its shape altered as one follows this portion along in its motion. This situation can also be described in terms of the various horizontal layers of the gas dragging across each other and exerting forces on the adjacent layers as indicated by the arrows in the dashed parallelogram. The net result is a tendency to slow down the faster layers and speed up the slower layers, so that there is a shearing

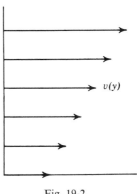

Fig. 19-2

stress in the gas, that is, a force F_x which is tangential to the surface of area A which is perpendicular to the direction in which the mass velocity is changing and which bounds this portion of the gas. It is found experimentally that the stress, that is, the tangential force per unit area, is proportional to the gradient of the mass velocity; thus we have

$$\frac{F_x}{A} = \eta \frac{\partial v}{\partial y} \tag{19-6}$$

where the proportionality factor η is called the *coefficient of viscosity* or simply the *viscosity*.

Since viscosity has many of the attributes associated with friction, it will be helpful in understanding both the origin of viscosity and our

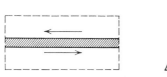
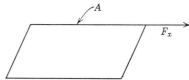

Fig. 19-3

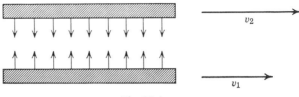

Fig. 19-4

subsequent calculation of η to consider the following question: *How* can there be viscosity in an ideal gas in which the only processes we consider are perfectly elastic collisions between smooth molecules? In order to answer this question, let us consider a rather rough analogy. Suppose we have two very long trains running along parallel tracks but with different speeds $v_2 > v_1$ as shown in Fig. 19-4. Now suppose also that at a given instant the passengers in each train begin firing machine guns at the other train, aiming so that the bullets are fired perpendicular to the motion of the train as indicated by the short arrows in the figure. Assuming that when the bullets hit they lodge in the train and are carried along with it, we see that each bullet which strikes train 2 has its momentum in the direction parallel to the track suddenly increased by $m(v_2 - v_1)$. Therefore, if $\mathscr{R}$ is the rate at which bullets are striking train 2, the force which the train must exert in order to continue moving at speed v_2 equals the rate of change of the momentum of the bullets and is given by

$$F_x = m(v_2 - v_1)\mathscr{R}$$

If the train is not able to exert this force, the net effect will be to slow the train down. Similarly, the bullets of higher momentum coming from train 2 and striking the lower momentum region of train 1 tend to speed up the slower moving train 1. The eventual result of this process would be to make both trains travel at the same speed—a result similar to that expected from viscosity.

If we look again at the layer in the gas shown shaded in Fig. 19-3 and recall that the molecules above the layer have a greater x component of momentum than those below, we see that, as the gas molecules move about, the net effect will be to give the gas below the layer an increase in momentum. Therefore, in order to find the viscosity, we need to calculate the net transport of x component of momentum, and, in particular, we want the net gain of momentum of the material below a given plane which we choose at $y = 0$ as shown in Fig. 19-5a.

We shall assume, for simplicity, that all molecules passing through the plane have come from a distance equal to the mean free path. Thus, in effect, they have originated from the surface of the sphere of radius l from where their last collision directed them across the $y = 0$ plane. Therefore a molecule coming from above and traveling at an angle θ from the y axis brings down to this plane an x component of momentum given by

$$p_d = mv(y) = mv(l \cos \theta) \simeq mv(0) + ml \cos \theta \left(\frac{\partial v}{\partial y}\right)_0 \qquad (19\text{-}7)$$

Similarly, for a molecule traveling upward at the corresponding angle θ, we have

$$p_u = mv(-l \cos \theta) \simeq mv(0) - ml \cos \theta \left(\frac{\partial v}{\partial y}\right)_0 \qquad (19\text{-}8)$$

For every downward molecule of this velocity type there is an upward one since there is no mass motion in the y direction; hence the net increase of x momentum of the gas below the plane for each downward moving molecule is

$$\Delta p = p_d - p_u = 2ml \cos \theta \left(\frac{\partial v}{\partial y}\right)_0 \qquad (19\text{-}9)$$

In order to find the number of downward moving molecules in a time interval Δt, we construct the cylinder on the area ΔA in the xz plane shown in Fig. 19-5b; as before, the generators of the cylinder are parallel to **u** and of length $u \, \Delta t$ and the number of molecules of this type which have crossed ΔA in Δt equals the number in the volume. Using (16-15), (18-1), (18-14), and (18-16), we find this number to be

$$u \, \Delta t \cos \theta \, \Delta A \cdot nF \cdot du_x \, du_y \, du_z$$

$$= \Delta t \, \Delta A \cdot nu \cos \theta \cdot \frac{\phi(u)}{4\pi u^2} \cdot u^2 \sin \theta \, du \, d\theta \, d\varphi \qquad (19\text{-}10)$$

When we multiply (19-9) and (19-10), we obtain the net increase of momentum due to these molecules. If we now integrate this quantity over

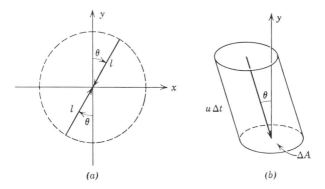

Fig. 19-5

all possible velocities for downward moving molecules, we find the total transfer of x component of momentum to the material below the plane to be given by

$$\bar{P}\Delta t\,\Delta A = \Delta t\,\Delta A\,\frac{nm}{2\pi}\left(\frac{\partial v}{\partial y}\right)_0 \int_0^\infty lu\phi(u)\,du \int_0^{\pi/2}\cos^2\theta\sin\theta\,d\theta \int_0^{2\pi} d\varphi \quad (19\text{-}11)$$

where $\bar{P}$ is defined as the total rate of downward transfer of x momentum per unit area. If we neglect any dependence of l on speed, we find from (19-11) that

$$\bar{P} = \frac{1}{3}\,nml\left(\frac{\partial v}{\partial y}\right)_0 \int_0^\infty u\phi(u)\,du$$

$$= \frac{1}{3}\,nml\bar{u}\left(\frac{\partial v}{\partial y}\right)_0 \quad (19\text{-}12)$$

Since force is rate of change of momentum, we also have $\bar{P} = F_x/A = \eta(\partial v/\partial y)_0$ because of (19-6); combining the last equation with (19-12), we find the viscosity to be given by

$$\eta = \tfrac{1}{3}nml\bar{u} \quad (19\text{-}13)$$

Since this result involves l, we see that measurements of the viscosity will enable us to evaluate the mean free path—something which is obviously impracticable to do directly from its definition. In addition, we can use this value of l to find the cross section for collision and then the molecular radius. Measurements of this kind were among the first which gave quantitative information about molecular sizes.

The dependence of η on the density, indicated by (19-13), is only superficial because we have seen in (19-5) that the mean free path is inversely proportional to n so that the product nl is independent of the density or, equivalently, independent of the pressure because of (17-15). Hence the kinetic theory quite unequivocally predicts that *the viscosity of an ideal gas is independent of the density*. This prediction has been verified experimentally over a considerable range of densities and represents an outstanding achievement in the historical development of kinetic theory. This independence of the density may seem surprising at first because one might think that the "friction" might decrease as the amount of gas decreases and hence that the viscosity would also be less. But if we recall the origin of viscosity we can see now that if, for example, we double the density, the number of molecules carrying excess x momentum across a given plane will also double; the molecules come, however, from an average distance only half as far away, hence their excess mass velocity is only half as great as before—the net result is that the excess x momentum will be unchanged and therefore the viscosity will be the same.

We can also see, however, that this prediction actually cannot hold for extreme values of the density. If the density is very large, the gas molecules are comparatively close together and the short range intermolecular forces which we have been neglecting become important. At the other extreme where the density is very small, the mean free path becomes comparable to or larger than the dimensions of the container; the collisions with the walls then may become more important than collisions with other molecules, and our method of calculation will no longer be applicable.

The result (19-13) does make a prediction about the temperature dependence of the viscosity because, if we also use (18-18), we see that

$$\eta \sim \bar{u} \sim \sqrt{T} \qquad (19\text{-}14)$$

Therefore *the viscosity increases with the temperature.* This behavior is in contrast to that of liquids whose viscosity generally decreases rapidly as the temperature increases, the proverbial example being molasses. The temperature dependence given by (19-14) is in fair agreement with experiment; we can see that (19-14) cannot be entirely correct because the molecules are not completely rigid and elastic as we have been assuming—this effect can be expected to make the effective size at collision as well as the mean free path depend on speed, and therefore the temperature will be involved in a more complicated way than in (19-14).

19-3   General transport and thermal conductivity

If we now define momentum flow to be positive if it is in the positive y direction and let $\bar{P}'$ be the total average rate of momentum transfer per unit area, (19-12) takes the form

$$\bar{P}' = -\frac{1}{3} n l \bar{u} \left[\frac{\partial(mv)}{\partial y} \right]_0 \qquad (19\text{-}15)$$

Suppose we now consider any general quantity G which can be transferred by the motion of molecules and also define a net rate of transfer of G per unit area which we write as Γ. We can now find Γ by simply repeating the calculations which led to (19-15) and replacing mv by G; the result is

$$\Gamma = -\frac{1}{3} n l \bar{u} \left(\frac{\partial G}{\partial y} \right)_0 \qquad (19\text{-}16)$$

We can make an immediate application of this general transport equation to the calculation of the thermal conductivity of an ideal gas.

If there is a temperature gradient in a gas so that $T = T(y)$, then (17-14) becomes $\overline{\varepsilon}_t = \frac{3}{2}kT(y)$ and there can be a net transfer of energy because of the motion of the molecules. If we let the corresponding rate per unit area be represented by $\bar{Q}$, we can immediately find $\bar{Q}$ from (19-16) by letting $G = \overline{\varepsilon}_t$; therefore

$$\bar{Q} = -\frac{1}{3}\,nl\bar{u}\left(\frac{\partial\overline{\varepsilon}_t}{\partial y}\right)_0 = -\frac{1}{2}\,knl\bar{u}\left(\frac{\partial T}{\partial y}\right)_0 \qquad (19\text{-}17)$$

The coefficient of thermal conductivity K is defined by

$$\bar{Q} = -K\left(\frac{\partial T}{\partial y}\right)_0 \qquad (19\text{-}18)$$

so that we have

$$K = \tfrac{1}{2}knl\bar{u} \qquad (19\text{-}19)$$

We see from this result that the thermal conductivity has the same properties as the viscosity, that is, K is independent of the density and proportional to $\sqrt{T}$; both of these predictions have been quite well confirmed by experiment.

If we divide (19-13) by (19-19), we find that

$$\frac{\eta}{K} = \frac{2m}{3k} \qquad (19\text{-}20)$$

This simple and interesting expression is reminiscent of thermodynamic results and has the virtue that it is independent of l and $\bar{u}$ and hence of many of the simplifying assumptions we have made. We can put (19-20) into a more useful form by multiplying numerator and denominator by L, using (17-14') and (17-17), and introducing the molecular weight $\mu = Lm$; in this way we find that

$$\frac{\eta c_v}{K\mu} = 1 \qquad (19\text{-}21)$$

which is an expression making a definite prediction about this particular combination of *directly measurable* quantities.

When the expression on the left in (19-21) is evaluated from experimental results on some monatomic gases, we find that it has the following values: for helium, 0.402; for neon, 0.424; and, for argon, 0.404. Although the value is not unity as predicted by (19-21), we do see that it is remarkably constant and hence is strong evidence for the *general* validity of our theory, which is what first led us to consider looking at this particular combination of quantities. That our predicted numerical value is 1 rather than about 0.4 is a consequence of the extreme simplifying assumptions we have made in deriving our formulas. A more elaborate theory which evaluates the transported quantities more accurately, and which also takes into account the fact that the gas molecules are not completely elastic, results in a different numerical factor which is more in accord with experiment.

Viscosity and heat conduction are both examples of *non-equilibrium* phenomena. Thus we see that kinetic theory enables us to deal with this type of problem as well as purely equilibrium situations. We shall not discuss the specialized methods of kinetic theory any further, however, but instead we shall again consider the problems associated with equilibrium, but in much more general terms than before.

Exercises

19-1. Verify (19-16) in detail.

19-2. Show that the viscosity of a gas which is constrained to move in two dimensions is given by $\eta = \frac{1}{2} n_a m l \bar{u}$.

19-3. If there is a concentration gradient in a gas, there will be a transport of molecules given by $\bar{\Gamma}_N = -D \, (\partial n/\partial y)$, where D is called the diffusion coefficient. Show that $D = \frac{1}{3} l \bar{u}$ and therefore that $D = \eta/nm$. What is the value of K/D?

19-4. A container of gas is separated into two parts by a thin wall with a very small hole in it. If the two parts are kept at different pressures and temperatures, show that there will be no net flow of molecules through the hole when

$$p_1/\sqrt{T_1} = p_2/\sqrt{T_2}$$

Part Four

Statistical Mechanics

20 *Fundamental principles*

Our brief discussion of kinetic theory has shown us that we are able to discuss states of thermodynamic equilibrium by means of statistical considerations. We were able to derive the equation of state of an ideal gas and to calculate the absolute values of its heat capacities. From this experience we can reasonably conclude that probability considerations will play a vital role when we discuss other systems by less specialized methods. On the other hand, the concept of entropy which is so important in thermodynamics is virtually absent from much of kinetic theory. The principal contribution of Boltzmann to the creation of statistical mechanics was his showing that there is an intimate connection between the two concepts of entropy and probability.

As we saw in the examples of Sec. 16-1, however, we cannot make any calculations of specific probabilities until we have made some assumptions about what corresponds to events of "equal probability." In all our kinetic theory calculations, we assumed without hesitation that the *probability* of finding a molecule in a certain range of position and velocity was given by

$$\frac{f}{N} \, dx \, dy \, dz \, du_x \, du_y \, du_z$$

according to (16-15). Thus we assumed that the probability was *proportional to the size of the volume element* in the six-dimensional space we effectively used to describe the motion of a single molecule. In other words, we assumed that *equal volumes have equal probability*, in so far as their size alone is concerned. This is a very simple idea, and it seems as if it would be an attractive starting point for our consideration of general systems. The difficulty which immediately arises, however, is: In *what space* does equal size correspond to equal probability? A hint about the appropriate space to use can be obtained from Hamiltonian mechanics.

20-1 Γ-space and ensembles

Let us begin by considering a conservative system which has a total of $\mathcal{N}$ degrees of freedom; for example, if it were comprised of a total of N particles, each of which had l degrees of freedom, then

$$\mathcal{N} = lN \tag{20-1}$$

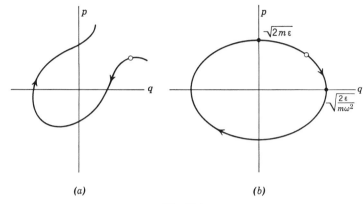

(a)   (b)

Fig. 20-1

The equations of motion of the system are Hamilton's equations

$$\dot{p_j} = -\frac{\partial H}{\partial q_j}, \quad \dot{q_j} = \frac{\partial H}{\partial p_j} \qquad (j = 1, 2, \ldots, \mathcal{N}) \qquad (20\text{-}2)$$

according to (I: 10-7). The Hamiltonian function H is numerically equal to the energy and is written as a function of the generalized coordinates q_j and the momenta p_j; that is, $H = H(p_1, \ldots, p_{\mathcal{N}}, q_1, \ldots, q_{\mathcal{N}})$.

We can now define a $2\mathcal{N}$-dimensional space which has the p_j and q_j as coordinates; this space is called Γ-*space* or *phase space*. If our system of interest is a kilomole of gas, for example, then $\mathcal{N} \approx 10^{27}$. Since the *instantaneous state* of the system is defined by the $2\mathcal{N}$ values of the p_j and q_j, we see that the instantaneous state can be represented by a *single point* in Γ-space whose coordinates are these $2\mathcal{N}$ quantities. As time goes on and the state of the system changes so that the p_j and q_j change, this representative point traces out a path in Γ-space as illustrated schematically in Fig. 20-1a, where p and q represent a particular two-dimensional projection of Γ-space.

Example. One-Dimensional Harmonic Oscillator. The Hamiltonian of this system of one degree of freedom is

$$H(p, q) = \frac{p^2}{2m} + \frac{1}{2} m\omega^2 q^2 = \varepsilon \qquad (20\text{-}3)$$

according to (I: 10-10 and 5-9), where m is the mass, $\omega = 2\pi\nu$ is its circular frequency, and ε is its energy. If we write (20-3) in the form

$$\frac{p^2}{2m\varepsilon} + \frac{q^2}{(2\varepsilon/m\omega^2)} = 1 \qquad (20\text{-}4)$$

we see that the path of the representative point of this system in its two-dimensional Γ-space is the ellipse of semiaxes $\sqrt{2m\varepsilon}$ and $\sqrt{2\varepsilon/m\omega^2}$ shown in Fig. 20-1b.

The physical quantities which we measure and which are of interest to us for a system in thermodynamic equilibrium almost always are *time averages* of suitable properties of the system which are averaged over the portion of the path in Γ-space corresponding to the time interval devoted to the measurement. We know from experience that such averages are reproducible later provided that external conditions are unchanged—we keep the temperature constant, for example. It is extremely difficult to set up mathematical machinery for calculating these time averages for a general system, and, even if we could perform the calculation in principle, it would be essentially impossible in practice because we can never hope to know with any degree of certainty all the very many initial conditions of the motion which would be required.

Since a direct attack on the problem of interest to us appears to be impossible, we can ask whether it might not be possible to devise some other kind of averaging process which would be equivalent, for computational purposes, to the one which we need for comparison with experiment. A very great contribution to statistical mechanics was made by Gibbs, who suggested that we imagine a group of similar systems which are suitably chosen and have appropriate random properties and then that we calculate our averages over this whole group *at a given time* rather than find a time average for a single system. Such a group of similar systems is called an *ensemble*. It is an intellectual construction which is to simulate and to represent, at one time, the properties of the actual system of interest as they are developed in the natural course of time. The properties of the ensemble must be so chosen as to reflect as accurately as possible whatever knowledge we do have of the system.

An ensemble is imagined to be composed of very many systems which are all identical in type to the system of interest, that is, they are all described by the identical form of Hamiltonian; the members of the ensemble do differ, however, in their initial conditions. As a result of these requirements, we see that the members of an ensemble which have almost equal energies will be *macroscopically* indistinguishable. Since each member of an ensemble can be represented by a single point in Γ-space, the ensemble as a whole is represented by a collection of points in Γ-space; these points can be assumed to have an almost continuous distribution for an ensemble with the extremely large number of members which we are visualizing. Since all the systems have the same Hamiltonian, they also have the same equations of motion; thus, as time goes on, these various points in Γ-space will all trace out their individual paths as determined by their different initial conditions.

Thus the basic idea of Gibbs is that of replacing the calculation of the time average for a single system by an *ensemble average* at a fixed time. The problem of demonstrating the equivalence of these two averages is the subject of ergodic theory; we shall show that it is plausible that these two are the same, although it has never been generally proved. In fact, we shall eventually adopt this equality as a basic hypothesis and trust to the comparison of our calculated results with experiment to justify our methods.

20-2   Liouville's theorem

Let us consider those ensemble points which are initially in the small volume element $\Delta\Omega$ in Γ-space given by

$$\Delta\Omega = \Delta p_1 \, \Delta p_2 \cdots \Delta p_{\mathcal{N}} \, \Delta q_1 \, \Delta q_2 \cdots \Delta q_{\mathcal{N}} \tag{20-5}$$

As time goes on and the various representative points contained in $\Delta\Omega$ move about, the shape of $\Delta\Omega$ can change considerably in order to continue to surround the same points; we want to show that the volume nevertheless remains constant.

We define a *density D* of points in Γ-space so that the number in $\Delta\Omega$ is $D\,\Delta\Omega$. We shall show that D is constant, and for this purpose we need to obtain an equation of continuity applicable to Γ-space. Let us consider a volume $\Delta\Omega'$ which is fixed in Γ-space. In a time *dt*, the gain in the number of points in $\Delta\Omega'$ can be written

$$\text{Gain} = \frac{\partial(D\,\Delta\Omega')}{\partial t}\,dt \tag{20-6}$$

We can calculate this gain in another way by considering the flow through the surfaces bounding $\Delta\Omega'$. In Fig. 20-2 we show the projection of $\Delta\Omega'$

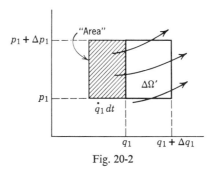

Fig. 20-2

on the $p_1 q_1$ plane; if we construct a cylinder of length $\dot{q}_1 \, dt$ on the surface of $\Delta\Omega'$, the "area" of the base will be $\Delta q_2 \cdots \Delta q_{\mathcal{N}} \, \Delta p_1 \cdots \Delta p_{\mathcal{N}}$, and the "volume" will be $\dot{q}_1 \, dt \, \Delta q_2 \cdots \Delta q_{\mathcal{N}} \, \Delta p_1 \cdots \Delta p_{\mathcal{N}}$. Since all the points contained in this cylinder will have passed through the bounding surface of $\Delta\Omega'$, we can say that the number into $\Delta\Omega'$ through the surface "normal" to q_1 is

$$(D\dot{q}_1 \, dt)_{q_1} \Delta q_2 \cdots \Delta q_{\mathcal{N}} \, \Delta p_1 \cdots \Delta p_{\mathcal{N}} \tag{20-7}$$

while the number of points which have passed out of $\Delta\Omega'$ through the surface normal to q_1 is

$$(D\dot{q}_1 \, dt)_{q_1 + \Delta q_1} \Delta q_2 \cdots \Delta q_{\mathcal{N}} \, \Delta p_1 \cdots \Delta p_{\mathcal{N}} \tag{20-8}$$

Therefore the net gain due to flow through the faces of $\Delta\Omega'$ normal to q_1 is (20-7) minus (20-8), which becomes

$$\text{Gain through } q_1 = -\frac{\partial}{\partial q_1} (D\dot{q}_1) \, dt \, \Delta\Omega' \tag{20-9}$$

with the use of $f(q_1 + \Delta q_1) - f(q_1) = (\partial f/\partial q_1) \, \Delta q_1$ and (20-5). We can discuss the flow of points through the surface normal to p_1 in the same way, and we shall find that

$$\text{Gain through } p_1 = -\frac{\partial}{\partial p_1} (D\dot{p}_1) \, dt \, \Delta\Omega' \tag{20-10}$$

There will be similar expressions for all the rest of the p's and q's; adding all of them, we obtain the following expression for the gain of points in $\Delta\Omega'$:

$$\text{Gain} = -\sum_j \left[\frac{\partial}{\partial p_j} (D\dot{p}_j) + \frac{\partial}{\partial q_j} (D\dot{q}_j) \right] dt \, \Delta\Omega' \tag{20-11}$$

If we equate (20-6) and (20-11) and cancel the common factor $dt \, \Delta\Omega'$, we obtain the *equation of continuity*,

$$\frac{\partial D}{\partial t} + \sum_{j=1}^{\mathcal{N}} \left[\frac{\partial}{\partial p_j} (D\dot{p}_j) + \frac{\partial}{\partial q_j} (D\dot{q}_j) \right] = 0 \tag{20-12}$$

In order to prove Liouville's theorem, we differentiate the products in (20-12) and *use the equations of motion* (20-2); the general term of the sum in (20-12) then becomes

$$\frac{\partial D}{\partial p_j} \dot{p}_j + D \frac{\partial \dot{p}_j}{\partial p_j} + \frac{\partial D}{\partial q_j} \dot{q}_j + D \frac{\partial \dot{q}_j}{\partial q_j}$$

$$= \left(\frac{\partial D}{\partial p_j} \dot{p}_j + \frac{\partial D}{\partial q_j} \dot{q}_j \right) + D \left(-\frac{\partial^2 H}{\partial p_j \, \partial q_j} + \frac{\partial^2 H}{\partial q_j \, \partial p_j} \right) \tag{20-13}$$

The last term in parentheses in (20-13) vanishes because of the equality of mixed second partial derivatives, and (20-12) finally becomes

$$\frac{\partial D}{\partial t} + \sum_j \left(\frac{\partial D}{\partial p_j} \dot{p}_j + \frac{\partial D}{\partial q_j} \dot{q}_j \right) = \frac{dD}{dt} = 0 \qquad (20\text{-}14)$$

so that

$$D = \text{const.} \qquad (20\text{-}15)$$

Therefore Liouville's theorem (20-15) tells us that, if we follow a representative point along its path in Γ-space, the density of points in its immediate neighborhood will remain constant.

There is another way of expressing Liouville's theorem. Suppose we consider the volume $\Delta\Omega$ which moves along with one of the points as shown in Fig. 20-3. The boundaries of the two regions are defined by the same set of points whose paths are determined by Hamilton's equations of motion. Then it is easy to show that Liouville's theorem (20-15) leads to

$$\Delta\Omega = \text{const.} \qquad (20\text{-}16)$$

The number of points contained in $\Delta\Omega$ is $D\,\Delta\Omega$ by the definition of D; however,

$$D\,\Delta\Omega = \text{const.} \qquad (20\text{-}17)$$

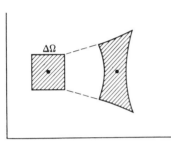

Fig. 20-3

because the boundaries of the volume elements were defined by the same set of phase points so that the two volumes of Fig. 20-3 always contain the same points by their construction. If we combine (20-15) and (20-17), we immediately obtain (20-16) as a direct consequence of Liouville's theorem.

20-3   The basic hypotheses of statistical mechanics

It is natural for us to interpret the density D as being proportional to the probability of finding a representative point in a given volume element of Γ-space. If we do this, Liouville's theorem also tells us: If the assumption that equal volume elements, $\Delta\Omega_1$ and $\Delta\Omega_2$, enclose regions of equal probability is correct at a given time, then it is correct at all times. The reason is that, if the densities associated with the volume elements are D_1 and D_2, then, if $D_1 = D_2$ at a given time, we shall have $D_1 = D_2$ for all times because of (20-15), and consequently the probabilities associated with $\Delta\Omega_1$ and $\Delta\Omega_2$ will remain equal if they ever were.

As a result, it is plausible for us to make the hypothesis that equal volume elements in Γ-space are associated with equal probabilities, or, in other words:

> The probability of finding a system in a given range of states (that is, of finding a representative point of the ensemble in a given volume element) is proportional to the size of the corresponding volume element in Γ-space. (20-18)

This is the basic reason for our use of Γ-space because it is only in this space that Liouville's theorem holds. It is important to emphasize that Liouville's theorem does *not* demand this basic assumption (20-18), but only shows that the laws of Hamiltonian mechanics are compatible with it.

We now want to show in a qualitative way that Liouville's theorem combined with (20-18) makes plausible our second basic hypothesis:

> The ensemble average at a given time is equivalent to the time average for a single system when used as the theoretical quantity to be compared with the corresponding experimental value of a given macroscopic property of the system. (20-19)

Let us consider two systems A and B traveling along the same trajectory in Γ-space. Thus the constants of motion are the same for the two, but they are displaced in time so that, for example, if $p_{jA} = f(t)$ then $p_{jB} = f(t - \tau)$; hence the point B occupies the same points in Γ-space as does A, but always a time τ later—this general situation is illustrated in Fig. 20-4. At the time t_0 they are in the positions shown; B arrives at A's original position at the time $t_0 + \tau$, hence B spent the time τ in $\Delta\Omega_0$. Similarly, B will also spend the time τ in the volume $\Delta\Omega_1$ shown farther along the path at t_1. But, from (20-16), $\Delta\Omega_1 = \Delta\Omega_0$, so that B *spends equal times in equal volumes.*

Since the time spent by a system in a given volume element in Γ-space is proportional to the size of the volume element, we see from (20-18) that

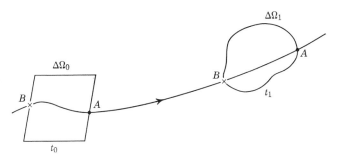

Fig. 20-4

the *time spent* is also *proportional to the probability* of finding a member of the ensemble in the volume element. Thus, if we were to calculate the time average of a given quantity by a formula of the form (16-9), we could replace the original integral over the time by an equal integral over the volume Ω of Γ-space and hence by an ensemble average. In this way we see that our hypothesis (20-19) about the equivalence of the time and ensemble averages is consistent with our other basic hypothesis (20-18) about probability being proportional to volume in Γ-space.

20-4   The microcanonical ensemble

We recall that a very important concept in thermodynamics was that of an isolated system—one which did not interact with its surroundings and hence was characterized by constant energy and volume; that is,

$$U = \text{const.}, \quad V = \text{const.} \tag{20-20}$$

We want to devise an ensemble which is to represent an isolated system; such an ensemble is called a *microcanonical ensemble*.

Since the energy is constant, the $2\mathcal{N}$ coordinates of a representative point are subject to the equation of constraint,

$$H(p_1, \ldots, p_{\mathcal{N}}, q_1, \ldots, q_{\mathcal{N}}) = U = \text{const.} \tag{20-21}$$

In other words, the representative point is always on the *surface* in Γ-space given by (20-21). (For the example of a one-dimensional oscillator, the corresponding surface is the ellipse of Fig. 20-1*b*.) Therefore, when we visualize our microcanonical ensemble, the representative points can be distributed only on this surface and nowhere else; the density D must correspondingly be zero everywhere except on this surface.

Such a representation as this is both undesirable and unrealistic. It is undesirable in that we have been considering only volume elements in Γ-space up to now and the use of this surface would make all the volumes zero. It is unrealistic in that experimentally we cannot know the value of the energy of our isolated system with complete precision; a more accurate appraisal of our knowledge would be that we know the energy to have the value U within limits δU; that is, as far as we know the energy is somewhere in the range

$$U - \delta U \leqslant U \leqslant U + \delta U \tag{20-22}$$

Therefore the points of our ensemble should be distributed so that they occupy the *shell* in Γ-space between the two surfaces defined by $H = U \pm \delta U$. Since as far as we know all values of the energy in this range are equally likely, the density D should be constant in this shell and zero outside as we know enough to be able to say confidently that the energy of the system does not have a value corresponding to a point in Γ-space outside the shell.

Therefore our microcanonical ensemble is defined by giving the value of D for each point P of Γ-space as

$$D(P) = \text{const.}, \quad U - \delta U \leqslant U(P) \leqslant U + \delta U$$
$$D(P) = 0, \quad \text{otherwise}$$

(20-23)

where $U(P)$ is evaluated by means of (20-21). In this way we have obtained a statistical mechanical representation of an isolated system.

Rather than continuing at present with a discussion of these very general systems, we shall now turn to a specialized type of system which is of great historical and practical importance.

Exercise

20-1. Assume the system to be a single particle of mass m moving vertically in a constant gravitational field. Draw a figure showing the surfaces in Γ-space which bound the representative points of the microcanonical ensemble. Choose a small area between these surfaces, and show that points within this area at $t = 0$ are in a corresponding area at a later time T. Show directly that these two areas are equal.

21 Systems of independent subsystems

We shall now restrict our considerations to systems which can be regarded as being composed of N independent identical subsystems, that is, where the interactions among these subsystems can be neglected. An example is an ideal gas consisting of N molecules whose mutual forces can be neglected. As a matter of fact, most of the applications we shall make of our results obtained in this chapter will be to systems of particles, such as gases, so that the subsystems will be the particles; accordingly, we shall frequently refer to our subsystems as particles for simplicity and definiteness. However, it is important to keep in mind that our results are more generally applicable.

If the subsystem has l degrees of freedom, the total number of degrees of freedom is given by (20-1). If the Hamiltonian of the kth subsystem is $H_k(p_1{}^k, \ldots, q_l{}^k)$, the Hamiltonian of the system is

$$H = \sum_{k=1}^{N} H_k(p_1{}^k, \ldots, q_l{}^k) \tag{21-1}$$

where all terms in the sum are identical in form. There are no terms in (21-1) which involve the coordinates of two or more subsystems because of our assumption that they are independent.

Since the subsystems move independently, Γ-space can be divided into separate portions which are identical in nature and each of which is associated with one subsystem. In other words, we can imagine Γ-space as "factored" into a separate phase space for each subsystem. This separate phase space is called *μ-space*; it has only $2l$ dimensions—six for a monatomic gas, for example. The coordinates of a point in μ-space are p_1, $p_2, \ldots, q_l$; the instantaneous state of a subsystem is given by the $2l$ values of these quantities, that is, by a *point in μ-space*. Since this can be done for every subsystem, we see that the instantaneous state of the system as a whole can be represented in two equivalent ways: by *one* point in Γ-space *or* by N points in μ-space. Similarly, an ensemble with $\mathscr{M}$ members can be represented by $\mathscr{M}$ points in Γ-space or by $N\mathscr{M}$ points in μ-space.

If we imagine μ-space divided into volumes ("cells") of equal size $\Delta\Omega_\mu$ where

$$\Delta\Omega_\mu = \Delta p_1 \cdots \Delta p_l \, \Delta q_1 \cdots \Delta q_l \tag{21-2}$$

the corresponding volume in Γ-space, $\Delta\Omega$, is given by

$$\Delta\Omega = (\Delta\Omega_\mu)^N \tag{21-3}$$

Since we have associated equal probability with equal volumes $\Delta\Omega$, by (20-18), we can conclude from (21-3) that we can also assume equal probabilities to be associated with volumes of equal size in μ-space, that is, with the $\Delta\Omega_\mu$.

21-1   Probability of a state

We assume that our system occupies a definite volume V and has a constant energy U; hence it is an isolated system and is described by the microcanonical ensemble of (20-23). Let us now divide all of μ-space into a total of M cells of equal volume $\Delta\Omega_\mu$; we label the cells by an index $i = 1, 2, \ldots, M$.

A given state of the system can be described by giving the number of points (subsystems) in each of these cells, that is, by the set of numbers $n_1, n_2, \ldots, n_i, \ldots, n_M$, where n_i is the number in the ith cell and where $\Sigma_i n_i = N$. This set of numbers n_i is called a *macrostate* or a *distribution*. The individual coordinates are not specified for each particle; hence a macrostate represents a particular macroscopic state of the system in the same sense in which we used the distribution function in kinetic theory, as discussed in connection with Fig. 16-2.

Since the particles are of the same type, we can interchange them at will; if we do this without changing the set n_i, we shall obtain the same macrostate and hence the same macroscopic physical state. Every such arrangement of particles among and within the cells is called a *microstate* or *complexion*; thus in a microstate we visualize a definite specification of the particular cell in which each particle is located in μ-space as contrasted to the mere counting of the number in a cell which is required to find a macrostate. Accordingly, we see that there are generally many microstates which correspond to the same macrostate. However, each microstate corresponds to a different volume element in Γ-space although these volumes are all the same size, as given by (21-3). This statement is illustrated in Fig. 21-1, which shows the projection of Γ-space on the $q_j{}^1 q_j{}^2$ plane; the corresponding coordinates of two microstates I and II which differ only in the interchange of particles 1 and 2 is also shown. The figure shows that these two microstates correspond to different regions of Γ-space, although each has the same number of particles in the appropriate cells in μ-space.

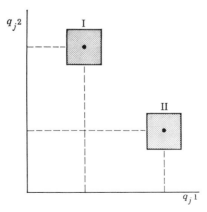

Fig. 21-1

According to our basic hypothesis (20-18), the probability of a macrostate is proportional to the corresponding volume in Γ-space; combining this statement with the preceding discussion, we have:

Relative probability of a macrostate $(n_1, n_2, \ldots, n_i, \ldots)$

$= $ total corresponding volume in Γ-space

$= $ (number of microstates) times (volume per microstate)

$= $ (number of possible combinations of N things taken $n_1, n_2, \ldots, n_i, \ldots$ at a time) times $(\Delta\Omega)$

$$= \frac{N!}{n_1! \, n_2! \cdots n_i! \cdots n_M!} \Delta\Omega = W_B \, \Delta\Omega$$

so that

$$W_B = \frac{N!}{n_1! \, n_2! \cdots n_i! \cdots n_M!} = \frac{N!}{\prod_i n_i!} \tag{21-4}$$

is *proportional* to the probability of a macrostate. The result (21-4) is the one originally obtained and used by Boltzmann. For identical subsystems, it is necessary to divide it by $N!$ and take

$$W = \frac{1}{n_1! \cdots n_i! \cdots n_M!} \tag{21-5}$$

as the *thermodynamic probability*; from now on we generally need use only W. The division by $N!$ is called "corrected Boltzmann counting"; there are many good reasons for this seemingly arbitrary step, and we shall discuss them as they subsequently arise.

As a simple illustration of (21-5), suppose that $N = 2$ and $M = 2$. The possible macrostates with their corresponding probabilities are

$$n_1 = 1, \quad n_2 = 1 \qquad W = \frac{1}{1! \, 1!} = 1$$

$$n_1 = 2, \quad n_2 = 0 \qquad W = \frac{1}{2! \, 0!} = \tfrac{1}{2}$$

$$n_1 = 0, \quad n_2 = 2 \qquad W = \frac{1}{0! \, 2!} = \tfrac{1}{2}$$

This example also shows why W is called a relative probability, for it is not normalized and does not satisfy (16-10). The normalized probability w is obtained by dividing W by its sum over all possible macrostates so that

$$w = \frac{W}{\sum_{\text{macrostates}} W} = \frac{W}{\sum_{(n_i)} W} \tag{21-6}$$

if we use (n_i) as a symbol for a given macrostate. w as defined in this way satisfies (16-10).

The distribution (n_i) is not completely arbitrary but must satisfy the conditions that the number of particles and the energy remain constant; that is,

$$\sum_i n_i = N = \text{const.} \tag{21-7}$$

$$\sum_i n_i \varepsilon_i = U = \text{const.} \tag{21-8}$$

In (21-8), ε_i is the energy corresponding to a particle in the ith cell with coordinates $p_{1i}, p_{2i}, \ldots, q_{li}$ and is found by evaluating the particle Hamiltonian [any of the H_k of (21-1)] for these values of the p's and q's.

Our basic problem has now been solved in principle, for, if G is any system property of interest to us, its average value is

$$\bar{G} = \sum_{\text{macrostates}} G w = \frac{\sum_{(n_i)} G W}{\sum_{(n_i)} W} \tag{21-9}$$

For example, the average number of particles in the rth cell is

$$\bar{n}_r = \frac{\sum_{(n_i)} n_r W}{\sum_{(n_i)} W} \tag{21-10}$$

In both of these formulas, the sums are to be taken over all possible macrostates, that is, those which satisfy the conditions (21-7) and (21-8). These averages can be calculated by methods developed by Darwin and Fowler, but the mathematics involved is rather formidable. The results obtained in this way are the same as those obtained by Boltzmann in his original approach, which we shall follow.

Boltzmann did not try to evaluate average values but instead found which macrostate had *maximum probability* and regarded this state as the *equilibrium* state. The calculated properties of the maximum probability macrostate were then to be compared with experiment. This method is based on the very plausible argument that, since the equilibrium state is what we are virtually certain of observing, its probability of occurrence must be overwhelmingly large and therefore a maximum. However, this method is different from our original aim of finding averages, and we have already seen an example of the fact that the most probable value is generally different from the average value in the specific case (18-19). Nevertheless, we shall proceed to calculate most probable values, and later we shall show by various methods that the difference between the most probable and the average values of a quantity are completely insignificant for systems of interest in statistical mechanics; the basic reason for this is the very large number of particles involved.

We can write W in a more convenient form, however, and, in fact, it is more useful to consider $\ln W$; from (21-5), we find

$$\ln W = -\sum_i \ln n_i! \tag{21-11}$$

It is customary to use the Stirling approximation for the factorial:

$$n! \simeq \left(\frac{n}{e}\right)^n \tag{21-12}$$

so that

$$\ln n! \simeq n \ln \frac{n}{e} = n \ln n - n \tag{21-13}$$

Substituting (21-13) into (21-11) and using (21-7), we find that our approximation is

$$\ln W = -\sum_i n_i \ln n_i + N \tag{21-14}$$

21-2   Lagrange's method of multipliers

In order to maximize $\ln W$, we cannot simply differentiate (21-14) with respect to each of the n_i in turn and set each derivative equal to zero because the n_i are not independent. The n_i are subject to the auxiliary conditions (21-7) and (21-8) and cannot be arbitrarily varied. A way for solving such a problem was devised by Lagrange and is known as the *method of (undetermined) multipliers*.

Suppose we wish to find the values of the variables $x_1, x_2, \ldots, x_K$ which correspond to an extreme value of the function $\psi(x_1, x_2, \ldots, x_K)$. We also assume that the variables are not all independent but are subject to L equations of constraint of the general form

$$\phi_j(x_1, x_2, \ldots, x_K) = \text{const.} \qquad (j = 1, 2, \ldots, L) \tag{21-15}$$

where $L \leqslant K$; the number of independent variables is therefore $K - L$. In principle, we could solve each of the equations (21-15) for a given variable and substitute the result into ψ so that ψ would finally be expressed as a function of independent variables only. This procedure is not always practicable, however, and we can proceed differently.

If we imagine virtual variations δx_i in the variables from their values that correspond to the extreme value of ψ, the condition for the extreme value is that the corresponding first order variation $\delta\psi$ vanish so that

$$\delta\psi = \sum_{i=1}^{K} \frac{\partial\psi}{\partial x_i} \delta x_i = 0 \qquad (21\text{-}16)$$

We cannot set the coefficient of each δx_i separately equal to zero because the x_i are not independent. Similarly, we can differentiate the constraint equations (21-15) and obtain the L equations

$$\delta\phi_j = \sum_{i=1}^{K} \frac{\partial\phi_j}{\partial x_i} \delta x_i = 0 \qquad (21\text{-}17)$$

Let us multiply each of the equations (21-17) by an arbitrary parameter λ_j, sum the results, and obtain

$$\sum_{j=1}^{L} \lambda_j \delta\phi_j = \sum_{j=1}^{L} \sum_{i=1}^{K} \lambda_j \frac{\partial\phi_j}{\partial x_i} \delta x_i = 0 \qquad (21\text{-}18)$$

If we add (21-18) to (21-16), we find that

$$\delta\psi + \sum_{j=1}^{L} \lambda_j \delta\phi_j = \sum_{i=1}^{K} \left(\frac{\partial\psi}{\partial x_i} + \sum_{j=1}^{L} \lambda_j \frac{\partial\phi_j}{\partial x_i} \right) \delta x_i = 0 \qquad (21\text{-}19)$$

Because the λ_j are arbitrary, we can choose them to have any value which suits our purposes; therefore we shall require that the λ_j be chosen so that the coefficients of the first L of the δx_i in (21-19) are zero; that is,

$$\frac{\partial\psi}{\partial x_i} + \sum_{j=1}^{L} \lambda_j \frac{\partial\phi_j}{\partial x_i} = 0 \qquad (i = 1, 2, \ldots, L) \qquad (21\text{-}20)$$

These are L equations which can be solved for the L unknown λ_j; hence they can now be considered as known functions of the x_i, that is,

$$\lambda_j = \lambda_j(x_1, x_2, \ldots, x_K) \qquad (j = 1, 2, \ldots, L) \qquad (21\text{-}21)$$

Equation (21-19) now becomes

$$\sum_{i=L+1}^{K} \left(\frac{\partial\psi}{\partial x_i} + \sum_{j=1}^{L} \lambda_j \frac{\partial\phi_j}{\partial x_i} \right) \delta x_i = 0 \qquad (21\text{-}22)$$

Since we have so far not decided which of the x_i we are going to consider to be the independent variables and which the dependent ones, we can now choose the first L of the x_i to be the dependent variables and the remaining $K - L$ of the x_i to be independent. We can solve the L equations (21-21) for the first L of the x_i to obtain

$$x_i = x_i(x_{L+1}, \ldots, x_K, \lambda_1, \ldots, \lambda_L) \qquad (i = 1, 2, \ldots, L) \qquad (21\text{-}23)$$

If these equations are now substituted into (21-22), the resultant equation will involve only the *independent* variables $x_{L+1}, \ldots, x_K$. Therefore the variations δx_i in (21-22) are independently arbitrary, and the only way in which (21-22) can always be zero is for the coefficients of the δx_i to be zero separately; in this way we obtain the $K - L$ equations

$$\frac{\partial \psi}{\partial x_i} + \sum_{j=1}^{L} \lambda_j \frac{\partial \phi_j}{\partial x_i} = 0 \qquad (i = L+1, \ldots, K) \tag{21-24}$$

These resultant equations when combined with (21-20) as previously chosen give us a total of K equations as the conditions for the extreme value of ψ subject to the conditions (21-15).

All these equations are seen to be of exactly the same form and, according to (21-19), are exactly what we would have obtained *if* we had used

$$\delta \psi + \sum_j \lambda_j \, \delta \phi_j = 0 \tag{21-25}$$

and treated all the x_i as if they were independent. In other words, if we look for the extreme value of the function $\psi + \Sigma_j \lambda_j \phi_j$ by treating the variables *as if they were all independent*, the results are the same as those which will give the extreme value of ψ alone subject to the constraints ϕ_j.

21-3   State of maximum probability

In order to maximize ln W, we consider virtual variations δn_i in the number of particles in the cells. The variation in the conditions (21-7) and (21-8) yield

$$\sum_i \delta n_i = 0 \tag{21-26}$$

$$\sum_i \varepsilon_i \, \delta n_i = 0 \tag{21-27}$$

If we differentiate (21-14) and use (21-26), we find that

$$\delta \ln W = 0 = -\sum_i \left(\delta n_i \ln n_i + n_i \frac{\delta n_i}{n_i} \right)$$

$$= -\sum_i \delta n_i \ln n_i \tag{21-28}$$

Following (21-25), we multiply (21-26) and (21-27) by α and β, respectively, and subtract the results from (21-28) to find that the condition for the maximum is

$$\sum_i (\ln n_i + \alpha + \beta \varepsilon_i) \, \delta n_i = 0$$

Since the δn_i can now be treated as independent, we equate the coefficients separately to zero so that

$$\ln n_i + \alpha + \beta \varepsilon_i = 0 \qquad (21\text{-}29)$$

and therefore the set

$$n_i = e^{-\alpha - \beta \varepsilon_i} \qquad (21\text{-}30)$$

is the macrostate of maximum probability W_m.

If we substitute (21-29) into (21-14) and use (21-7) and (21-8), we see that

$$\ln W_m = \alpha N + \beta U + N \qquad (21\text{-}31)$$

The multipliers α and β can be determined from the constraints. If we substitute (21-30) into (21-7), we find

$$e^{-\alpha} = \frac{N}{\sum_i e^{-\beta \varepsilon_i}} \qquad (21\text{-}32)$$

so that (21-30) can also be written as

$$n_i = \frac{N e^{-\beta \varepsilon_i}}{\sum_i e^{-\beta \varepsilon_i}} \qquad (21\text{-}33)$$

When we substitute (21-33) into (21-8), we obtain

$$U = \frac{N \sum_i \varepsilon_i e^{-\beta \varepsilon_i}}{\sum_i e^{-\beta \varepsilon_i}} \qquad (21\text{-}34)$$

Thus, in principle, β can be found from this result as soon as the dependence of ε_i on the location of the cell is known; we shall soon find an easier and better way of determining β.

It is convenient to define the *partition function* Z_0 by

$$Z_0 = \sum_i e^{-\beta \varepsilon_i} \qquad (21\text{-}35)$$

We see from (21-35) and (21-34) that

$$\frac{\partial \ln Z_0}{\partial \beta} = -\frac{1}{Z_0} \sum_i \varepsilon_i e^{-\beta \varepsilon_i} = -\frac{U}{N}$$

and therefore

$$U = -N \frac{\partial \ln Z_0}{\partial \beta} \qquad (21\text{-}36)$$

Similarly, if we use (21-35) and (21-33), we obtain

$$n_i = -\frac{N}{\beta} \frac{\partial \ln Z_0}{\partial \varepsilon_i} \qquad (21\text{-}37)$$

The fundamental results for the macrostate of maximum probability are summarized in the last three numbered equations.

Before we go on, it will be useful to see how the probability of any other distribution compares with that of maximum probability. We let n_i' be a macrostate of probability W' given by (21-14) as

$$\ln W' = -\sum_i n_i' \ln n_i' + N \qquad (21\text{-}38)$$

while n_i corresponds to W_m so that

$$\ln W_m = -\sum_i n_i \ln n_i + N$$

Subtracting the last two equations, we obtain

$$\ln \frac{W'}{W_m} = -\sum_i (n_i' \ln n_i' - n_i \ln n_i) \qquad (21\text{-}39)$$

We now set

$$n_i' = n_i + \Delta n_i \qquad (21\text{-}40)$$

The differences Δn_i need not be small in absolute value, but we shall assume that $|\Delta n_i/n_i| \ll 1$ so that the primed macrostate can be thought of as "near" that of maximum probability. Since we must always have $N = \Sigma_i\, n_i = \Sigma_i\, n_i'$, we find that

$$\sum_i \Delta n_i = 0 \qquad (21\text{-}41)$$

Using (21-40), and $\ln (1 + x) = x - \frac{1}{2}x^2 + \cdots$ for $x \ll 1$, we obtain

$$\begin{aligned}
n_i' \ln n_i' &= (n_i + \Delta n_i) \ln (n_i + \Delta n_i) \\
&= (n_i + \Delta n_i)\left\{\ln n_i + \ln\left[1 + \frac{\Delta n_i}{n_i}\right]\right\} \\
&\simeq (n_i + \Delta n_i)\left[\ln n_i + \left(\frac{\Delta n_i}{n_i}\right) - \frac{1}{2}\left(\frac{\Delta n_i}{n_i}\right)^2\right] \\
&= n_i \ln n_i + \Delta n_i + \Delta n_i \ln n_i + \frac{(\Delta n_i)^2}{2n_i} \qquad (21\text{-}42)
\end{aligned}$$

which is correct to terms of order $(\Delta n_i/n_i)^2$. Substituting (21-42) into (21-39), using (21-41) and the condition (21-28) that n_i correspond to W_m, we find that

$$\ln \frac{W'}{W_m} = -\sum_i \frac{(\Delta n_i)^2}{2n_i}$$

and therefore

$$\frac{W'}{W_m} = e^{-\frac{1}{2}\Sigma_i (\Delta n_i)^2/n_i} \qquad (21\text{-}43)$$

In order to get a numerical example, let us assume a special situation in which the fractional change in each cell is the same:

$$|\Delta n_i/n_i| = \text{const.} = |\Delta n/n| \qquad (21\text{-}44)$$

If we substitute (21-44) into (21-43) and use (21-7), we obtain

$$\frac{W'}{W_m} = e^{-\frac{1}{2}N(\Delta n/n)^2} \qquad (21\text{-}45)$$

Suppose we consider a kilomole of gas for which $N \approx 10^{27}$ and also choose $|\Delta n/n| \approx 10^{-8}$, that is, a fractional difference between the two states of only one part in a hundred million. Substituting these numbers into (21-45), we obtain

$$\frac{W'}{W_m} \simeq e^{-\frac{1}{2} \times 10^{11}} \simeq 0$$

Since this ratio is so very small, we can confidently say that the probability of any other state is completely insignificant compared to that of maximum probability. In other words, all distributions which would have a significant physical difference for us have a negligible probability compared to the maximum probability distribution *provided that N is sufficiently large.* Consequently, only the values associated with the maximum probability state will contribute appreciably to the sum for the average in (21-9) and hence the average of any quantity will be negligibly different from its value of maximum probability. Thus we see some quantitative justification for Boltzmann's method of procedure.

21-4   Entropy and probability

The next thermodynamic parameter we wish to identify is the entropy S. Boltzmann made the fundamental suggestion that the entropy can be written as a function of the probability of the equilibrium state, that is,

$$S = S(W_m) \qquad (21\text{-}46)$$

In order to find the form of this function we use the basic properties of the two quantities involved. By the second law of thermodynamics, S is a maximum for an isolated system at equilibrium for which we assume maximum probability W_m. Entropy is an extensive quantity and therefore additive; if we combine two systems to form a single system, the entropy S_{12} of the combined system will be

$$S_{12} = S_1 + S_2 \qquad (21\text{-}47)$$

The probability, on the other hand, is multiplicative and thus

$$W_{12} = W_1 W_2 \qquad (21\text{-}48)$$

Combining the last three equations, we obtain

$$S_{12}(W_{12}) = S_{12}(W_1 W_2) = S_1(W_1) + S_2(W_2) \qquad (21\text{-}49)$$

If we differentiate (21-49) with respect to W_1 and W_2, we find the two equations

$$\frac{\partial S_{12}}{\partial W_1} = \frac{dS_{12}}{dW_{12}} \frac{\partial W_{12}}{\partial W_1} = W_2 \frac{dS_{12}}{dW_{12}} = \frac{dS_1}{dW_1} \qquad (21\text{-}50a)$$

$$\frac{\partial S_{12}}{\partial W_2} = \frac{dS_{12}}{dW_{12}} \frac{\partial W_{12}}{\partial W_2} = W_1 \frac{dS_{12}}{dW_{12}} = \frac{dS_2}{dW_2} \qquad (21\text{-}50b)$$

By multiplying these by W_1 and W_2, respectively, and by using (21-48) and the same arguments which led to (18-7) from (18-6), we obtain

$$W_{12} \frac{dS_{12}}{dW_{12}} = W_1 \frac{dS_1}{dW_1} = W_2 \frac{dS_2}{dW_2} = \text{const.} = k$$

which, when we drop the numerical subscripts and note (21-46), leads to the general result

$$dS = k \frac{dW_m}{W_m} = k \, d \ln W_m$$

and therefore to

$$S = k \ln W_m \qquad (21\text{-}51)$$

after we drop the constant of integration. Equation (21-51) is Boltzmann's famous result. Later, we shall show that k is actually the Boltzmann constant defined in (17-14').

We can express S in terms of other variables by substituting (21-31) into (21-51). The multiplier α as evaluated from (21-32) and (21-35) is

$$\alpha = \ln Z_0 - \ln N \qquad (21\text{-}52)$$

and, if we also use (21-13), we obtain the various forms

$$S = \beta k U + Nk \ln Z_0 + Nk - Nk \ln N \qquad (21\text{-}53a)$$

$$= \beta k U + Nk \ln Z_0 + Nk \ln \frac{e}{N} \qquad (21\text{-}53b)$$

$$= \beta k U + Nk \ln Z_0 - k \ln N! \qquad (21\text{-}53c)$$

$$= \beta k U + k \ln \frac{Z_0^N}{N!} \qquad (21\text{-}53d)$$

Of course, nothing we have done so far proves that the quantity S has the same properties as the thermodynamic entropy which is defined by (10-27). In order to do this, we must first find how the *work* done in a small change of state can be described.

In general, the energy ε_i of a subsystem in the ith cell depends not only on the coordinates of the cell but also on other external parameters a_λ which appear in the Hamiltonian. The most common of these parameters are the volume and the electric and magnetic field components. Thus one has

$$\varepsilon_i = \varepsilon_i(p_{1i}, \ldots, q_{li}; \; a_1, \ldots, a_\lambda, \ldots) \qquad (21\text{-}54)$$

If the parameter a_λ is changed by the amount da_λ, the energy of a subsystem in the ith cell will be changed by

$$d\varepsilon_i = \frac{\partial \varepsilon_i}{\partial a_\lambda} \, da_\lambda$$

so that, if we sum this over all the cells, we find the total change in energy of the system resulting from a change in the parameter to be given by

$$\sum_i n_i \, d\varepsilon_i = \sum_i n_i \frac{\partial \varepsilon_i}{\partial a_\lambda} \, da_\lambda \qquad (21\text{-}55)$$

which also equals the work done on the whole system in order to change a_λ. There will be expressions similar to (21-55) for each parameter that is altered; if we sum these, we get the total work dW done on the system resulting from a general change of state; therefore

$$dW = \sum_\lambda \sum_i n_i \frac{\partial \varepsilon_i}{\partial a_\lambda} \, da_\lambda = \sum_\lambda F_\lambda \, da_\lambda \qquad (21\text{-}56)$$

where

$$F_\lambda = \sum_i n_i \frac{\partial \varepsilon_i}{\partial a_\lambda} \qquad (21\text{-}57)$$

is defined as the *generalized force* acting on the system. If $a_\lambda = V$, for example, then $F_\lambda = -p$, and $dW = -p \, dV$ in agreement with (8-6).

We can also express the generalized forces as derivatives of the partition function. If we use (21-35), (21-33), and (21-57), we find

$$\frac{\partial \ln Z_0}{\partial a_\lambda} = -\frac{\beta}{Z_0} \sum_i e^{-\beta \varepsilon_i} \frac{\partial \varepsilon_i}{\partial a_\lambda} = -\frac{\beta}{N} \sum_i n_i \frac{\partial \varepsilon_i}{\partial a_\lambda}$$

and therefore

$$F_\lambda = -\frac{N}{\beta} \frac{\partial \ln Z_0}{\partial a_\lambda} \qquad (21\text{-}58)$$

If we now calculate dS from (21-53a) with the use of (21-35), (21-36), (21-58), and (21-56), we find

$$dS = \beta k\, dU + kU\, d\beta + Nk\, d\ln Z_0$$

$$= \beta k\, dU + kU\, d\beta + Nk\, \frac{\partial \ln Z_0}{\partial \beta}\, d\beta + Nk\, \sum_\lambda \frac{\partial \ln Z_0}{\partial a_\lambda}\, da_\lambda$$

$$= \beta k\, (dU - \sum_\lambda F_\lambda\, da_\lambda)$$

$$= \beta k\, (dU - dW) \qquad (21\text{-}59)$$

This agrees with the defining equations (10-27) and (9-1) for the thermodynamic entropy provided that $\beta k = 1/T$. Therefore, if we adopt

$$\beta = \frac{1}{kT} \qquad (21\text{-}60)$$

as a universal relation, then $S = k \ln W_m$ is completely identified with the thermodynamic entropy and, for example, (21-53b) becomes

$$S = \frac{U}{T} + Nk \ln Z_0 + Nk \ln \frac{e}{N} \qquad (21\text{-}61)$$

(We note that we have not yet identified k.)

We can now easily find the Helmholtz function from (11-4b) and (21-61); the result is

$$F = -NkT \ln Z_0 - NkT \ln \frac{e}{N} \qquad (21\text{-}62)$$

We can use our thermodynamic result (11-6b) to obtain a formula for the equation of state:

$$p = -\left(\frac{\partial F}{\partial V}\right)_T = NkT \left(\frac{\partial \ln Z_0}{\partial V}\right)_T \qquad (21\text{-}63)$$

This result agrees, of course, with the general formula (21-58) for the generalized forces and again demonstrates how a knowledge of the partition function Z_0 is sufficient to determine all the thermodynamic properties of a system composed of independent subsystems.

Exercises

21-1. Discuss and compare the Γ-space and μ-space for a system of N independent one-dimensional harmonic oscillators.

21-2. Show that the expression (21-4) for W_B is correct.

21-3. Show that the entropy can be written

$$S = -Nk \overline{\ln p_i} + Nk \ln (e/N)$$

where p_i is the probability that a subsystem will be in the ith cell of μ-space.

21-4. If the subsystems are actually *distinguishable* (as was implied by our labeling them in our derivation of W_B) rather than completely identical (and accordingly *indistinguishable* in principle), show that one should use the uncorrected Boltzmann probability W_B rather than (21-5). Also show that then (21-36) and (21-37) are unchanged, while the entropy and Helmholtz function are given by

$$S = (U/T) + Nk \ln Z_0 \qquad (21\text{-}64)$$

$$F = -NkT \ln Z_0 \qquad (21\text{-}65)$$

rather than by (21-61) and (21-62). An example of distinguishable subsystems would be the *localizable* atoms of a solid which are fixed at their average positions. What other examples can you think of?

22 *Ideal gases*

Let us assume our system to be a gas containing N molecules. We let x, y, z, p_x, p_y, p_z be the coordinates and momenta of the center of mass of a molecule; we let them be the $q_1, q_2, q_3, p_1, p_2, p_3$ and let any remaining degrees of freedom of the molecule be described by $q_4, \ldots, q_l, p_4, \ldots, p_l$. The Hamiltonian of the molecule can then be written as the sum of the energy associated with the motion of the center of mass and a term H' which includes the rest of the energy; therefore

$$H = \frac{1}{2m} (p_x{}^2 + p_y{}^2 + p_z{}^2) + \phi(x, y, z) + H'(p_4, \ldots, q_l) = \varepsilon \qquad (22\text{-}1)$$

where $\phi(x, y, z)$ is the external potential energy which depends on the position of the center of mass.

22-1   The Maxwell-Boltzmann distribution

We shall use our results to answer the question: How many molecules have $x, y, \ldots, p_z$ in the range $dx \, dy \, dz \, dp_x \, dp_y \, dp_z$ regardless of the values of the rest of the coordinates and momenta?

The number of molecules in the cell of volume

$$d\Omega_\mu = dx \, dy \, dz \, dp_x \, dp_y \, dp_z \, dq_4 \cdots dp_l \qquad (22\text{-}2)$$

in μ-space is given by (21-33). If we multiply (21-33) by $d\Omega_\mu/d\Omega_\mu = 1$, we can change the sum over cells in μ-space to the $2l$-fold integral over all values of the p's and q's since both procedures cover the total volume in

μ-space; if we also use (22-1) and (22-2), we find

$$n_i = \frac{Ne^{-\beta\varepsilon_i}}{\sum_i e^{-\beta\varepsilon_i}} = \frac{Ne^{-\beta\varepsilon_i}\,d\Omega_\mu}{\int e^{-\beta\varepsilon}\,d\Omega_\mu}$$

$$= \frac{Ne^{-\beta p^2/2m-\beta\phi-\beta H'}\,dx\cdots dp_z\,dq_4\cdots dp_l}{\int e^{-\beta p^2/2m-\beta\phi}dx\cdots dp_z\int e^{-\beta H'}\,dq_4\cdots dp_l} \qquad (22\text{-}3)$$

We actually want only the number with coordinates in the range $dx \cdots dp_z$ which we shall call n_{cm}. We can obtain n_{cm} from (22-3) by integrating over all permissible values of $q_4, \ldots, p_l$; when we do this, the integral involving H' will appear in both numerator and denominator and can be cancelled with the result that

$$n_{cm} = \text{const.}e^{-\beta p^2/2m-\beta\phi}dx\,dy\,dz\,dp_x\,dp_y\,dp_z \qquad (22\text{-}4)$$

If we express this result in terms of the molecular velocity $\mathbf{u} = \mathbf{p}/m$, the number n_{cm} can be written in terms of the molecular distribution function f defined in (16-15); then (22-4) becomes

$$f\,dx \cdots du_z = \text{const.}e^{-\frac{1}{2}\beta mu^2-\beta\phi}dx\,dy\,dz\,du_x\,du_y\,du_z \qquad (22\text{-}5)$$

This distribution function is known as the *Maxwell-Boltzmann distribution*.

We can obtain the fraction of the molecules whose velocity components fall in the range $du_x\,du_y\,du_z$ regardless of position by summing (22-5) over the coordinates x, y, z; the result is

$$F(u)\,du_x\,du_y\,du_z = \text{const.}e^{-\frac{1}{2}\beta mu^2}du_x\,du_y\,du_z \qquad (22\text{-}6)$$

On comparing with (18-14), we see that (22-6) is identical with the Maxwell velocity distribution function provided that $\beta = 1/kT$; this agrees with (21-60) and proves that the k introduced in (21-51) is actually the Boltzmann constant R/L. Our derivation of (22-6) has been very general and has used only our basic ideas about equilibrium. We also see that the Maxwell velocity distribution is not restricted to point molecules, or to hard sphere molecules, but is applicable to molecules of any complexity as long as they can be assumed to be independent.

We can obtain the density n by using (22-5) in (16-16); the result is

$$n = \text{const.}e^{-\beta\phi}$$

and, if we let n_0 be the density where $\phi = 0$, we obtain

$$n(x, y, z) = n_0 e^{-\beta\phi(x,y,z)} = n_0 e^{-\phi/kT} \qquad (22\text{-}7)$$

The result tells us how the density of a gas in equilibrium varies with position and shows that the general tendency is for the density to be greater at locations where the potential energy is smaller. The factor $e^{-\phi/kT}$ is sometimes called the *Boltzmann factor*; the result (22-7) is often called the *law of atmospheres* since it would describe the density variation in an isothermal planetary atmosphere if ϕ is set equal to the gravitational potential energy. We shall discuss several of the many other uses of (22-7) as we proceed.

22-2   Ideal monatomic gas

We want to calculate all the thermodynamic properties of the gas when the molecules are assumed to be mass points. Each molecule thus has three degrees of freedom and (22-1) becomes

$$\varepsilon = \frac{1}{2m} (p_x^2 + p_y^2 + p_z^2) + \phi \tag{22-8}$$

Although we shall neglect other external forces, we require the potential energy ϕ to describe our assumption that the gas is kept in a container of volume V while otherwise free to move anywhere within the container. Thus we let $\phi = 0$ *inside* the container, and $\phi \to \infty$ at the walls and everywhere *outside* the container; as a result, $e^{-\beta\varepsilon} = 0$ for all points *outside* the container and we need consider in our calculations only those values of x, y, z which are inside.

We need to find the partition function Z_0. If we let h^3 represent the volume of a cell in μ-space, we can multiply the sum in (21-35) by $d\Omega_\mu/h^3$ and convert the sum to an integral. If we also change to spherical coordinates in momentum space and use (18-9), we obtain

$$Z_0 = \sum_i e^{-\beta\varepsilon_i}$$

$$= \iiint_{\text{volume}} \iiint e^{-\beta(p_x^2 + p_y^2 + p_z^2)/2m} \frac{dx\,dy\,dz\,dp_x\,dp_y\,dp_z}{h^3}$$

$$= \frac{V}{h^3} \iiint e^{-\beta(p_x^2 + p_y^2 + p_z^2)/2m}\,dp_x\,dp_y\,dp_z$$

$$= \frac{V}{h^3} \int_0^{2\pi} \int_0^\pi \int_0^\infty e^{-\beta p^2/2m}\,p^2 \sin\theta\,dp\,d\theta\,d\varphi$$

$$= \frac{4\pi V}{h^3} \int_0^\infty e^{-\beta p^2/2m}\,p^2\,dp = \frac{V}{h^3}\left(\frac{2\pi m}{\beta}\right)^{3/2} \tag{22-9}$$

which can also be put in the form

$$Z_0 = \frac{V}{h^3}(2\pi m k T)^{3/2} \tag{22-10}$$

with the use of (21-60).

From (22-9) we find that

$$\ln Z_0 = -\frac{3}{2}\ln \beta + \ln V + \frac{3}{2}\ln \frac{2\pi m}{h^2} \tag{22-11a}$$

$$\ln Z_0 = \frac{3}{2}\ln T + \ln V + \frac{3}{2}\ln \frac{2\pi m k}{h^2} \tag{22-11b}$$

If we apply (21-36) to (22-11a), we obtain

$$U = \frac{3N}{2\beta} = \frac{3}{2}NkT \tag{22-12}$$

which is equivalent to the result (17-16) we previously obtained for an ideal monatomic gas by kinetic theory methods and again identifies k as the Boltzmann constant.

The entropy is obtained by inserting (22-11b) and (22-12) into (21-61) and is

$$S = \frac{3}{2}Nk \ln T + Nk \ln V + Nk \ln \left[\frac{(2\pi m k)^{3/2}\, e^{5/2}}{Nh^3}\right] \tag{22-13}$$

Since $Nk = (\nu L)(R/L) = \nu R$, we can also write (22-13) as

$$S = C_v \ln T + \nu R \ln V + \text{const.} \tag{22-14}$$

if we use (17-17). We see that (22-14) is exactly the same as the expression (9-43) we first found for the entropy of an ideal gas by purely thermodynamic means.

The equation of state as found from (21-63) and (22-11) is

$$p = \frac{NkT}{V} \tag{22-15}$$

and is the equation of state of an ideal gas (17-15) which we have succeeded in obtaining by the general methods of statistical mechanics. If we review our calculation of Z_0, we see that the volume V will enter into Z_0 in the same way as in (22-10), no matter how complicated the molecules might be, as long as they can be treated as independent. As a result, we shall always obtain (22-15); thus we also find that the same equation of state applies to all ideal gases and is not restricted to those which are monatomic.

22-3   The absolute value of the entropy

If we rewrite (22-13) so that it involves only one logarithm, we obtain the *Sackur-Tetrode formula*

$$S = Nk \ln \left[\left(\frac{V}{N} \right) \frac{(2\pi m k T)^{3/2} e^{5/2}}{h^3} \right] \tag{22-16}$$

Since the ratio (V/N) is intensive, $S \sim N$ and therefore our entropy expression is extensive, as it should be.

The extensive property of S is a consequence of our use of corrected Boltzmann counting, that is, (21-5) rather than (21-4). We see from (21-4) and (21-51) that the use of uncorrected Boltzmann counting is equivalent to adding

$$k \ln N! = Nk \ln \frac{N}{e}$$

to (22-16), so that the entropy formula would be

$$S = Nk \ln \frac{V(2\pi m k T)^{3/2} e^{3/2}}{h^3}$$

This result is *not* extensive because only V appears under the logarithm. Thus we have found one of the reasons for the use of corrected Boltzmann counting for identical subsystems; we shall defer a more complete discussion until later.

We have also obtained the absolute value of the entropy; we could not do this in thermodynamics. If we apply (22-13) to a kilomole and use (17-17) again, we find that

$$s = c_v \ln T + R \ln v + s_{v0}$$

which is exactly the same as (15-16) except that now we have found that

$$s_{v0} = R \ln \frac{(2\pi m k)^{3/2} e^{5/2}}{L h^3} \tag{22-17}$$

If we combine (15-18) and (22-17), we find the entropy constant s_{p0}, which appears in the vapor pressure equation (15-23), to be given by

$$s_{p0} = R \ln \frac{(2\pi m)^{3/2} (ek)^{5/2}}{h^3} \tag{22-18}$$

These results show that the entropy involves the size h^3 of the cells in μ-space which we have not yet specified. This fact did not disturb Boltzmann because the entropy as originally defined always involved an additive constant and he was free to choose his cell size in any arbitrary way. The third law of thermodynamics, however, requires that the entropy have a definite value, and this means that the cell size h^3 can no longer be chosen arbitrarily but must be fixed to agree with experimental results for the entropy. For example, from a study of the vapor pressure curve, one can obtain an experimental value for s_{p0} and then find h from the theoretical expression (22-18). It is found that, within experimental error, h is equal to *Planck's constant* (6.625 × 10⁻³⁴ joule-second) which was introduced by Planck at the beginning of quantum theory.

Thus there is a natural size for the cells in μ-space; for the monatomic ideal gas it equals h^3. This is in agreement with the general results of quantum theory which show that we cannot know both a momentum and its conjugate coordinate exactly, but only to within the "uncertainties" Δp_i and Δq_i which are limited according to the uncertainty principle by

$$\Delta p_i \, \Delta q_i \approx h \qquad (22\text{-}19)$$

Accordingly, for a monatomic gas we would have

$$\Delta\Omega_\mu = \Delta p_x \, \Delta x \, \Delta p_y \, \Delta y \, \Delta p_z \, \Delta z \approx h^3$$

which agrees with what we found above. In general, then, if a system has l degrees of freedom, the cell size in μ-space must be chosen to be

$$\Delta\Omega_\mu = h^l \qquad (22\text{-}20)$$

Although (22-20) is correct, its real justification can only be given by means of the complete formalism of quantum mechanics.

22-4 Mixtures of gases

Before we go on, we should make certain that our methods will describe equilibrium if there is more than one type of molecule, as would be the case for a mixture of gases. We shall discuss this problem only enough to see that we are getting reasonable results.

For simplicity, we restrict ourselves to the case of only two gases occupying the same volume V and possessing a total energy U. The masses of the molecules are m_1 and m_2, and their numbers are N_1 and N_2. We define a μ-space for each gas and let the numbers of molecules per cell in each μ-space be denoted by $n_i^{(1)}$ and $n_j^{(2)}$.

The probabilities for the two gases as obtained from (21-5) are

$$W_1 = \frac{1}{n_1^{(1)}! \, n_2^{(1)}! \cdots}, \qquad W_2 = \frac{1}{n_1^{(2)}! \, n_2^{(2)}! \cdots} \qquad (22\text{-}21)$$

and the probability for the mixture is $W = W_1 W_2$. Using (22-21) and (21-13), we obtain

$$\ln W = N_1 + N_2 - \sum_i n_i^{(1)} \ln n_i^{(1)} - \sum_j n_j^{(2)} \ln n_j^{(2)} \qquad (22\text{-}22)$$

We want to find the maximum of $\ln W$ subject to the conditions of constant number of particles and energy, namely,

$$\sum_i n_i^{(1)} = N_1, \quad \sum_j n_j^{(2)} = N_2,$$

$$\sum_i n_i^{(1)} \varepsilon_i^{(1)} + \sum_j n_j^{(2)} \varepsilon_j^{(2)} = U$$

Proceeding as in Sec. 21-3, we introduce three Lagrange multipliers α_1, α_2, β corresponding to these three constraints, and we find the condition for the maximum to be

$$\sum_i \delta n_i^{(1)} [\ln n_i^{(1)} + \alpha_1 + \beta \varepsilon_i^{(1)}] + \sum_j \delta n_j^{(2)} [\ln n_j^{(2)} + \alpha_2 + \beta \varepsilon_j^{(2)}] = 0$$

which leads to

$$n_i^{(1)} = e^{-\alpha_1 - \beta \varepsilon_i^{(1)}}, \quad n_j^{(2)} = e^{-\alpha_2 - \beta \varepsilon_j^{(2)}} \qquad (22\text{-}23)$$

If we had done these calculations before we had identified β as $1/kT$, the results (22-23) would have shown us that β must somehow be connected with the temperature. If the two gases are in mutual equilibrium, they must have the same temperature and β is the only quantity in (22-23) which is the *same* for the two distributions and hence could possibly describe what the gases have in common.

If we calculate the partition functions as in (22-9), we find

$$Z_1 = \left(\frac{V}{h^3}\right)(2\pi m_1 kT)^{3/2}, \quad Z_2 = \left(\frac{V}{h^3}\right)(2\pi m_2 kT)^{3/2}$$

so that the Helmholtz functions as found from (21-62) are

$$F_1 = -N_1 kT \ln V + F_{10}, \quad F_2 = -N_2 kT \ln V + F_{20} \qquad (22\text{-}24)$$

where F_{10} and F_{20} are independent of V. The total Helmholtz function of the system therefore is

$$F = F_1 + F_2 = -(N_1 + N_2)kT \ln V + F_{10} + F_{20} \qquad (22\text{-}25)$$

The pressure is found from (21-63) and (22-25) to be

$$p = \frac{(N_1 + N_2)kT}{V} = \frac{N_1 kT}{V} + \frac{N_2 kT}{V} = p_1 + p_2 \qquad (22\text{-}26)$$

We also see that $p_1 = -(\partial F_1/\partial V)_T$ and $p_2 = -(\partial F_2/\partial V)_T$, so that p_1 and p_2 are the partial pressures of the constituents of the mixture. Therefore we have derived Dalton's law of partial pressures (8-22) by our statistical mechanical methods.

Exercises

22-1. Find expressions for the multiplicative constants of (22-4), (22-5), and (22-6).

22-2. Find the density as a function of position for a gas comprised of N molecules contained in a cylinder of radius a and length l which is rotating about its axis with angular velocity ω.

22-3. Suppose that the particles of an ideal gas have the relativistic dependence of energy on momentum

$$\varepsilon = c(p_x^2 + p_y^2 + p_z^2 + m_0^2c^2)^{1/2} \qquad (22\text{-}27)$$

as found from (5-24). Find the energy, Helmholtz function, and equation of state for this ideal gas in the extreme relativistic range where $m_0c \ll p_j$, and compare the results with (22-12) and (22-15).

23 Equations of state of real gases

There are forces between the molecules of real gases; hence these molecules cannot be regarded as completely independent particles and the methods we have developed are not directly applicable to them. If we restrict ourselves to situations where the gas does not deviate too much from ideal behavior, we can hope to develop approximation methods which will enable us to calculate the corrections to our results for ideal gases which arise from the intermolecular forces. In this chapter we shall show how the Boltzmann factor $e^{-\phi/kT}$ can be used to calculate the equation of state and to verify more accurately some of the remarks we made about the van der Waals gas in Chapter 12.

23-1 Virial coefficients and the general equation of state

If we write van der Waals' equation of state (12-6) in terms of the number of molecules N by using $N = \nu L$, we obtain

$$\left(p + \frac{a'N^2}{V^2}\right)(V - Nb') = NkT \qquad (23\text{-}1)$$

where

$$a' = \frac{a}{L^2}, \quad b' = \frac{b}{L} \tag{23-2}$$

In order to illustrate the motivation for our later calculations let us expand (23-1) to first order in small quantities; if we multiply out the left side and neglect the second order term $-a'b'N^3/V^2$, we obtain

$$pV - b'Np + \frac{a'N^2}{V} \simeq NkT \tag{23-3}$$

so that, to first order,

$$p \simeq \frac{NkT}{V} \tag{23-4}$$

Since the correction terms to (23-4) are of first order, we can replace p in the second term of (23-3) by (23-4) and still get a result which differs from (23-3) only by second order terms which we are neglecting anyhow. When we do this, we obtain

$$pV - b'N\left(\frac{NkT}{V}\right) + \left(\frac{a'N^2}{V}\right) \simeq NkT$$

which becomes

$$pV = NkT + \frac{N^2(b'kT - a')}{V} \tag{23-5}$$

The terms we have neglected would appear on the right side of (23-5) as inversely proportional to V^2.

It is clear from this example that we can expand the equation of state for any gas in the general form

$$pV = NkT + \frac{B(T)}{V} + \frac{C(T)}{V^2} + \cdots \tag{23-6}$$

since this form approaches the ideal gas law for large V, as do those equations found empirically. The coefficients in this expansion are called *virial coefficients*; NkT is the first virial coefficient, $B(T)$ is the second virial coefficient, etc. The more virial coefficients we can obtain, the more terms we shall have in the expansion; hence the equation of state (23-6) could be expected to be more accurate for small V.

We see from (23-5) and (23-6) that the second virial coefficient of a van der Waals gas is

$$B(T) = N^2(b'kT - a') \tag{23-7}$$

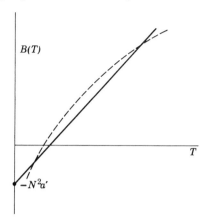

Fig. 23-1

and is a linear function of T as shown by the straight line of Fig. 23-1. Experimental values of $B(T)$ for real gases yield a curve with a slight curvature which is like the dashed curve in the same figure. Thus the van der Waals equation predicts a second virial coefficient which is remarkably like those observed.

We shall see how we can calculate the second virial coefficient for a general real gas and thus find the first correction term to the ideal gas equation of state. In order to do this, we must first discuss a theorem of classical mechanics.

23-2 The virial theorem

This theorem is quite different from most theorems in mechanics because it is statistical in nature; that is, it deals with time averages of certain mechanical quantities.

Let us consider a general system composed of mass points whose position vectors are $\mathbf{r}_i$; the force on the ith particle is $\mathbf{F}_i$ and may include forces of constraint. The equations of motion of the system are

$$\mathbf{F}_i = \frac{d\mathbf{p}_i}{dt} = m_i \frac{d^2\mathbf{r}_i}{dt^2} \tag{23-8}$$

We define a quantity

$$G = \sum_i \mathbf{p}_i \cdot \mathbf{r}_i \tag{23-9}$$

If we calculate dG/dt from (23-9) and use (23-8), we find that

$$\frac{dG}{dt} = \sum_i \mathbf{p}_i \cdot \frac{d\mathbf{r}_i}{dt} + \sum_i \frac{d\mathbf{p}_i}{dt} \cdot \mathbf{r}_i$$

$$= 2E_t + \sum_i \mathbf{F}_i \cdot \mathbf{r}_i \qquad (23\text{-}10)$$

where

$$E_t = \frac{1}{2} \sum_i m_i \left(\frac{d\mathbf{r}_i}{dt}\right)^2$$

is the total kinetic energy of the system.

If we calculate the time average of (23-10) over an interval τ, we obtain

$$\overline{\frac{dG}{dt}} = \frac{1}{\tau} \int_0^\tau \frac{dG}{dt}\, dt = 2\overline{E_t} + \overline{\sum_i \mathbf{F}_i \cdot \mathbf{r}_i} = \frac{G(\tau) - G(0)}{\tau} \qquad (23\text{-}11)$$

If the motion of the system is periodic, we can choose τ to be the period and the right side of (23-11) will be zero. If the motion is not periodic, but is bounded so that the coordinates and momenta remain finite, then we see from (23-9) that G will never become greater than some finite upper bound; in this case, we can make the right side of (23-11) vanish by choosing τ sufficiently large. Thus we can conclude in general that $\overline{dG/dt} = 0$ and therefore

$$\overline{E_t} = -\tfrac{1}{2} \overline{\sum_i \mathbf{F}_i \cdot \mathbf{r}_i} \qquad (23\text{-}12)$$

This is the *virial theorem*; the right side is called *the virial of Clausius*.

The virial theorem deals with time averages which are basically what we are looking for in statistical mechanics. However, we have decided that time averages and ensemble averages are equivalent for our purposes; thus we can also interpret (23-12) as expressing a relation between ensemble averages, or as a relation involving both time and ensemble averages.

23-3 Contribution of the pressure

We have seen in (17-14) and (22-12) that $\overline{E_t} = \tfrac{3}{2} NkT$ for monatomic gases so that (23-12) becomes

$$NkT = -\tfrac{1}{3} \overline{\sum_i \mathbf{F}_i \cdot \mathbf{r}_i} \qquad (23\text{-}13)$$

We shall neglect all external body forces such as gravity; the only forces on a molecule which we need consider then are the force exerted by the wall of the container, F_{iw}, and that due to the other molecules, F_i'. Thus we can write $F_i = F_{iw} + F_i'$ and (23-13) becomes

$$NkT = -\tfrac{1}{3} \overline{\sum_i F_{iw} \cdot r_i} - \tfrac{1}{3} \overline{\sum_i F_i' \cdot r_i} \qquad (23\text{-}14)$$

We consider first the contribution to NkT from the wall forces. Since the wall will act on a molecule only when it is very near the wall, it will be a good approximation to replace r_i by the position vector r of the element of area of the wall da which the molecule is near. Since r is constant, the first sum in (23-14) will now involve only $\overline{F_{iw}}$; however, the average force exerted *by* the wall on the gas near the area da is $-p\, da$ since the direction of da is along the outer normal. In other words, we have

$$\overline{\sum_{\text{molecules at } da} F_{iw} \cdot r_i} = -p\, da \cdot r$$

so that the sum over all the molecules can be replaced by an integration over the total bounding surface S of the volume V. If we also use the divergence theorem (I: 1-33), the first sum in (23-14) can be evaluated as follows:

$$\overline{\sum_i F_{iw} \cdot r_i} = \int_S (-p r \cdot da) = -p \int_S r \cdot da$$

$$= -p \int_V \text{div } r \, dV = -3p \int_V dV = -3pV \qquad (23\text{-}15)$$

If we insert (23-15) into (23-14), we finally obtain

$$pV = NkT + \tfrac{1}{3} \overline{\sum_i F_i' \cdot r_i} \qquad (23\text{-}16)$$

which includes all forces except those exerted by the wall. If $F_i' = 0$, we find that $pV = NkT$, as we would expect. On comparing (23-16) and (23-6), we see that we should be able to calculate the virial coefficients from a knowledge of the intermolecular forces F_i'.

23-4   Contribution from intermolecular forces

For simplicity, we shall consider only the case of *central forces* so that, if r is the separation of two molecules, the force between them is $f(r)$. The force is repulsive if f is positive, and attractive if f is negative.

Consider the pair consisting of the jth and kth molecules as shown in Fig. 23-2. Since $\mathbf{r}_{jk} = \mathbf{r}_k - \mathbf{r}_j$ and $\mathbf{F}_j' = -\mathbf{F}_k'$ by (I: 3-10), we obtain

$$\sum_{jk\,\text{pair}} \mathbf{F}_i' \cdot \mathbf{r}_i = \mathbf{F}_j' \cdot \mathbf{r}_j + \mathbf{F}_k' \cdot \mathbf{r}_k = \mathbf{F}_k' \cdot \mathbf{r}_{jk} = f(r_{jk})r_{jk}$$

so that, for central forces, (23-16) becomes

$$pV = NkT + \tfrac{1}{3} \overline{\sum_{\text{pairs}} rf(r)} \qquad (23\text{-}17)$$

The number of pairs that can be obtained from N molecules is $\tfrac{1}{2}N(N-1) \simeq \tfrac{1}{2}N^2$; hence the sum in (23-17) can also be written in terms of the result for a typical pair as

$$pV = NkT + \tfrac{1}{6}N^2\overline{[rf(r)]}_{\text{pair}} \quad (23\text{-}18)$$

If we let $\phi(r)$ be the potential energy for the forces, we have

$$f(r) = -\frac{d\phi}{dr}, \quad \phi(r) \xrightarrow[r\to\infty]{} 0 \quad (23\text{-}19)$$

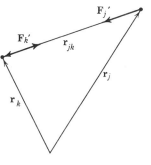

Fig. 23-2

where the potential energy is chosen to be zero when the molecules are a great distance apart. The dependence of ϕ on r is generally assumed to be similar to that shown in Fig. 23-3. The steep rise in ϕ for small values of r describes a repulsive force which is effective when the molecules are close together; for greater separations the force is attractive and becomes very small at large distances.

We shall calculate only the second virial coefficient $B(T)$; because of (23-6), therefore, we need only include terms to the order $1/V$ and can neglect terms proportional to $1/V^2$, $1/V^3$, etc. From (16-9), we see that in order to find $\overline{rf(r)} = \overline{-r(d\phi/dr)}$ for a given pair we need the probability that they will be a distance r apart. According to (22-7), we can take this probability to be proportional to the Boltzmann factor $e^{-\phi/kT}$. Therefore, if $w(r)\,dr$ is the probability that the second molecule of the pair will be in the spherical shell of thickness dr at a distance r from the first so that it is in the volume $4\pi r^2\,dr$, we have

$$w(r)\,dr = A4\pi r^2 e^{-\phi(r)/kT}\,dr \qquad (23\text{-}20)$$

where A is a normalization constant determined, according to (16-10), by

$$\int w(r)\,dr = 1 = A\int 4\pi r^2 e^{-\phi/kT}\,dr \qquad (23\text{-}21)$$

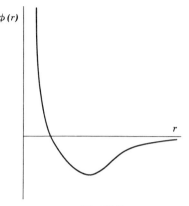

Fig. 23-3

If we plot $e^{-\phi/kT}$ as a function of r for a potential of the general form shown in Fig. 23-3, we get a curve like that of Fig. 23-4. Since the integral over r must cover the volume V, whose dimensions are extremely large compared to average molecular separations, the figure shows that $e^{-\phi/kT} \simeq 1$ except for a very small portion of the range of integration of r and therefore we can approximate (23-21) by

$$1 \simeq A \int 4\pi r^2 \, dr = AV \quad \text{and} \quad A \simeq \frac{1}{V} \tag{23-22}$$

If we combine (16-9), (23-19), (23-20), and (23-22), we obtain

$$\overline{[rf(r)]}_{\text{pair}} = \overline{\left(-r\frac{d\phi}{dr}\right)} = -\frac{4\pi}{V}\int_0^\infty r^3 \frac{d\phi}{dr} e^{-\phi/kT} \, dr \tag{23-23}$$

We have been able to extend the upper limit of integration out to infinity, for any error introduced in this way would be of higher order than the

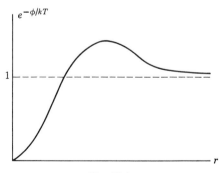

Fig. 23-4

terms we are keeping since (23-23) is already inversely proportional to $1/V$. It is convenient to integrate by parts in (23-23); taking account of the fact that our result must vanish in the absence of molecular forces ($\phi = 0$), we obtain

$$\int_0^\infty r^3 \frac{d\phi}{dr} e^{-\phi/kT} \, dr = \left[kT(1 - e^{-\phi/kT})r^3 \right]_0^\infty - 3kT \int_0^\infty r^2(1 - e^{-\phi/kT}) \, dr$$

$$= -3kT \int_0^\infty r^2(1 - e^{-\phi/kT}) \, dr \qquad (23\text{-}24)$$

where we have used (23-19) and assumed that the potential falls off rapidly enough with r so that, as $r \to \infty$,

$$kT(1 - e^{-\phi/kT})r^3 \to r^3\phi \to 0$$

If we now use (23-24) in (23-23) and compare the resultant form of (23-18) with (23-6), we see that the second virial coefficient is given by

$$B(T) = 2\pi N^2 kT \int_0^\infty r^2(1 - e^{-\phi/kT}) \, dr \qquad (23\text{-}25)$$

The result applies to a gas for which the central force potential vanishes sufficiently rapidly at large separation; as a check on (23-25), we see that $B = 0$ when $\phi = 0$, as it should.

Example. van der Waals Gas. Let us assume that the molecules are impenetrable spheres of radius $\frac{1}{2}s$, and that they have a *weak* mutual attraction when separated by more than the collision diameter s. Therefore ϕ will have the general appearance shown in Fig. 23-5 which

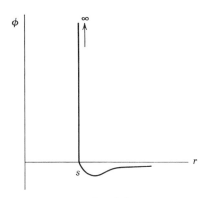

Fig. 23-5

approximately corresponds to that envisioned for a van der Waals gas. If we assume that $\phi \ll kT$ so that

$$1 - e^{-\phi/kT} \simeq \phi/kT \qquad (r \geqslant s)$$

we obtain

$$\int_0^\infty r^2(1 - e^{-\phi/kT}) \, dr = \int_0^s [\cdots] + \int_s^\infty [\cdots]$$

$$= \int_0^s r^2 \, dr + \int_s^\infty r^2(1 - e^{-\phi/kT}) \, dr \simeq \frac{1}{3}s^3 + \frac{1}{kT}\int_s^\infty \phi r^2 \, dr$$

Therefore we find from (23-25) that

$$B(T) = N^2\left(\frac{2\pi s^3 kT}{3} + 2\pi\int_s^\infty \phi r^2 \, dr\right) \qquad (23\text{-}26)$$

which is exactly of the form (23-7) obtained for a van der Waals gas where

$$b' = \tfrac{2}{3}\pi s^3, \quad a' = -2\pi\int_s^\infty \phi(r) r^2 \, dr \qquad (23\text{-}27)$$

We see that a' will be positive for attractive forces, as we assumed in our original discussion in Chapter 12.

Since the molecular radius is $\tfrac{1}{2}s$, we also see that

$$b' = 4\left[\frac{4\pi}{3}\left(\frac{s}{2}\right)^3\right]$$

and hence is four times the volume of a molecule. This is precisely the interpretation of b' which we made in our initial discussion of van der Waals' equation as given after (12-1).

Exercises

23-1. A system of mass points moves in three dimensions under the influence of an external inverse square central force. Show that the average value of the potential energy per molecule is $-3kT$.

23-2. Find the second virial coefficient for a gas for which the mutual repulsion between pairs of molecules is described by the potential energy $\phi = \text{const.}/r^n$ where $n > 3$.

23-3. Calculate the Joule-Thomson coefficient μ for the equation of state (23-6), and thereby show that the inversion temperature is determined approximately by the condition $dB/dT = B/T$. How can one use this condition to determine T_i graphically from an actual curve of B vs. T such as the dashed one of Fig. 23-1?

24 *Paramagnetism and ferromagnetism*

The additional variables which are appropriate for the thermodynamic description of a magnetic system have been discussed in Chapter 14. In order to calculate them, we now assume that each subsystem possesses enough internal structure that it has a permanent magnetic dipole moment μ. As has been shown in (I: 38-19 and 23-15), the energy of a permanent dipole in an external magnetic field is

$$\varepsilon_m = -\mu \cdot \mathbf{B} = -\mu B \cos \theta \qquad (24\text{-}1)$$

where θ is the angle between the directions of μ and $\mathbf{B}$. If $\mathscr{M}$ is the total component of the magnetic dipole moment of the system in the direction of the applied field,

$$\mathscr{M} = \sum_k (\mu \cos \theta)_k = N\overline{\mu \cos \theta} \qquad (24\text{-}2)$$

since $(\mu \cos \theta)_k$ is the component of the kth subsystem.

If the energy corresponding to the ith cell is written $\varepsilon_i = \varepsilon_0 + \varepsilon_m$, where ε_0 is that part of the energy which is independent of the magnetic field, we have

$$Z_0 = \sum_i e^{-\beta \varepsilon_i} = \sum_i e^{-\beta \varepsilon_0 - \beta \varepsilon_m}$$

$$= \sum_i e^{-\beta \varepsilon_0 + \beta \mu B \cos \theta} \qquad (24\text{-}3)$$

If we calculate $\partial \ln Z_0 / \partial B$ and use (21-33) and (24-2), we obtain

$$\mathscr{M} = \frac{N}{\beta} \frac{\partial \ln Z_0}{\partial B} \qquad (24\text{-}4)$$

as our basic result.

24-1 Langevin paramagnetism

The first calculation of the magnetization of a paramagnetic system, that is, one comprised of independent subsystems, was made by Langevin. He used the Boltzmann factor to evaluate the probability of $\mu \cos \theta$ in a way which is intuitively very appealing and leads to the correct result. However, Langevin's basic assumption is not an immediate consequence of our result (21-33) for the probability of occupation of a cell in μ-space, nor does it follow directly from the Boltzmann distribution (22-7) for the center of mass of the molecules. Consequently, we shall derive Langevin's result in a different and more accurate manner while leaving it as an exercise to apply his method to this problem.

Since our molecule possesses a dipole moment $\mathbf{\mu}$, it cannot have spherical symmetry but must have an *axis* of symmetry as one of its properties. Therefore any model we adopt must also be of this type and, for example, cannot be a mass point. It will be sufficient for our purposes to use the simplest model which has this property. This is the *rigid rotator* or *dumbbell diatomic molecule*, and it consists of two particles at the constant distance a apart; the energy associated with the motion with respect to the center of mass is given in terms of the reduced mass m' by

$$\varepsilon_r = \frac{1}{2m'a^2}\left(p_\theta{}^2 + \frac{p_\varphi{}^2}{\sin^2\theta}\right) \tag{24-5}$$

as can be seen from (I: Exercise 10-1). If the z axis is chosen to be along the external field, then θ in (24-5) is the angle between $\mathbf{B}$ and the line connecting the two particles; since this line is the only axis of symmetry, it necessarily coincides with the direction of $\mathbf{\mu}$, and hence θ is also the same angle used in (24-1).

The total energy ε_i of a particle in a cell is then found, from (22-1), (24-1), and (24-5), to have the form

$$\varepsilon_i = \varepsilon_0{}'' + \frac{p_\varphi{}^2}{2m'a^2\sin^2\theta} - \mu B\cos\theta \tag{24-6}$$

where $\varepsilon_0{}''$ is independent of θ and B. We can multiply (24-3) by $d\Omega_\mu/h^5$ and write it as an integral where

$$d\Omega_\mu = dx\,dy\,dz\,d\theta\,d\varphi\,dp_x\,dp_y\,dp_z\,dp_\theta\,dp_\varphi$$

and also use (24-6) for ε_i; the result is that Z_0 has the form

$$Z_0 = Z_0{}'' \int_0^\pi e^{\beta\mu B\cos\theta}\,d\theta \int_{-\infty}^{\infty} e^{-\beta p_\varphi{}^2/2m'a^2\sin^2\theta}\,dp_\varphi \tag{24-7}$$

where $Z_0{}''$ is independent of B. If we integrate over p_φ with the aid of (18-9a), we find that (24-7) becomes

$$Z_0 = Z_0{}' \int_0^\pi e^{\beta\mu B\cos\theta}\sin\theta\,d\theta = Z_0{}'Z_B \tag{24-8}$$

where Z_0' is independent of B. We can evaluate Z_B by setting $x = \cos\theta$ so that

$$Z_B = \int_{-1}^{1} e^{\beta\mu Bx}\, dx = \frac{2\sinh\beta\mu B}{\beta\mu B} \tag{24-9}$$

If we substitute (24-8) into (24-4), note that $\ln Z_0 = \ln Z_0' + \ln Z_B$, use (24-9) and (21-60), we obtain

$$\mathscr{M} = \frac{N}{\beta}\frac{\partial\ln Z_B}{\partial B} = N\mu\left[\operatorname{ctnh}\left(\frac{\mu B}{kT}\right) - \frac{kT}{\mu B}\right] = \mathscr{M}_0\mathscr{B}\left(\frac{\mu B}{kT}\right) \tag{24-10}$$

where

$$\alpha = \frac{\mu B}{kT} \tag{24-11}$$

and the function

$$\mathscr{B}(\alpha) = \operatorname{ctnh}\alpha - \frac{1}{\alpha} \tag{24-12}$$

is called the *Langevin function*; also,

$$\mathscr{M}_0 = N\mu \tag{24-13}$$

is the value of $\mathscr{M}$ when all the individual dipoles are parallel to the field; $\mathscr{M}_0$ therefore is the maximum possible value of the total moment and is called the *saturation moment*.

The general dependence of $\mathscr{B}(\alpha)$ on α is shown in Fig. 24-1. As $\alpha \to \infty$, corresponding to large fields and low temperatures,

$$\operatorname{ctnh}\alpha \xrightarrow[\alpha\to\infty]{} \frac{e^{\alpha}}{e^{\alpha}} = 1$$

so that we can approximate $\mathscr{B}$ by

$$\mathscr{B}(\alpha) = 1 - \frac{1}{\alpha} + \cdots \qquad (\alpha \gg 1) \tag{24-14}$$

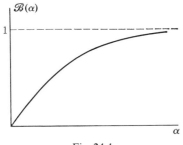

Fig. 24-1

showing that $\mathscr{B}(\alpha) \to 1$ as $\alpha \to \infty$ as indicated in the figure. At the other extreme, generally corresponding to low fields and high temperatures, $\alpha \ll 1$, and if we use the series expansion for ctnh α we find that

$$\mathscr{B}(\alpha) = \frac{\alpha}{3} - \frac{\alpha^3}{45} + \cdots \qquad (\alpha \ll 1) \qquad (24\text{-}15)$$

showing that the initial slope of the curve in Fig. 24-1 is

$$\mathscr{B}'(\alpha)_0 = \left(\frac{d\mathscr{B}}{d\alpha}\right)_{\alpha=0} = \frac{1}{3} \qquad (24\text{-}16)$$

If α is extremely small, we need use only the first term of (24-15), and (24-10) becomes

$$\mathscr{M} = \frac{1}{3}\mathscr{M}_0\alpha = \frac{N\mu^2 B}{3kT} = \left(\frac{N\mu^2\mu_0}{3k}\right)\frac{H}{T} = \frac{\mathscr{C}H}{T} \qquad (24\text{-}17)$$

with the use of the good approximation, $B \simeq \mu_0 H$. Equation (24-17) is the *Curie law* (14-14) which we discussed earlier. Thus we have obtained a theoretical expression for the Curie constant

$$\mathscr{C} = \frac{\mu_0 N\mu^2}{3k} \qquad (24\text{-}18)$$

It enables us to determine the magnitudes of the molecular dipole moments from measurements of the magnetic susceptibility of various materials. We also see that the Curie law is a special case of the Langevin magnetic equation of state (24-10) which itself is seen to be a function of the ratio $B/T \simeq \mu_0 H/T$ and thus describes an ideal magnetic material according to (14-13).

24-2   Weiss theory of ferromagnetism

A notable characteristic of ferromagnetic materials, such as the metals iron, nickel, and cobalt, is that they can have a net magnetization in the absence of a field. Below a temperature characteristic of the material, the magnetization is very large, is virtually independent of the external field, and is almost independent of the temperature over a large temperature range.

According to current ideas about ferromagnetism, the elementary magnetic moments interact very strongly with each other. Strictly speaking, therefore, they are *not* independent; hence the classical Boltzmann statistical mechanics we have been using should not be applicable. Weiss, however, made use of a simple artifice in order to apply the independent particle results even for ferromagnetic materials; in this manner, he obtained a surprisingly satisfactory theory.

Since the magnetization is relatively independent of the external field, we can conclude that the *actual* field acting on an individual magnetic moment is much larger than the external field. Thus we try to describe the over-all effect of the interactions within the system by an *internal field* H_i which we assume to be proportional to the total moment:

$$H_i = \lambda \mathcal{M} \tag{24-19}$$

In (24-19), λ is an empirical constant which is very large and characteristic of the material. Thus the *effective field* H_e acting on the magnetic moment is to be taken as

$$H_e = H + H_i = H + \lambda \mathcal{M} \tag{24-20}$$

We now use H_e in the Langevin formulas:

$$\alpha = \frac{\mu \mu_0 H_e}{kT} = \frac{\mu_0 \mathcal{M}_0}{NkT}(H + \lambda \mathcal{M}) \tag{24-21}$$

$$\mathcal{M} = \mathcal{M}_0 \mathcal{B}(\alpha) = \mathcal{M}_0 \mathcal{B}\left[\frac{\mu_0 \mathcal{M}_0}{NkT}(H + \lambda \mathcal{M})\right] \tag{24-22}$$

The last equation is the *Weiss equation of state*.

If $\alpha \ll 1$, we can take $\mathcal{B}(\alpha) \simeq \frac{1}{3}\alpha$ by (24-15), so that (24-22) becomes

$$\mathcal{M} = \frac{\mu_0 \mathcal{M}_0^2}{3NkT}(H + \lambda \mathcal{M})$$

which can be solved for $\mathcal{M}$; the result is

$$\mathcal{M} = \frac{\mathscr{C}H}{T - \theta_c} \tag{24-23}$$

where $\mathscr{C}$ is given by (24-18) and

$$\theta_c = \lambda \mathscr{C} \tag{24-24}$$

is called the *Curie temperature*. Equation (24-23) is known as the *Curie-Weiss law*; P. Curie had found that (24-23) describes quite accurately the experimental results for the "paramagnetic" moment of ferromagnetic materials, that is, the field proportional moment above the characteristic temperature of the system. The value of θ_c can be determined most easily from a plot of the reciprocal of the ratio of total moment to field as a function of T as shown in Fig. 24-2. We also see from (24-23) that the slope of this curve is $1/\mathscr{C}$. Once θ_c and $\mathscr{C}$ have been determined, the value of λ can be found from (24-24). In this way it has been shown that the observed values of λ are about a thousand times larger than can be accounted for by any classical theory; these large internal fields are now generally regarded as basically a phenomenon of quantum theory.

When α is not small compared to unity, we can proceed differently. We

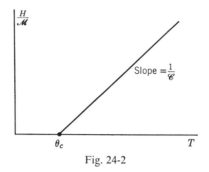

Fig. 24-2

obtain the following two equations from (24-21) and (24-22) with the use of (24-18) and (24-24):

$$\frac{\mathscr{M}}{\mathscr{M}_0} = \mathscr{B}(\alpha) \tag{24-25a}$$

$$\frac{\mathscr{M}}{\mathscr{M}_0} = \frac{T}{3\theta_c} \alpha - \frac{H}{\lambda \mathscr{M}_0} \tag{24-25b}$$

These are simultaneous equations which must be satisfied by $\mathscr{M}/\mathscr{M}_0$; in other words, if both of these equations are plotted as a function of α, the value of $\mathscr{M}/\mathscr{M}_0$ which simultaneously satisfies the equations (24-25) is that given by the intersection of the two curves. This graphical calculation is illustrated in Fig. 24-3.

The case $H = 0$ is of particular interest, and, as shown in Fig. 24-4, it is still possible for the curves to intersect at a value of $\mathscr{M} \neq 0$. In other words, the Weiss theory predicts that it is possible for the system to be magnetized in the absence of an external field as is observed for ferromagnetic materials; this net magnetic moment $\mathscr{M}_s$ is called the *spontaneous moment*. As T increases, the slope of the straight line (24-25b)

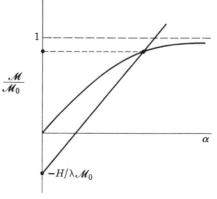

Fig. 24-3

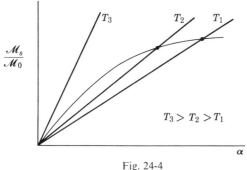

$T_3 > T_2 > T_1$

Fig. 24-4

increases so that the point of intersection moves down toward the origin as is also illustrated in Fig. 24-4. Thus the spontaneous moment decreases as the temperature increases. We also see from the same figure that the spontaneous moment will be zero when the slope of the straight line (24-25*b*) is greater than or equal to the initial slope of the Langevin function. Thus, from (24-25*b*) and (24-16), we find that $\mathcal{M}_s = 0$ when $T/3\theta_c \geqslant \frac{1}{3}$, or

$$\mathcal{M}_s = 0 \quad \text{when } T \geqslant \theta_c \qquad (24\text{-}26)$$

Thus the Curie temperature θ_c is not only the temperature at which the Curie-Weiss law (24-23) becomes meaningless, but it is also the highest temperature for which a spontaneous moment is possible.

It will be left as an exercise to calculate the numerical values of $\mathcal{M}_s/\mathcal{M}_0$ as a function of T/θ_c by the graphical method of Fig. 24-4. The general appearance of the resultant curve is shown in Fig. 24-5, and it agrees with the over-all trend observed for most ferromagnetic systems.

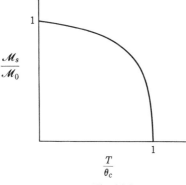

Fig. 24-5

24-3 Heat capacities

Let us investigate the properties of the heat capacities of a system described by the Weiss theory. We previously found the difference in the heat capacities at constant field and constant magnetic moment to be given by (14-21) as

$$C_H - C_{\mathscr{M}} = -\mu_0 T \left(\frac{\partial H}{\partial T}\right)_{\mathscr{M}} \left(\frac{\partial \mathscr{M}}{\partial T}\right)_H \qquad (24\text{-}27)$$

We shall have to evaluate the required derivatives indirectly since we have not obtained an explicit expression for $\mathscr{M}(H, T)$.

If we differentiate (24-22) with respect to T while keeping $\mathscr{M}$ constant. we obtain

$$0 = \mathscr{B}'(\alpha)\left(\frac{\partial \alpha}{\partial T}\right)_{\mathscr{M}} \qquad (24\text{-}28)$$

where

$$\mathscr{B}'(\alpha) = \frac{d\mathscr{B}}{d\alpha} \qquad (24\text{-}29)$$

Therefore, from (24-21) and (24-28), we obtain

$$\left(\frac{\partial \alpha}{\partial T}\right)_{\mathscr{M}} = 0 = -\frac{\mu\mu_0 H_e}{kT^2} + \frac{\mu_0 \mathscr{M}_0}{NkT}\left(\frac{\partial H}{\partial T}\right)_{\mathscr{M}}$$

$$= -\frac{\alpha}{T} + \frac{\mu_0 \mathscr{M}_0}{NkT}\left(\frac{\partial H}{\partial T}\right)_{\mathscr{M}}$$

so that

$$\left(\frac{\partial H}{\partial T}\right)_{\mathscr{M}} = \frac{Nk\alpha}{\mu_0 \mathscr{M}_0} \qquad (24\text{-}30)$$

Similarly, we differentiate (24-22) with respect to T at constant H to obtain

$$\left(\frac{\partial \mathscr{M}}{\partial T}\right)_H = \mathscr{M}_0 \mathscr{B}'(\alpha)\left(\frac{\partial \alpha}{\partial T}\right)_H$$

$$= \mathscr{M}_0 \mathscr{B}'(\alpha)\left[-\frac{\alpha}{T} + \frac{\mu_0 \mathscr{M}_0 \lambda}{NkT}\left(\frac{\partial \mathscr{M}}{\partial T}\right)_H\right]$$

The result of solving this equation for $(\partial \mathscr{M}/\partial T)_H$ and using (24-18) and (24-24) is

$$\left(\frac{\partial \mathscr{M}}{\partial T}\right)_H = -\frac{\alpha \mathscr{M}_0 \mathscr{B}'(\alpha)}{T - 3\theta_c \mathscr{B}'(\alpha)} \qquad (24\text{-}31)$$

If we substitute (24-30) and (24-31) into (24-27), we obtain

$$C_H - C_{\mathcal{M}} = \frac{Nk\alpha^2 \mathscr{B}'(\alpha)}{1 - 3(\theta_c/T)\mathscr{B}'(\alpha)} \qquad (24\text{-}32)$$

We shall consider only the case $H = 0$, $\mathcal{M} = \mathcal{M}_s$, and therefore

$$\alpha = \frac{\mu_0 \mathcal{M}_0 \lambda}{NkT} \mathcal{M}_s \qquad (24\text{-}33)$$

by (24-21).

If $T > \theta_c$, $\mathcal{M}_s = 0$ by (24-26) and therefore $\alpha = 0$; we then find from (24-32) that $C_H = C_{\mathcal{M}}$. Thus, above the Curie temperature, the heat capacities are equal in the absence of an external field, as we would expect for this unmagnetized state.

We now want to evaluate (24-32) for temperatures less than the Curie temperature yet very close to θ_c, that is, $T < \theta_c$ and $T \simeq \theta_c$. We see from Figs. 24-4 and 24-5 that $\mathcal{M}_s \simeq 0$, so that $\alpha \ll 1$. We can accordingly use the following approximations obtained from (24-22), (24-15), (24-24), (24-18), and (24-33):

$$\frac{\mathcal{M}_s}{\mathcal{M}_0} \simeq \frac{\alpha}{3}\left(1 - \frac{\alpha^2}{15}\right)$$

$$\mathscr{B}'(\alpha) \simeq \frac{1}{3}\left(1 - \frac{\alpha^2}{5}\right)$$

$$\frac{3\theta_c}{T} = \frac{\lambda\mu_0\mathcal{M}_0^2}{NkT} = \alpha \frac{\mathcal{M}_0}{\mathcal{M}_s} \simeq \frac{3}{[1 - (\alpha^2/15)]} \simeq 3\left(1 + \frac{\alpha^2}{15}\right)$$

$$\frac{3\theta_c}{T}\mathscr{B}'(\alpha) \simeq \left(1 + \frac{\alpha^2}{15}\right)\left(1 - \frac{\alpha^2}{5}\right) \simeq 1 - \frac{2\alpha^2}{15}$$

When these expressions are substituted into (24-32), we obtain

$$C_H - C_{\mathcal{M}} = \frac{5}{2} Nk\left(1 - \frac{\alpha^2}{5}\right) \xrightarrow[\alpha \to 0]{} \frac{5}{2} Nk \qquad (24\text{-}34)$$

Therefore the heat capacities differ by $\frac{5}{2}Nk$ immediately below the Curie temperature and are equal right above this temperature. Similar results can be obtained for the more general situation in which $H \neq 0$. In other words, there is a *discontinuity* in the heat capacities at the Curie temperature. Experimentally, jumps in the heat capacity of this order of magnitude are indeed observed for ferromagnetic materials.

The Weiss theory thus provides us with an example of a *second order phase transition* since we previously saw after (15-30) that such a transition is characterized by a heat capacity discontinuity. This type of transition is also called an *order-disorder transition* because the system changes from the highly ordered ferromagnetic state in which the elementary dipoles are essentially parallel to the very disordered "paramagnetic" state in which the dipoles are randomly oriented. Since the disordered state corresponds to many more possible microstates, it also has a greater entropy so that the heat capacity must rise suddenly as the transition point is approached in order to produce the large entropy change which is required.

Exercises

24-1. In a simple derivation of Langevin paramagnetism, one assumes that the probability dW that the direction of the dipole μ is in the solid angle $d\omega = \sin \theta \, d\theta \, d\varphi$ and hence that μ has the z component $\mu \cos \theta$ is given by $dW = \text{const.} \, e^{-\beta \varepsilon_m} \, d\omega$. Show that this assumption also leads to (24-10). Why does this method give the correct answer?

24-2. Calculate the numerical values of $\mathcal{M}_s/\mathcal{M}_0$ as a function of T/θ_c and thus construct an accurate version of Fig. 24-5.

24-3. Show that the Weiss theory of ferromagnetism violates the third law by showing that $(d\mathcal{M}_s/dT)_{T=0} \neq 0$.

25 *The equipartition theorem and applications*

The question of how the total energy of a system in equilibrium can be associated with average contributions from various aspects of its motion is partially answered by the famous general result of classical statistical mechanics called the *equipartition theorem*. After we have obtained this result, we shall apply it to a few examples whose diversity will illustrate anew the over-all power and applicability of statistical mechanical methods.

25-1 Separate contributions to the heat capacity

If we let $\bar{\varepsilon}$ be the average energy of one of the independent subsystems, we see from (21-36) that

$$\bar{\varepsilon} = \frac{U}{N} = -\frac{\partial \ln Z_0}{\partial \beta} \tag{25-1}$$

We can also define a subsystem heat capacity $\bar{c}_v$ by

$$\bar{c}_v = \left(\frac{\partial \bar{\varepsilon}}{\partial T}\right)_V \tag{25-2}$$

so that the heat capacity of the whole system is given by

$$C_v = N\bar{c}_v \tag{25-3}$$

Frequently the energy ε_i can be written as a sum of terms each of which involves variables which do not appear in any other term; that is, ε_i has the form

$$\varepsilon_i = \varepsilon_a(p_a, q_a) + \varepsilon_b(p_b, q_b) + \cdots \tag{25-4}$$

where (p_a, q_a) stands for the whole *set* of variables in ε_a, (p_b, q_b) is the set of different variables in ε_b, etc.

Writing the partition function as an integral over μ-space in the usual way by means of (22-20), we see that it can be written as a product:

$$Z_0 = \frac{1}{h^l} \int e^{-\beta\varepsilon_a - \beta\varepsilon_b - \cdots} dp_1 \cdots dq_l = \frac{Z_a Z_b \cdots}{h^l} \tag{25-5}$$

where

$$Z_j = \int e^{-\beta\varepsilon_j} (dq_j\, dp_j) \tag{25-6}$$

and involves an integration over all the variables involved in ε_j as symbolized by $(dq_j\, dp_j)$. Substituting (25-5) into (25-1), we see that $\bar{\varepsilon}$ becomes

$$\bar{\varepsilon} = -\frac{\partial \ln Z_a}{\partial \beta} - \frac{\partial \ln Z_b}{\partial \beta} - \cdots = \bar{\varepsilon}_a + \bar{\varepsilon}_b + \cdots \tag{25-7}$$

and is in the form of a sum of contributions from the individual terms in (25-4). Similarly, we find from (25-2) and (25-7) that the heat capacity can also be written as a sum of separate contributions:

$$\bar{c}_v = \left(\frac{\partial \bar{\varepsilon}_a}{\partial T}\right)_V + \left(\frac{\partial \bar{\varepsilon}_b}{\partial T}\right)_V + \cdots = \bar{c}_{va} + \bar{c}_{vb} + \cdots \tag{25-8}$$

Example. Linear Harmonic Oscillator. We see from (20-3) that ε can be written in the form (25-4) as the sum of a kinetic energy term and a potential energy term. From (25-6) and (18-9) it is seen that

$$Z_a = \int_{-\infty}^{\infty} e^{-\beta p^2/2m}\, dp = \left(\frac{2\pi m}{\beta}\right)^{1/2}$$

$$Z_b = \int_{-\infty}^{\infty} e^{-\frac{1}{2}\beta m\omega^2 q^2}\, dq = \left(\frac{2\pi}{\beta m\omega^2}\right)^{1/2}$$

and, therefore,

$$\ln Z_a = -\tfrac{1}{2}\ln \beta + \tfrac{1}{2}\ln (2\pi m)$$

so that

$$\bar{\varepsilon}_a = \bar{\varepsilon}_{\text{kin}} = -\frac{\partial \ln Z_a}{\partial \beta} = \frac{1}{2\beta} = \tfrac{1}{2}kT \qquad (25\text{-}9)$$

Similarly,

$$\bar{\varepsilon}_b = \bar{\varepsilon}_{\text{pot}} = \tfrac{1}{2}kT, \quad \bar{c}_{v\,\text{kin}} = \bar{c}_{v\,\text{pot}} = \tfrac{1}{2}k \qquad (25\text{-}10)$$

and, because of (25-7) and (25-8),

$$\bar{\varepsilon} = kT, \quad \bar{c}_v = k \qquad (25\text{-}11)$$

This example shows that the kinetic and potential energies of the oscillator contribute equally to its average energy; it is also a known result of mechanics that the time averages of the kinetic and potential energies of an oscillator are equal.

25-2   Equipartition theorem

It follows from (21-33) and (21-35) that

$$w_i = \frac{n_i}{N} = \frac{e^{-\beta \varepsilon_i}}{Z_0} \qquad (25\text{-}12)$$

is the probability that a subsystem will be found in the ith cell of volume $d\Omega_\mu = h^l$ in μ-space.

Let us consider the following average:

$$\overline{p_1 \frac{\partial \varepsilon}{\partial p_1}} = \frac{1}{h^l Z_0} \int p_1 \frac{\partial \varepsilon}{\partial p_1} e^{-\beta \varepsilon} dp_1 \cdots dp_l \, dq_1 \cdots dq_l \qquad (25\text{-}13)$$

where

$$h^l Z_0 = \int e^{-\beta \varepsilon} dp_1 \cdots dp_l \, dq_1 \cdots dq_l \qquad (25\text{-}14)$$

If we first integrate by parts with respect to p_1, noting that, for this purpose,

$$\frac{\partial \varepsilon}{\partial p_1} e^{-\beta \varepsilon} dp_1 = d\left(-\frac{e^{-\beta \varepsilon}}{\beta} \right)$$

the integral in (25-13) becomes

$$\int dp_2 \cdots dq_l \left[-\frac{p_1}{\beta} e^{-\beta \varepsilon} \right]_{p_1\,\text{min}}^{p_1\,\text{max}} + \frac{1}{\beta} \int dp_2 \cdots dq_l \int e^{-\beta \varepsilon} dp_1 \qquad (25\text{-}15)$$

Usually a momentum ranges from $-\infty$ to $+\infty$, and $\varepsilon \to \infty$ at these limits; consequently $e^{-\beta \varepsilon} = 0$ at the limits $p_1\,\text{max}$ and $p_1\,\text{min}$, so that the first integral in (25-15) vanishes. All that remains in (25-15) is the second integral which equals $h^l Z_0/\beta$ by (25-14); substituting this resultant value for the integral of (25-13), we find that

$$\overline{p_1 \frac{\partial \varepsilon}{\partial p_1}} = \frac{1}{\beta} = kT \qquad (25\text{-}16)$$

The same result would have been obtained for any choice of p_j, and therefore we can say in general that

$$\overline{p_j \frac{\partial \varepsilon}{\partial p_j}} = kT \qquad (25\text{-}17)$$

Proceeding in exactly the same manner, we find that

$$\overline{q_j \frac{\partial \varepsilon}{\partial q_j}} = kT \qquad (25\text{-}18)$$

provided that

$$\left[q_j e^{-\beta \varepsilon} \right]_{q_j \min}^{q_j \max} = 0 \qquad (25\text{-}19)$$

The last condition will be valid for all the cases to which we shall apply (25-18); for example, from (20-4) it is easily seen to hold for the oscillator and also for the free particle in a box according to the discussion in connection with (22-8).

In order to apply these results in a general manner we shall let $p_1, \ldots, p_l, q_1, \ldots, q_l$ be denoted by $x_1, x_2, \ldots, x_{2l}$ which are chosen in an appropriate order as shown below. Let us suppose that

$$\varepsilon = \varepsilon' + \varepsilon'' \qquad (25\text{-}20)$$

where

$$\varepsilon' = \sum_{i=1}^{f} \sum_{k=1}^{f} a_{ik}(x_{f+1}, \ldots, x_{2l}) x_i x_k \qquad (f \leqslant 2l) \qquad (25\text{-}21)$$

and where $\varepsilon'' = \varepsilon''(x_{f+1}, \ldots, x_{2l})$ and, in addition, ε'' has no quadratic parts. Therefore the variables $x_1, \ldots, x_f$ appear only quadratically in the energy expression, while the rest do not appear quadratically. In all practical cases, ε' will be a positive quadratic form, so that $\varepsilon \to \infty$ if $x_i \to \pm \infty$ and (25-17) and (25-18) therefore apply to ε. If $j = 1, 2, \ldots, f$, then it follows from (25-20) and (25-21) that

$$x_j \frac{\partial \varepsilon}{\partial x_j} = x_j \frac{\partial \varepsilon'}{\partial x_j} = x_j \left(\sum_i a_{ij} x_i + \sum_k a_{jk} x_k \right)$$

and therefore

$$\sum_{j=1}^{f} x_j \frac{\partial \varepsilon}{\partial x_j} = \sum_{i,j} a_{ij} x_i x_j + \sum_{j,k} a_{jk} x_j x_k = 2\varepsilon'$$

If we solve for ε' and use (25-17) and (25-18), we obtain

$$\overline{\varepsilon'} = \frac{1}{2} \sum_{j=1}^{f} \overline{x_j \frac{\partial \varepsilon}{\partial x_j}} = \frac{1}{2} \sum_{j=1}^{f} kT = \frac{1}{2} fkT \tag{25-22}$$

which is our desired result. It can also be stated as:

EQUIPARTITION THEOREM. Any dynamical variable (p or q) which appears in the energy ε of a subsystem quadratically, and *only* quadratically, contributes $\frac{1}{2}kT$ to the average energy $\bar{\varepsilon}$ and, therefore, $\frac{1}{2}k$ to the subsystem heat capacity $\bar{c}_v$.

This theorem is a purely classical result since it depends on our use of integrals to evaluate the averages in μ-space.

Example. Monatomic Gas. According to (22-8),

$$\varepsilon = \frac{1}{2m} (p_x{}^2 + p_y{}^2 + p_z{}^2)$$

in the container. Since there are *three* dynamical variables entering quadratically, we obtain

$$\bar{\varepsilon} = \tfrac{3}{2}kT, \quad \bar{c}_v = \tfrac{3}{2}k, \quad U = \tfrac{3}{2}NkT, \quad c_v = \tfrac{3}{2}R$$

which agree with our previous results (17-14) and (17-17) which were obtained in a more detailed manner.

Example. Rigid Rotator. If we neglect external forces such as gravity, we find from (22-1) and (24-5) that

$$\varepsilon = \frac{1}{2m} (p_x{}^2 + p_y{}^2 + p_z{}^2) + \frac{1}{2m'a^2} \left(p_\theta{}^2 + \frac{p_\varphi{}^2}{\sin^2 \theta} \right) \tag{25-23}$$

Thus we have five variables entering in the proper way; the coefficient of $p_\varphi{}^2$ is independent of the variables which do appear quadratically in (25-23). Therefore

$$\bar{\varepsilon} = \tfrac{5}{2}kT, \quad \bar{c}_v = \tfrac{5}{2}k$$

so that, if we use (9-13), the molar heat capacities are

$$c_v = \frac{5}{2}R, \quad c_p = \frac{7}{2}R, \quad \frac{c_p}{c_v} = \frac{7}{5} = 1.40 \tag{25-24}$$

These results agree very well with the measured heat capacities of diatomic gases. In this example, we could say that $\bar{\varepsilon}$ has a translational contribution of $\frac{3}{2}kT$ and a rotational contribution of $\frac{2}{2}kT$.

25-3 Monatomic crystals

We consider only the crystal type for which there are N atoms, rather than molecules, at the lattice points; an example of such a crystal is a diamond. In a real crystal there are large forces binding the atoms together; hence we certainly cannot consider the N atoms to be independent subsystems. However, if the displacements of the atoms from their equilibrium positions are not too large, we can determine an appropriate choice of subsystems by using some of the results from the mechanics of coupled systems as discussed for example in (I: Chapter 12).

For small displacements u_j, the potential energy of the system has the form

$$V = \tfrac{1}{2} \sum_{j,k} v_{jk} u_j u_k$$

where the v_{jk} are constants. If one introduces the normal coordinates ζ_j, the potential energy takes the form

$$V = \sum_j \tfrac{1}{2}\,\omega_j{}^2 \zeta_j{}^2$$

where the ω_j are the normal (circular) frequencies of the coupled system. The Lagrangian then has the form

$$L = \sum_j \tfrac{1}{2}(\dot{\zeta}_j{}^2 - \omega_j{}^2 \zeta_j{}^2)$$

and the Hamiltonian becomes

$$H = \sum_j \tfrac{1}{2}(p_j{}^2 + \omega_j{}^2 \zeta_j{}^2) \qquad (25\text{-}25)$$

where p_j is the generalized momentum conjugate to the normal coordinate ζ_j. Therefore we see from (25-25) that the coupled system is completely equivalent to a collection of *independent harmonic oscillators*. In other words, the independent subsystems are the *normal modes* of the coupled system; the Hamiltonian (25-25) is of the form we assumed in (21-1), so that all our results are applicable to the monatomic crystal considered as a superposition of its normal modes.

We have seen in (25-11) that the average energy of an oscillator with its two quadratic variables is kT, so that the average energy of the jth normal mode of the crystal is

$$\bar{\varepsilon}_j = kT \qquad (25\text{-}26)$$

For the N particles, $3N$ coordinates will be needed. Of this number, three will describe translations of the crystal as a whole, and three the

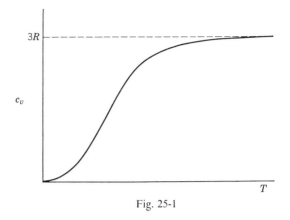

Fig. 25-1

rotation. Hence there will be $3N - 6$ coordinates describing the oscillations, so that there will be $3N - 6$ normal modes of the crystal, each of which will contribute kT to the total energy U. Therefore

$$U = (3N - 6)kT \simeq 3NkT \qquad (25\text{-}27)$$

Using (17-14') and (9-14), we find the molar energy to be $u = 3RT$, so that the molar heat capacity is

$$c_v = 3R \simeq 6 \text{ kilocalories/kilomole-degree} \qquad (25\text{-}28)$$

The last result is the famous *empirical* law of Dulong and Petit, and we see how it is accounted for by classical statistical mechanics. The theory predicts not only that these solids should all have about the same heat capacity but also that c_v should be independent of temperature, and this is found to be approximately true. However, (25-28) cannot be completely correct because it violates the third law of thermodynamics from which we found that c_v should vanish as $T \to 0$; the experimental values of c_v for solids depend on temperature in the manner shown in Fig. 25-1 and begin to decrease from the Dulong-Petit value (25-28) at a temperature characteristic of the material. We shall return to this problem in the next chapter.

25-4   Thermal radiation

The next application of the equipartition theorem will be to a system which is a continuum, in contrast to the systems of discrete particles considered up to this point. The system consists of the electromagnetic fields in a box and in equilibrium with the walls of the box which are at the temperature T. In this way we can ascribe the temperature T to the electromagnetic energy, which is accordingly called *thermal radiation* or *black-body radiation*.

First of all, we shall use the second law of thermodynamics to show that, when a body is in temperature equilibrium with the radiation in the box, the radiation can be described by giving the energy density for the various frequencies, and that this energy density is a universal function of the temperature only.

Let us consider a box with perfectly reflecting walls which neither emit nor absorb radiation. The electromagnetic energy in the box is therefore isolated from its surroundings. Suppose we now assume that two different objects (1 and 2) are placed in the box and kept at the same temperature T. In addition, let us assume that we can place a filter between the objects so that the box is divided into two portions as shown in Fig. 25-2. The filter is assumed to be perfectly transparent for a single frequency ν and is perfectly reflecting for all other frequencies.

First we assume that the box is divided by a screen that is perfectly reflecting for *all* frequencies, thus isolating the two bodies from each other in their own portions of the box. Each body will separately absorb and emit radiation until it reaches equilibrium, that is, until the energy density about it is high enough that it absorbs as much energy as it radiates. Let us assume, for example, that the energy density of the radiation of frequency ν in equilibrium with body 1 is greater than for 2, that is, $u_{1\nu} > u_{2\nu}$. Were we now to imagine the filter for frequency ν to be put into position, there would be a net flow of electromagnetic energy through this screen from side 1 to side 2. As this would decrease $u_{1\nu}$, body 1 would emit more than it absorbs while the converse would be true for body 2. The net effect of the introduction of the filter would therefore be a transfer of energy between two objects at the same temperature without any work having been done in the process. Since this would violate the second law,

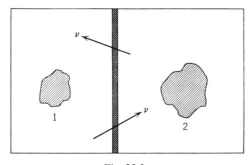

Fig. 25-2

we conclude that our initial assumption that $u_{1\nu} > u_{2\nu}$ is invalid. Similarly, we would find that $u_{2\nu} > u_{1\nu}$ is not possible; therefore the only possibility is $u_{1\nu} = u_{2\nu} = u_\nu$, so that the density at frequency ν is independent of the nature of the bodies in equilibrium with the radiation.

Since we can assume a filter for each possible frequency, we shall obtain the same result for every frequency. Therefore if we define a density function u by

> Electromagnetic energy per unit volume with frequencies
> in the range ν to $\nu + d\nu$ which is in equilibrium at
> a temperature $T = u(\nu, T) \, d\nu$ (25-29)

we know that $u(\nu, T)$ is a universal function of frequency and temperature. Our aim now is to calculate this function.

We can get an idea about how to proceed by recalling the results for the monatomic crystal; we introduced the normal modes and used the fact that the Hamiltonian of the system then corresponded to a collection of independent oscillators. Similarly, it is found in the study of cavities and wave guides that the electromagnetic fields in an enclosure can be written as superpositions of independent normal modes as discussed, for example, in (I: Chapter 30). Each normal mode in an enclosure is a standing wave which varies with time as $e^{-2\pi i\nu t}$ and thus is equivalent to a one-dimensional harmonic oscillator. Therefore we can again treat this system as a collection of *independent harmonic oscillators*. As we shall see below, if the box is sufficiently large, the frequencies are very close together and will have an almost continuous distribution. Accordingly, the principal problem in finding $u(\nu, T) \, d\nu$ is to find the number dZ of independent normal modes between ν and $\nu + d\nu$ since then we shall have the total energy in the frequency range given by

$$u(\nu, T)V \, d\nu = \overline{\varepsilon(\nu)}_{\text{osc}} \, dZ \qquad (25\text{-}30)$$

where V is the total volume.

If we consider a rectangular box of sides A, B, C whose walls are perfectly conducting and therefore perfectly reflecting, the frequencies of the normal modes are given by (I: 30-14) as

$$\left(\frac{2\nu}{c}\right)^2 = \left(\frac{m}{A}\right)^2 + \left(\frac{n}{B}\right)^2 + \left(\frac{p}{C}\right)^2 \qquad (25\text{-}31)$$

where m, n, and p are positive integers. Let us first find the number of modes whose frequency is less than a given frequency ν, that is, the number of possible sets of m, n, p which fulfill this condition. If we plot the possible values of m, n, p in a set of rectangular axes with these indices as coordinates, we get a set of lattice points, each point corresponding to a normal frequency. The points which lie in the mn plane are shown in Fig. 25-3a. If we write (25-31) in the form

$$\left(\frac{m}{2Av/c}\right)^2 + \left(\frac{n}{2Bv/c}\right)^2 + \left(\frac{p}{2Cv/c}\right)^2 = 1 \qquad (25\text{-}32)$$

we see that the surface of constant v in the mnp space is an ellipsoid with

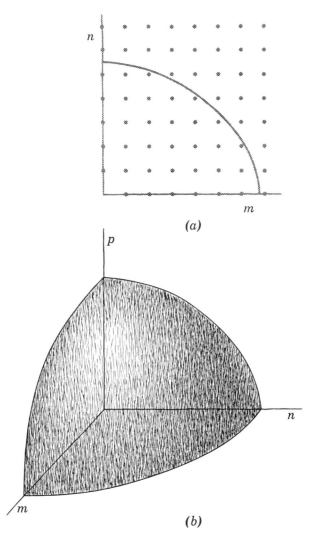

(a)

(b)

Fig. 25-3

semiaxes: $2Av/c, 2Bv/c, 2Cv/c$; this ellipsoid is shown in Fig. 25-3b, and its projection on the mn plane in Fig. 25-3a. Since m, n, and p are integers, the coordinates of the lattice points differ by unity; hence the volume corresponding to each lattice point is $1 \times 1 \times 1 = 1$.

If we let N_v be the number of normal frequencies which are less than the given frequency v, we see that N_v equals the total volume enclosed by the constant frequency surface divided by the (unit) volume associated with each lattice point. Since m, n, p are all positive, the volume involved is one-eighth that of the whole ellipsoid and therefore

$$N_v = \frac{1}{8} \times \frac{4\pi}{3} \times \left(\frac{2Av}{c}\right) \times \left(\frac{2Bv}{c}\right) \times \left(\frac{2Cv}{c}\right)$$

so that

$$N_v = \frac{4\pi V v^3}{3c^3} \tag{25-33}$$

where $V = ABC$ is the total volume of the box. The number of normal frequencies in the range dv is the differential of (25-33):

$$dN_v = \frac{4\pi V}{c^3} v^2 \, dv \tag{25-34}$$

For electromagnetic waves, however, the number of normal modes is twice as great as (25-34) because there are two independent directions of polarization which are possible for each standing wave of a given frequency, as discussed in connection with (I: 30-19). Therefore we find from (25-34) that

$$dZ = \frac{8\pi V}{c^3} v^2 \, dv \tag{25-35}$$

If we substitute this result into (25-30), we find the total energy in the frequency range v to $v + dv$ to be given by

$$U(v, T) \, dv = u(v, T)V \, dv = \frac{8\pi V}{c^3} v^2 \overline{\varepsilon(v)}_{\text{osc}} \, dv \tag{25-36}$$

so that the energy density per unit frequency interval is

$$u(v, T) = \frac{8\pi v^2}{c^3} \overline{\varepsilon(v)}_{\text{osc}} \tag{25-37}$$

If we substitute into (25-37) the value kT found for the average energy of an oscillator in (25-11), we obtain

$$u(v, T) = \frac{8\pi v^2}{c^3} kT \tag{25-38}$$

Equation (25-38) is called *the Rayleigh-Jeans law*, and we have derived it as an application of the equipartition theorem by substantially the original method. This law is in good agreement with experimental results at low enough frequencies, but it breaks down at high frequencies since we see that $u \to \infty$ as $v \to \infty$, which is physically impossible.

The examples of the heat capacity of solids and of the energy distribution of thermal radiation show that our statistical mechanics is not yet completely correct. We have obtained results which agree well with experiment in a certain range of the variables but become quite incorrect elsewhere. What we have left out of our considerations is the fact that it is quantum mechanics rather than classical mechanics which is the appropriate scheme to be used for the description of atoms and molecules. In the next two chapters, we show how the results of quantum mechanics can be incorporated into the theory of statistical mechanics.

Exercises

25-1. Show that the entropy of a system of linear harmonic oscillators as obtained from (21-64) is
$$S = Nk \ln (ekT/hv)$$
where $v = \omega/2\pi$. Show that, if (21-53) were used, the entropy would not have been extensive. What are the physical reasons for treating a system of oscillators as distinguishable?

25-2. Show that the quantities analogous to (25-17) and (25-18) are
$$\frac{\overline{c^2 p_x^{\,2}}}{\varepsilon} = \frac{\overline{c^2 p_y^{\,2}}}{\varepsilon} = \frac{\overline{c^2 p_z^{\,2}}}{\varepsilon} = kT$$

for relativistic particles where the energy dependence on momentum is given by (22-27). Use these expressions to find the heat capacity per molecule of an ideal gas in the extreme relativistic limit, and compare with the results of Exercise 22-3.

26 Classical quantum statistical mechanics

A complete discussion of the fundamentals of quantum mechanics will not be necessary for our purposes, and we shall mention only those principal results which are essential. We have already seen that the effect of the *uncertainty principle* is to make it necessary to choose the size of the cells in μ-space with the definite volume h^l as given by (22-20) where l is the number of degrees of freedom of a subsystem.

Another fundamental result of interest to us is that the energies of the system can no longer have any arbitrary value, as was possible in principle for classical mechanics. According to quantum mechanics, only certain states are possible for the system and *a definite energy corresponds to each possible state.* For the systems of most interest, these energies are usually discrete. Another useful result is that, in general, *there exists a state of lowest energy* for a given system. These allowed energies are calculated by the specific methods of quantum mechanics; the results for the only two cases which we shall need to consider are given below.

Free particle in a rectangular box of sides L_x, L_y, L_z

The classical energy as given by (22-1) is

$$\varepsilon = \frac{1}{2m}(p_x^{\ 2} + p_y^{\ 2} + p_z^{\ 2}) \tag{26-1}$$

The possible quantum mechanical energies are given by

$$\varepsilon_{n_x n_y n_z} = \frac{h^2}{8m}\left[\left(\frac{n_x}{L_x}\right)^2 + \left(\frac{n_y}{L_y}\right)^2 + \left(\frac{n_z}{L_z}\right)^2\right] \tag{26-2}$$

where $n_x = 1, 2, 3, \ldots$; $n_y = 1, 2, 3, \ldots$; $n_z = 1, 2, 3, \ldots$.

One-dimensional harmonic oscillator

The classical energy as given by (20-3) is

$$\varepsilon = \frac{p^2}{2m} + \frac{1}{2}m\omega^2 q^2 \tag{26-3}$$

The quantum energies are

$$\varepsilon_n = (n + \tfrac{1}{2})h\frac{\omega}{2\pi} = (n + \tfrac{1}{2})h\nu \tag{26-4}$$

where $n = 0, 1, 2, 3, \ldots$.

26-1 The quantum partition function

The partition function Z_0, which is so necessary for us, is defined by (21-35) as a sum over the cells in μ-space. However, from the quantum mechanical point of view, the only fundamental features of our subsystems which we can use are the possible states, and we can no longer describe the subsystems by giving their coordinates in μ-space. We must somehow be able to make a correspondence between the cells and the states. It is extremely difficult to do this rigorously; instead, we shall consider a simple example which shows quite clearly how this correspondence is obtained and which gives the correct result.

We saw in (20-4) and Fig. 20-1b that the surfaces of constant energy of the one-dimensional harmonic oscillator are the ellipses of semiaxes $\sqrt{2m\varepsilon}$ and $\sqrt{2\varepsilon/m\omega^2}$. The area enclosed by a given ellipse is

$$A = \pi\sqrt{2m\varepsilon}\sqrt{\frac{2\varepsilon}{m\omega^2}} = \frac{2\pi\varepsilon}{\omega} = \frac{\varepsilon}{\nu} \qquad (26\text{-}5)$$

According to (26-4), however, the oscillator energies are restricted to definite values and thereby correspond to particular ellipses in μ-space. In Fig. 26-1 we show the ellipses of areas A_n and A_{n+1} corresponding to the energies ε_n and ε_{n+1}. The difference in energy between these two states can be written as

$$\varepsilon_{n+1} - \varepsilon_n = h\nu = (A_{n+1} - A_n)\nu \qquad (26\text{-}6)$$

with the use of (26-4) and (26-5). Therefore the difference in area enclosed by these ellipses in μ-space is

$$A_{n+1} - A_n = h \qquad (26\text{-}7)$$

and is shown shaded in the figure. We also know from (22-20) that h is equal to the cell volume for a system of one degree of freedom. Consequently, as we go from one quantum state of the oscillator to the next, we

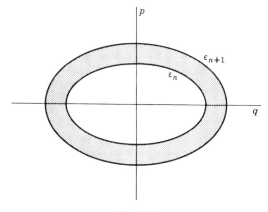

Fig. 26-1

increase the area enclosed by the ellipse by exactly the size of a cell in classical μ-space. In this way we can correlate each *state* of the oscillator with a *cell* in μ-space; the cells do not have the rectangular shapes we have been thinking about, but the size, not the shape, is the essential aspect of the argument.

Extending these results to a general system, we conclude that: *Each quantum state of a subsystem corresponds to one of the elementary cells of volume h^l*. Thus we see that a sum over cells in classical μ-space is equivalent to a sum over subsystem quantum states, and hence we can write (21-35) as

$$Z_0 = \sum_{\text{cells}} e^{-\beta\varepsilon_i} = \sum_{\substack{\text{quantum} \\ \text{states}}} e^{-\beta\varepsilon_i} \qquad (26\text{-}8)$$

In other words, we can continue to write

$$Z_0 = \sum_i e^{-\beta\varepsilon_i} \qquad (26\text{-}9)$$

except that now the index i labels each quantum state with corresponding energy ε_i. Similarly, all our basic formulas (21-36), (21-61), and (21-62) will remain unchanged and we can proceed by the same general methods as before.

As in classical mechanics, it is possible for quantum mechanical results also to have the property of *degeneracy*, that is, there can be several distinct states which have the same energy; also as in the classical case, degeneracy is generally a result of the particular symmetry possessed by the system. Often when there is degeneracy, it is convenient to group all the states with the same energy and to speak of this group as an *energy level*; the *degree of degeneracy* g_j is defined as the number of states in the level j with energy ε_j. It is clear that the sum over states (26-9) can also be written as a sum over levels as

$$Z_0 = \sum_i e^{-\beta\varepsilon_i} = \sum_j g_j e^{-\beta\varepsilon_j} \qquad (26\text{-}10)$$

Occasionally, it may be preferable to write the results in the latter way.

26-2   Subsystem with two states

As a simple but useful example, we consider a subsystem which has only two states with energies,

$$\varepsilon_1, \quad \varepsilon_2 = \varepsilon_1 + \Delta \qquad (26\text{-}11)$$

Substituting these energies into (26-9), we find that

$$Z_0 = e^{-\beta\varepsilon_1} + e^{-\beta\varepsilon_2} = e^{-\beta\varepsilon_1}(1 + e^{-\beta\Delta}) \tag{26-12}$$

$$\ln Z_0 = -\beta\varepsilon_1 + \ln(1 + e^{-\beta\Delta}) \tag{26-13}$$

We obtain the energy from (21-36) as

$$U = U_0 + \frac{N\Delta e^{-\Delta/kT}}{1 + e^{-\Delta/kT}} \tag{26-14}$$

where

$$U_0 = N\varepsilon_1 = \text{zero point energy} \tag{26-15}$$

The name "zero point energy" is used because $U \to U_0$ as $T \to 0$ since

$$e^{-\Delta/kT} \to 0$$

In the high-temperature limit, we have

$$\frac{\Delta}{kT} \ll 1, \quad e^{-\Delta/kT} \simeq 1 - \frac{\Delta}{kT} \tag{26-16}$$

and (26-14) becomes

$$U \simeq U_0 + \frac{1}{2}N\Delta\left(1 - \frac{\Delta}{2kT}\right) \tag{26-17}$$

so that $U - U_0$ approaches $\frac{1}{2}N\Delta$ for very high temperatures. The general dependence of $U - U_0$ on T is shown in Fig. 26-2.

We can understand why the energy approaches this limiting value by looking at the populations of the states. We find from (21-37), (26-11), and (26-12) that

$$n_1 = \frac{N}{1 + e^{-\Delta/kT}}, \quad n_2 = \frac{Ne^{-\Delta/kT}}{1 + e^{-\Delta/kT}} \tag{26-18}$$

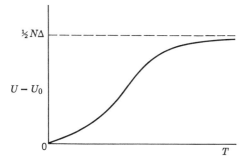

Fig. 26-2

from which we see that, as $T \to 0$, $n_1 \to N$, and $n_2 \to 0$, so that all subsystems are in the lower state. For very high temperatures, we can use (26-16) and see that, as $T \to \infty$,

$$n_1 \to \tfrac{1}{2}N, \quad n_2 \to \tfrac{1}{2}N \tag{26-19}$$

and the states become equally populated. Thus the energy becomes

$$U = n_1\varepsilon_1 + n_2\varepsilon_2 \xrightarrow[T \to \infty]{} \tfrac{1}{2}N(\varepsilon_1 + \varepsilon_2) = N\varepsilon_1 + \tfrac{1}{2}N\,\Delta$$

as found in (26-17). The populations of the two states are shown as functions of T in Fig. 26-3.

The heat capacity of the system can be found from (26-14) as

$$C_v = \left(\frac{\partial U}{\partial T}\right)_V = \left(\frac{\partial U}{\partial T}\right)_\Delta = Nk\left(\frac{\Delta/kT}{1 + e^{-\Delta/kT}}\right)^2 e^{-\Delta/kT} \tag{26-20}$$

which has the limiting forms:

$$\frac{\Delta}{kT} \gg 1: \quad C_v \simeq Nk\left(\frac{\Delta}{kT}\right)^2 e^{-\Delta/kT} \xrightarrow[T \to 0]{} 0 \tag{26-21}$$

$$\frac{\Delta}{kT} \ll 1: \quad C_v \simeq Nk\left(\frac{\Delta}{2kT}\right)^2 \xrightarrow[T \to \infty]{} 0 \tag{26-22}$$

We see that the heat capacity of this system now satisfies the third law of thermodynamics since it vanishes at absolute zero. Since C_v vanishes at both the upper and lower limits, it has a maximum which is found to occur at a temperature of about Δ/k; Fig. 26-4 shows the general temperature dependence of C_v. The physical reason for the vanishing of the heat capacity at high temperatures can be seen with the help of Fig. 26-3. Since the populations of the states become almost equal, any temperature increase has an almost negligible effect in changing the relative populations of the states; thus there is correspondingly almost no change in the energy, and this means that the heat capacity continually decreases with T and eventually is zero.

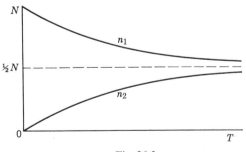

Fig. 26-3

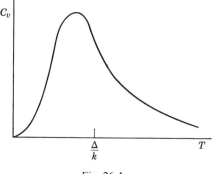

Fig. 26-4

Finally, we can briefly look at the entropy of this system. We find from (21-61), (26-13), and (26-14) that

$$\frac{S}{Nk} = \frac{(\Delta/kT)e^{-\Delta/kT}}{1 + e^{-\Delta/kT}} + \ln\left(1 + e^{-\Delta/kT}\right) + \ln\left(\frac{e}{N}\right) \qquad (26\text{-}23)$$

Using (26-16), we find the high-temperature value of (26-23) to be

$$S \underset{T \to \infty}{\longrightarrow} Nk \ln \frac{2e}{N} \qquad (26\text{-}24)$$

It is instructive to compare this result with our basic beginning formulas; if we insert (26-19) into (21-51) and (21-14), we find that

$$\frac{S}{k} = N - \tfrac{1}{2}N \ln \tfrac{1}{2}N - \tfrac{1}{2}N \ln \tfrac{1}{2}N = N \ln \frac{2e}{N}$$

which agrees exactly with (26-24).

26-3   Monatomic ideal gas

The partition function as obtained from (26-9) and (26-2) is

$$Z_0 = \sum_{n_x, n_y, n_z} e^{-(\beta h^2/8m)[(n_x/L_x)^2 + (n_y/L_y)^2 + (n_z/L_z)^2]}$$

$$= Z_x Z_y Z_z \qquad (26\text{-}25)$$

where

$$Z_j = \sum_{n_j=1}^{\infty} e^{-\beta h^2 n_j^2/8mL_j^2} = \sum_{n_j} e^{-\zeta_j n_j^2} = \sum_{n_j} e^{-\zeta_j n_j^2} \Delta n_j \qquad (26\text{-}26)$$

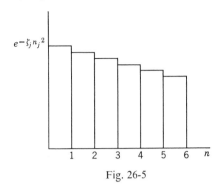

Fig. 26-5

and where

$$\zeta_j = \frac{\beta h^2}{8mL_j^2} \tag{26-27}$$

We were able to perform the last step of inserting the Δn_j in the sum in (26-26) since n_j takes on only integral values and therefore $\Delta n_j = 1$.

If the temperature is high enough, the box large enough, and m large enough, ζ_j is small according to (26-27); therefore $e^{-\zeta_j n_j^2}$ will not change very much as n_j changes in unit steps as is shown in Fig. 26-5, and we can approximate the sum (26-26) by an integral over n. In this way we obtain

$$Z_j \simeq \int_0^\infty e^{-\zeta_j n^2}\, dn = \left(\frac{\pi}{4\zeta_j}\right)^{1/2} = L_j \frac{(2\pi mkT)^{1/2}}{h} \tag{26-28}$$

with the aid of (18-9), (26-27), and (21-60). Substituting (26-28) into (26-25) and noting that $V = L_x L_y L_z$ is the volume of the box, we obtain

$$Z_0 = \frac{V}{h^3} (2\pi mkT)^{3/2} \tag{26-29}$$

which is exactly the result (22-10) previously obtained by the classical calculations, and consequently (26-29) will lead to all our previous results, such as the equation of state (22-15), for ideal gases. The result (26-29) justifies again the use of h^l as the cell size in μ-space since h entered through the quantum mechanical energy (26-2).

We note, however, that, if T is small, ζ_j as given by (26-27) will be large and it will *not* be permissible to replace the sum by an integral as we did in (26-28). Consequently, we see that the classical result (26-29) cannot be applicable at very low temperatures and we need to use a more exact calculation. We shall return to this question later.

26-4 One-dimensional harmonic oscillator

The partition function for this case is found from (26-9) and (26-4) to be

$$Z_0 = \sum_{n=0}^{\infty} e^{-\beta(n+\frac{1}{2})h\nu} = e^{-\frac{1}{2}\beta h\nu} \sum_{n=0}^{\infty} e^{-\beta n h\nu} = \frac{e^{-\frac{1}{2}\beta h\nu}}{1 - e^{-\beta h\nu}} \tag{26-30}$$

since the second sum in (26-30) is an infinite geometric series whose sum is given by

$$\sum_{n=0}^{\infty} x^n = \frac{1}{1 - x} \qquad (x < 1) \tag{26-31}$$

It is sometimes convenient to define a characteristic temperature θ of the oscillator by

$$\theta = \frac{h\nu}{k} \tag{26-32}$$

so that

$$\beta h\nu = \frac{\theta}{T} \tag{26-33}$$

Therefore Z_0 can also be written

$$Z_0 = \frac{e^{-\theta/2T}}{1 - e^{-\theta/T}} \tag{26-34}$$

From (26-30), we obtain

$$\ln Z_0 = -\tfrac{1}{2}\beta h\nu - \ln(1 - e^{-\beta h\nu}) \tag{26-35}$$

so that the average energy per oscillator as found from (25-1), (26-35), and (26-33) is

$$\bar{\varepsilon} = \frac{h\nu}{2} + \frac{h\nu}{e^{\beta h\nu} - 1} = \frac{k\theta}{2} + \frac{k\theta}{e^{\theta/T} - 1} \tag{26-36}$$

Similarly, the heat capacity per oscillator as found from (26-36) and (25-2) is

$$\bar{c}_v = k\left(\frac{\theta}{T}\right)^2 \frac{e^{\theta/T}}{(e^{\theta/T} - 1)^2} \tag{26-37}$$

The entropy per oscillator, $\bar{s} = S/N$, can be obtained from (21-64), (26-35), and (26-36); the result is

$$\bar{s} = \frac{k(\theta/T)}{e^{\theta/T} - 1} - k \ln(1 - e^{-\theta/T}) \tag{26-38}$$

We can see the nature of these results more clearly by looking at the usual extreme cases.

High temperature $(T \gg \theta)$

Since $\theta/T \ll 1$, we find from (26-36) through (26-38) that

$$\bar{\varepsilon} \simeq kT + [\text{terms of order } (\theta/T)^2] \to kT \qquad (26\text{-}39a)$$

$$\bar{c}_v \simeq k\left(1 + \frac{\theta}{T}\right) \to k \qquad (26\text{-}39b)$$

$$\bar{s} \simeq k \ln \frac{T}{\theta} + k = k \ln \frac{ekT}{h\nu} \qquad (26\text{-}39c)$$

These results agree in their limiting values for $T \to \infty$ with those of (25-11) and Exercise 25-1 found from the classical equipartition theorem.

Low temperature $(T \ll \theta)$

Similarly, since $\theta/T \gg 1$, we find that

$$\bar{\varepsilon} \simeq \tfrac{1}{2}k\theta + k\theta e^{-\theta/T} \to \tfrac{1}{2}k\theta = \tfrac{1}{2}h\nu \qquad (26\text{-}40a)$$

$$\bar{c}_v \simeq k\left(\frac{\theta}{T}\right)^2 e^{-\theta/T} \to 0 \qquad (26\text{-}40b)$$

$$\bar{s} \simeq k\frac{\theta}{T} e^{-\theta/T} \to 0 \qquad (26\text{-}40c)$$

Thus the energy approaches the zero point energy while the heat capacity becomes zero in agreement with the third law. The low-temperature limiting value of the entropy given by (26-40c) also agrees with the value zero required by the third law; this last result also shows again that the only imaginable system composed of linear oscillators is one in which each oscillator has its own equilibrium position so that they are localizable and hence distinguishable.

We have seen in this example of the oscillator that the introduction of the results of quantum theory has gone a long way toward resolving many of our previous difficulties. At high temperatures the results agreed with all our calculations based on classical mechanics. At low temperatures, where the classical results were in violent disagreement with experiment and the requirements of the third law, the results obtained with the use of quantum theory agreed with the third law. We shall now go on to show that our results also lead to much better agreement with experiment as well.

26-5 Heat capacity of monatomic crystals

We saw in our discussion of (25-25) and (25-27) that use of the normal modes enables us to treat the solid as a collection of $3N$ independent linear oscillators. Therefore, if $\bar{\varepsilon}_j$ is the average energy of the jth normal mode of frequency $\nu_j (= \omega_j/2\pi)$, the energy of the system can be found from (26-36) to be

$$U = \sum_j \bar{\varepsilon}_j = \sum_j \frac{h\nu_j}{2} + \sum_j \frac{h\nu_j}{e^{h\nu_j/kT} - 1} \tag{26-41}$$

and the heat capacity as obtained from (26-37) and (26-33) is

$$C_v = \sum_j \bar{c}_{vj} = \sum_j k \left(\frac{h\nu_j}{kT}\right)^2 \frac{e^{h\nu_j/kT}}{(e^{h\nu_j/kT} - 1)^2} \tag{26-42}$$

The sums can be evaluated once the frequencies of the normal modes of the crystal are known. In principle, the ν_j can be found from the knowledge of the mechanical properties of the crystal lattice by the methods appropriate to coupled mechanical systems as discussed in (1: Chapter 12). Such a program is quite difficult to carry out, but it has been done for some cases by Blackman and others, and the results obtained in this way from (26-42) agree very well with experimental results. We shall not discuss this method any further, but instead we shall turn to two approximations to (26-41) and (26-42) which have been historically very important and are still very useful for many purposes.

The first is due to Einstein, who made the very simple assumption that all the frequencies ν_j are the same and equal to ν; this would be the case if the N atoms oscillated independently with this same frequency. If we evaluate (26-42) for a kilomole so that there are $3N = 3L$ terms in the sum, and use (17-14'), we obtain

$$c_v = 3R \left(\frac{h\nu}{kT}\right)^2 \frac{e^{h\nu/kT}}{(e^{h\nu/kT} - 1)^2} \tag{26-43}$$

We know from (26-39b) that this result gives the Dulong-Petit value $3R$ as its high-temperature limit, and also vanishes as $T \to 0$ according to (26-40b) and in that sense is better than the classical result (25-28). The general dependence of c_v on T as given by (26-43) is like that shown in Fig. 25-1; however, the low-temperature behavior of c_v obtained from (26-40b) is much too rapid a decrease with temperature to agree generally with experiment. Nevertheless, the qualitative success of the Einstein theory led Debye to formulate his more accurate theory which we shall consider next.

Since there are so many normal modes, their frequencies will be almost continuously distributed; if we let dZ_c be the number of normal modes of the crystal with frequencies in the range v to $v + dv$, we can write (26-41) as the integral

$$U = \int \bar{\varepsilon}(v)\, dZ_c = \int \left(\frac{1}{2} hv + \frac{hv}{e^{\beta hv} - 1} \right) dZ_c \qquad (26\text{-}44)$$

In order to devise a theory of universal form, Debye obtained dZ_c by treating the crystal as a continuous isotropic solid whose normal modes as given by the theory of elasticity are the transverse and longitudinal elastic waves in the body.

In our discussion of thermal radiation following (25-31), we have already obtained the essential results we shall need. Although we were considering the frequency distribution of standing electromagnetic waves in a box, the essential feature of (25-31) is that it is a consequence of the boundary conditions that the waves had to satisfy at the surfaces of the box. One could do a similar calculation for the elastic body by solving the wave equation subject to the boundary conditions that the faces of the solid be free or held fixed. The calculation of the number of normal modes dN_v of a given type in the frequency interval dv would go exactly as before and the result (25-34) would again be obtained where c is now the speed appropriate to the wave. For the elastic body there can be longitudinal waves of one possible polarization and speed c_l so that their number dZ_l is found from (25-34) to be

$$dZ_l = \frac{4\pi V}{c_l^{3}} v^2\, dv \qquad (26\text{-}45)$$

In addition, there can be transverse elastic waves of two possible polarizations and speed c_t so that their number is

$$dZ_t = \frac{8\pi V}{c_t^{3}} v^2\, dv \qquad (26\text{-}46)$$

making the total

$$dZ_c = dZ_l + dZ_t = 4\pi V \left(\frac{1}{c_l^{3}} + \frac{2}{c_t^{3}} \right) v^2\, dv \qquad (26\text{-}47)$$

A continuum with its infinite number of degrees of freedom will have an infinite number of normal modes; our solid, however, has only $3N$ normal modes. In order to take this fact into account, Debye assumed that (26-47) holds up to a maximum frequency v_g which is so defined as to make the total number of modes equal to the actual number, that is,

$$\int_0^{v_g} dZ_c = 3N = \frac{4\pi V}{3} \left(\frac{1}{c_l^{3}} + \frac{2}{c_t^{3}} \right) v_g^{3} \qquad (26\text{-}48)$$

If (26-47) and (26-48) are combined, we obtain the simpler expression

$$dZ_c = \frac{9Nv^2\,dv}{v_g^{\ 3}} \tag{26-49}$$

so that (26-44) becomes

$$U = \frac{9Nh}{v_g^{\ 3}} \int_0^{v_g} \left(\frac{v^3}{2} + \frac{v^3}{e^{\beta h v} - 1} \right) dv \tag{26-50}$$

If we define the *Debye temperature* Θ by

$$\Theta = \frac{hv_g}{k} \tag{26-51}$$

and replace v by the dimensionless variable $x = \beta h v = hv/kT$, we find that (26-50) becomes

$$U = \frac{9}{8} Nk\Theta + 3NkT D\left(\frac{\Theta}{T}\right) \tag{26-52}$$

where

$$D(\alpha) = \frac{3}{\alpha^3} \int_0^\alpha \frac{x^3\,dx}{e^x - 1} \tag{26-53}$$

is called the *Debye function*. This function $D(\alpha)$ can be evaluated by numerical methods, and tables of its values for various α are available.

According to its definition (26-51), Θ should be a definite constant for a given crystal and should be independent of the temperature. Since different crystals will have unlike elastic constants and therefore c_l and c_t will vary from crystal to crystal, we can expect the values of Θ to depend considerably on the nature of the particular solid.

In the high-temperature limit, $\alpha = \Theta/T \ll 1$. Therefore, in (26-53), $x \ll 1$ over the whole range of integration and we can replace the denominator in the integrand by the expansion

$$e^x - 1 \simeq x + \tfrac{1}{2}x^2 + \tfrac{1}{6}x^3 + \cdots$$

If we then use the expansion

$$\frac{1}{1+y} \simeq 1 - y + y^2 + \cdots$$

with $y = \tfrac{1}{2}x + \tfrac{1}{6}x^2$, keep all terms to the order of x^4 in the integrand of (26-53), and integrate term by term, we find the following approximation for the Debye function:

$$D(\alpha) \simeq 1 - \frac{3}{8}\alpha + \frac{\alpha^2}{20} + \cdots \qquad (\alpha \ll 1) \tag{26-54}$$

If we insert (26-54) into (26-52) and evaluate the energy for a kilomole so that $Nk = R$, we find

$$u = 3RT + \frac{3R\Theta^2}{20T} + \cdots \tag{26-55a}$$

$$c_v = \left(\frac{\partial u}{\partial T}\right)_\Theta = 3R - \frac{3R}{20}\left(\frac{\Theta}{T}\right)^2 + \cdots \xrightarrow[T \to \infty]{} 3R \tag{26-55b}$$

which again yields the classical Dulong-Petit value.

In the low-temperature limit where $\alpha = \Theta/T \gg 1$, we can approximate $D(\alpha)$ by extending the upper limit in (26-53) to infinity; we obtain

$$D(\alpha) \simeq \frac{3}{\alpha^3} \int_0^\infty \frac{x^3 \, dx}{e^x - 1} \tag{26-56}$$

The integral can be evaluated by a series expansion in $e^{-x} \leqslant 1$ and then by use of the relation

$$\int_0^\infty x^n e^{-ax} \, dx = \frac{n!}{a^{n+1}} \tag{26-57}$$

which applies when n is a positive integer:

$$\int_0^\infty \frac{x^3 \, dx}{e^x - 1} = \int_0^\infty \frac{x^3 e^{-x} \, dx}{1 - e^{-x}} = \int_0^\infty x^3 e^{-x} \, dx \left(\sum_{m=0}^\infty e^{-mx}\right)$$

$$= \sum_{p=1}^\infty \int_0^\infty x^3 e^{-px} \, dx = 3! \sum_{p=1}^\infty \frac{1}{p^4} = \frac{\pi^4}{15} \tag{26-58}$$

The last sum in (26-58) is a Riemann zeta function with the value $\pi^4/90$. Substituting (26-58) into (26-56), we obtain

$$D(\alpha) \simeq \frac{\pi^4}{5\alpha^3} \quad (\alpha \gg 1) \tag{26-59}$$

and when we evaluate (26-52) for a kilomole we obtain

$$u \simeq \frac{9}{8} R\Theta + \frac{3\pi^4 RT^4}{5\Theta^3} + \cdots \tag{26-60a}$$

$$c_v = \left(\frac{\partial u}{\partial T}\right)_\Theta \simeq \frac{12\pi^4 R}{5}\left(\frac{T}{\Theta}\right)^3 + \cdots \tag{26-60b}$$

Thus the low-temperature heat capacity is proportional to T^3 and vanishes as $T \to 0$, in agreement with the third law. The T^3 dependence at low temperature is not as rapid a decrease as the exponential decrease given by the Einstein theory and is experimentally very well verified for simple ionic crystals. This result does not agree with the low-temperature heat capacities observed for metals for which $c_v \sim T$; we shall see later that this can be accounted for as a specifically quantum mechanical result arising from the free electrons in a metal.

If we look back at (26-52) as well as at the specific formulas given by (26-55b) and (26-60b), we see that the Debye theory essentially predicts a heat capacity which should be a universal curve when plotted as a function of T/Θ. Thus, by trying to fit experimental values to this curve, we can obtain an estimate of the value of Θ characteristic of a given crystal. We also see from (26-51) and (26-48) that

$$\Theta \sim v_g \sim \left(\frac{N}{V}\right)^{1/3} \bar{c} \qquad (26\text{-}61)$$

where $\bar{c}$ is an appropriate average speed of the elastic waves. In the theory of elasticity, it is shown that

$$\bar{c} \sim (\text{volume compressibility})^{-1/2} \qquad (26\text{-}62)$$

An example of such a relation is given for fluid systems in (I: Exercise 18-5). Therefore we would expect qualitatively that an incompressible or "hard" crystal would have a large value of Θ, while Θ would be small for a "soft" crystal. The few selected data given below which compare Θ_o obtained from the experimental heat capacity and Θ_c calculated from the elastic constants tend to verify this general prediction:

	Θ_o	Θ_c
Diamond	1800	1871
Aluminum	396	399
Copper	313	329
Lead	86	72

These temperatures are measured on the absolute temperature scale. The agreement is surprisingly good considering the very simplified assumptions which were made by Debye.

26-6   Thermal radiation

We could get some of the results of interest to us from the Debye theory, but it is preferable to begin anew. We saw that the basic problem is the calculation of the energy density per unit frequency interval given by (25-37). Rather than use kT for the average oscillator energy, we should now use the expression (26-36). In the discussion of black-body radiation, it is customary to drop the zero point energy $\frac{1}{2}h\nu$, as it would lead to an infinite (although constant) energy density when integrated over the whole frequency range since the possible frequencies extend from 0 to ∞ as far as we know. In this manner we obtain the *Planck distribution law*

$$u(\nu, T) = \frac{8\pi h \nu^3}{c^3(e^{h\nu/kT} - 1)} \tag{26-63}$$

which agrees well with experiment and represents the beginning of quantum theory.

For low frequencies, $h\nu/kT \ll 1$, (26-63) becomes

$$u(\nu, T) \simeq \frac{8\pi \nu^2 kT}{c^3} \tag{26-64}$$

which is the Rayleigh-Jeans law (25-38) we previously obtained. For high frequencies, $h\nu/kT \gg 1$, (26-63) is approximately given by *Wien's law*:

$$u(\nu, T) \simeq \frac{8\pi h \nu^3}{c^3} e^{-h\nu/kT} \tag{26-65}$$

The general dependence of u on ν as given by Planck's law is shown in Fig. 26-6. The location of the frequency ν_m for which u is a maximum can be obtained from (26-63) by setting $du/d\nu = 0$; the resulting condition can be written as

$$(3 - x)e^x = 3 \tag{26-66}$$

with $x = h\nu/kT$. The solution of (26-66) is most easily found by successive approximations; the result is that $x = 2.84$, so that

$$\nu_m = \frac{2.84kT}{h} = \text{const. } T \tag{26-67}$$

which is known as *Wien's displacement law* and was discovered experimentally by Wien before the formulation of Planck's theory. Equation

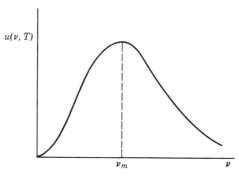

Fig. 26-6

(26-67) shows that the frequency at which the maximum energy density occurs increases as the temperature increases; this effect accounts qualitatively for the observed change in color of objects as they are heated.

We can find the total energy density U/V by integrating (26-63) over all frequencies; if we set $x = h\nu/kT$ and use (26-58), we obtain

$$\frac{U}{V} = \int_0^\infty u(\nu, T) \, d\nu = \frac{8\pi^5 k^4 T^4}{15(hc)^3} = \sigma T^4 \qquad (26\text{-}68)$$

which is the empirical *Stefan-Boltzmann law*; we see that the constant of proportionality σ is a universal constant.

We can now obtain other thermodynamic functions of the radiation. The entropy per oscillator is given by (26-38) with $\theta/T = h\nu/kT$; this is the appropriate form to use since the normal modes are *distinguishable*, differing as they do by their directions of propagation and polarization as indicated by our ability to associate each mode with a definite (and different) point in Fig. 25-3a. Using (25-35), (26-38), (26-63), and (26-68), we obtain

$$\frac{S}{V} = \int_0^\infty \frac{8\pi\nu^2 \, d\nu}{c^3} \left[\frac{h\nu/T}{e^{h\nu/kT} - 1} - k \ln\left(1 - e^{-h\nu/kT}\right) \right]$$

$$= \frac{U}{VT} - \frac{8\pi k^4 T^3}{(hc)^3} \int_0^\infty x^2 \ln\left(1 - e^{-x}\right) dx \qquad (26\text{-}69)$$

If we use the series expansion

$$\ln(1 - \varphi) = -\sum_{n=1}^\infty \frac{\varphi^n}{n} \qquad (26\text{-}70)$$

we can evaluate the integral in (26-69) by integrating term by term, and we find that

$$\int_0^\infty x^2 \ln\left(1 - e^{-x}\right) dx = -\sum_{n=1}^\infty \frac{1}{n} \int_0^\infty x^2 e^{-nx} \, dx$$

$$= -2\sum_{n=1}^\infty \frac{1}{n^4} = -\frac{\pi^4}{45} \qquad (26\text{-}71)$$

with the use of (26-57) and (26-58). If we substitute (26-71) into (26-69) and use (26-68), we find that

$$S = \frac{4U}{3T} \qquad (26\text{-}72)$$

The Helmholtz function is

$$F = U - TS = -\tfrac{1}{3}U \qquad (26\text{-}73)$$

so that the pressure can be found from (11-6b), (26-73), and (26-68) to be

$$p = -\left(\frac{\partial F}{\partial V}\right)_T = \frac{1}{3}\left(\frac{\partial U}{\partial V}\right)_T = \frac{1}{3}\left(\frac{U}{V}\right)$$

so that the equation of state is

$$pV = \tfrac{1}{3}U \tag{26-74}$$

which is the same as we previously found by thermodynamic methods in Exercise 10-5.

Finally, the Gibbs function of the radiation is found to be

$$G = U + pV - TS = 0 \tag{26-75}$$

The significance of this result will become clearer when we reconsider this whole problem from another point of view.

Exercises

26-1. A material is composed of atoms having a magnetic moment μ which may be oriented in the direction of, or opposite to, a field B with energy $-\mu B$ and $+\mu B$ respectively. Find the paramagnetic moment and Curie constant. Show that the equation of state obtained for this system leads to a Weiss ferromagnetism which is compatible with the third law.

26-2. The quantum energy levels of a rigid rotator are $\varepsilon_j = [j(j+1)h^2]/8\pi^2 m' a^2$, where $j = 0, 1, 2, \ldots$. The degeneracy of each level is $g_j = 2j + 1$. Find the general expression for the partition function, and show that at high temperatures it can be approximated by an integral. Evaluate the high-temperature energy and heat capacity and compare your results with (25-24). Also find the low-temperature approximations to Z_0, U, and C_v.

26-3. A system is composed of subsystems each of which has only two possible states. Suppose that the number in the upper state is found to be greater than the number in the lower. How would you describe the state of the whole system? Plot the temperature as a function of the ratio $n_{\text{upper}}/n_{\text{lower}}$.

26-4. Show that the next term in the series for c_v gives the formula

$$c_v = 3R\left[1 - \frac{1}{20}\left(\frac{\Theta}{T}\right)^2 + \frac{1}{560}\left(\frac{\Theta}{T}\right)^4 + \cdots\right]$$

rather than (26-55b).

26-5. Derive the Debye heat capacity for a two-dimensional crystal. Similarly, find the Stefan-Boltzmann radiation law for a two-dimensional space.

27 *Identical particles*

Our fundamental results need a further modification because of the recognition that elementary entities such as electrons, atoms, etc., are *indistinguishable in principle*. In our calculation of the number of complexions in a given distribution given by (21-4), we counted all complexions which differed by an interchange of the identical subsystems as actually different; that is, we assumed that we could distinguish among the subsystems. However, this is not possible for truly identical quantities, and we now need to go back and take this feature into account. We shall find that all our previous calculations were sufficiently accurate under the conditions for which we have applied them so far.

This recognition of the fact that the elementary units are indistinguishable is often described as another correction due to quantum mechanics. This is not strictly true, of course; the necessity of such a step was first strongly emphasized when statistical mechanical calculations were first made for quantum mechanical systems. As a matter of fact, the necessity of correcting for indistinguishability had already been discussed by Gibbs about twenty years before the development of modern quantum mechanics.

27-1 Introductory considerations

While we are carrying out the correction discussed above, we shall, however, simultaneously take another quantum effect into account. For certain types of systems, there are restrictions on the number of particles that can simultaneously be in the same quantum state. The most famous example of this type of restriction is the *Pauli exclusion principle for electrons*, which states that no more than one electron can occupy a given state. It has been found that one can divide all particles into two classes which are characterized by the possible values of n_i—the number of particles in the ith quantum state of the particle. If there are no restrictions on n_i, so that $n_i = 0, 1, 2, 3, \ldots$, we obtain *Bose-Einstein statistics*. If the particles obey an exclusion principle like that for electrons so that $n_i = 0, 1$, we obtain *Fermi-Dirac statistics*. It should be emphasized that this conventional terminology is somewhat misleading because the *basic ideas* of our calculations are *unchanged*; only the specific methods of calculating the thermodynamic probabilities need to be modified.

We should also point out that, although our previous method of calculation in Secs. 21-1 and 21-3 gave the correct answer, we used throughout an assumption which is not justified by the results; that is, we assumed that n_i was large enough that Stirling's formula (21-12) could be used to approximate $n_i!$. We can estimate the value of n_i for a typical situation from (21-33) and (22-10); we see that the largest value of n_i for a monatomic gas is about

$$n_i \approx \frac{N}{Z_0} = \frac{Nh^3}{V(2\pi mkT)^{3/2}} \tag{27-1}$$

If we evaluate (27-1) for helium under standard conditions, we find that $n_i \approx 1/240{,}000$; in other words, in μ-space only about one cell out of each 240,000 even has a helium atom in it. Therefore n_i is generally very small rather than very large as was assumed in the use of Stirling's formula to obtain (21-14); the basic reason why this problem has arisen is that initially there was no necessity for using a cell size as small as h^l which we now know to be an essential requirement.

We can easily avoid this difficulty by a slight change of procedure. Since the fundamental cell in μ-space is so very small, the energy of a particle in a given cell is very little different from that in neighboring cells. Therefore we can collect the cells into groups such that the energy of a particle is practically uniform within the group and the number N_j of particles in the jth group is quite large. For convenience, we shall choose the same number g of cells in each group although we shall see that this is not necessary. Since the total number of cells in μ-space is M, we have

$$\text{Number of groups} = \frac{M}{g} \tag{27-2}$$

Now we can do all our calculations in terms of the groups, and the numbers involved will be large enough to justify completely the use of Stirling's formula.

27-2 Bose-Einstein probability

Let us represent the N_j identical particles by N_j identical zeros and let us also number the g cells so that they can be represented by the symbols $i_1, i_2, \ldots, i_g$. We now imagine mixing the i's and the zeros and then arranging them in any sequence; for example,

$$i_1 0 i_2 0 0 i_3 i_4 i_5 0 0 0 i_6 i_7 0 i_8 0 i_9 i_{10} \cdots \tag{27-3}$$

If we now require that the first symbol be an i, we can assume that the zeros represent particles which are located in the cell represented by the preceding i. For example, in the sequence above, cell 5 has three particles, cell 2 has two, cells 1, 7, and 8 have one each, while the others shown contain none.

The number of complexions which can be obtained from the N_j particles in the g cells of the group is clearly equal to the number of arrangements like (27-3) which we can make with these symbols. Since the first symbol must be an i, it can be chosen in g ways. The remaining $g + N_j - 1$

symbols can be arranged in $(g + N_j - 1)!$ ways. Therefore the number of sequences such as (27-3) is

$$g(g + N_j - 1)! \qquad (27\text{-}4)$$

Although each of these sequences is a complexion, there are many duplications in (27-4). For example, it is clear that every complexion can be represented by one like (27-3) in which the cells are arranged in numerical order; therefore permuting the i's is unnecessary and, since this can be done in $g!$ ways, we must divide (27-4) by $g!$. Similarly, the zeros are indistinguishable, and hence their $N_j!$ possible arrangements do not correspond to different complexions. Therefore, if we let w_j be the thermodynamic probability given by the number of different complexions which are possible for the jth group of cells, we find from (27-4) that

$$w_j = \frac{g(g + N_j - 1)!}{g!\, N_j!} \qquad (27\text{-}5)$$

The probability W for the whole system is obtained by combining the probabilities for the independent groups according to (16-3), so that

$$W = w_1 w_2 \cdots w_j \cdots w_{M/g} \qquad (27\text{-}6)$$

and therefore

$$\ln W = \sum_{j=1}^{M/g} \ln w_j \qquad (27\text{-}7)$$

Using (21-13) and (27-5), we obtain

$$\ln w_j = \ln g + (g + N_j - 1) \ln (g + N_j - 1) - g \ln g - N_j \ln N_j + 1$$
$$\simeq (g + N_j) \ln (g + N_j) - g \ln g - N_j \ln N_j \qquad (27\text{-}8)$$

since $g \gg 1$ and $N_j \gg 1$. If we let

$$n_i = \frac{N_j}{g} \qquad (27\text{-}9)$$

be the *average* number of particles in a cell of the jth group, we can use (27-9) to eliminate N_j from (27-8); the result is

$$\ln w_j = g(n_i + 1) \ln g(1 + n_i) - g \ln g - g n_i \ln g n_i$$
$$= g[(n_i + 1) \ln (1 + n_i) - n_i \ln n_i] \qquad (27\text{-}10)$$

If we substitute (27-10) into (27-7), we obtain

$$\ln W = \sum_{j=1}^{M/g} g[(n_i + 1) \ln (1 + n_i) - n_i \ln n_i] \qquad (27\text{-}11)$$

Since the bracketed term in (27-11) is the same for each of the g cells of the group by the definition of n_i, each term in (27-11) of the form g multiplying a bracket equals the sum of the bracket over each of the g cells of the group; therefore (27-11) can actually be written as a sum over all the cells:

$$\ln W = \sum_{i=1}^{M} [(n_i + 1) \ln (1 + n_i) - n_i \ln n_i] \tag{27-12}$$

This result no longer contains the group size and involves only quantities characteristic of the cell.

27-3 Fermi-Dirac probability

Before we go on to use (27-12), let us calculate the equivalent quantity for the Fermi-Dirac case in which an n_i is restricted to the values 0 and 1. We could continue with our sequence of zeros and i's with the additional restriction that two zeros cannot be adjacent, but it is more convenient to start over.

In order to distribute the N_j particles among the g cells, we can put the first in any of the g cells, the second in any of the $g - 1$ remaining cells, the third in any of $g - 2$, etc.; in all, we can distribute them in the following number of ways:

$$g(g - 1)(g - 2) \cdots (g - N_j + 1) = \frac{g!}{(g - N_j)!} \tag{27-13}$$

In this process we have identified the particles as first, second, etc., but this is not possible; accordingly we must divide (27-13) by the $N_j!$ possible permutations of the identical particles in order to obtain the number of complexions w_j:

$$w_j = \frac{g!}{N_j! (g - N_j)!} \tag{27-14}$$

By proceeding as before and using (21-12) and (27-9), we can approximate w_j as

$$w_j = \left(\frac{g}{e}\right)^g \left(\frac{e}{N_j}\right)^{N_j} \left(\frac{e}{g - N_j}\right)^{g - N_j}$$

$$= (1 - n_i)^{N_j - g} n_i^{-N_j} \tag{27-15}$$

so that

$$\ln w_j = (N_j - g) \ln (1 - n_i) - N_j \ln n_i$$

$$= g[(n_i - 1) \ln (1 - n_i) - n_i \ln n_i] \tag{27-16}$$

Therefore we can also write ln W obtained from (27-7) as a sum over the cells:

$$\ln W = \sum_i [(n_i - 1) \ln (1 - n_i) - n_i \ln n_i] \qquad (27\text{-}17)$$

27-4   State of maximum probability

Equations (27-12) and (27-17) can be combined into the single equation

$$\ln W = \sum_i [(n_i \pm 1) \ln (1 \pm n_i) - n_i \ln n_i] \qquad (27\text{-}18)$$

if we always choose the upper sign for the Bose-Einstein case and the lower sign for Fermi-Dirac; we shall follow this convention throughout.

As in Sec. 21-3, we want to find the state of maximum probability and identify it with the equilibrium state. As before, our distribution n_i is subject to the conditions of constant number of particles N and constant energy U given by (21-7) and (21-8):

$$N = \sum_i n_i = \text{const.}, \quad U = \sum_i \varepsilon_i n_i = \text{const.} \qquad (27\text{-}19)$$

Consequently, the virtual variations δn_i are restricted by equations identical to (21-26) and (21-27):

$$\sum_i \delta n_i = 0, \quad \sum_i \varepsilon_i \, \delta n_i = 0 \qquad (27\text{-}20)$$

The corresponding first order variation in (27-18) which vanishes for the maximum of ln W is

$$\delta \ln W = 0 = \sum_i \left[\delta n_i \ln (1 \pm n_i) + (n_i \pm 1)\left(\frac{\pm \delta n_i}{1 \pm n_i} \right) \right.$$
$$\left. - \delta n_i \ln n_i - \delta n_i \right]$$
$$= \sum_i \delta n_i \ln \left(\frac{1}{n_i} \pm 1 \right) \qquad (27\text{-}21)$$

We multiply (27-20) by the respective Lagrange multipliers α and β and subtract from (27-21) to obtain

$$\sum_i \delta n_i \left[\ln \left(\frac{1}{n_i} \pm 1 \right) - \alpha - \beta \varepsilon_i \right] = 0 \qquad (27\text{-}22)$$

Setting the coefficient of each δn_i equal to zero, we get

$$\ln \left(\frac{1}{n_i} \pm 1 \right) = \alpha + \beta \varepsilon_i \qquad (27\text{-}23)$$

so that the distribution of maximum probability is given by

$$n_i = \frac{1}{e^{\alpha + \beta \varepsilon_i} \mp 1} \qquad (27\text{-}24)$$

The distributions for the two separate cases are therefore

$$\text{(Bose-Einstein)} \qquad n_i = \frac{1}{e^{\alpha + \beta \varepsilon_i} - 1} \qquad (27\text{-}25)$$

$$\text{(Fermi-Dirac)} \qquad n_i = \frac{1}{e^{\alpha + \beta \varepsilon_i} + 1} \qquad (27\text{-}26)$$

In general, the α's will be different for the two distributions.

The multipliers α and β can in principle be determined from the two conditions (27-19); thus, if we use (27-24), we find that

$$N = \sum_i \frac{1}{e^{\alpha + \beta \varepsilon_i} \mp 1} \qquad (27\text{-}27a)$$

$$U = \sum_i \frac{\varepsilon_i}{e^{\alpha + \beta \varepsilon_i} \mp 1} \qquad (27\text{-}27b)$$

These results are seen to differ from the Boltzmann ones by the appearance of the ∓ 1 in the denominators.

It is convenient to define a quantity Q by

$$\ln Q = \mp \sum_i \ln (1 \mp e^{-\alpha - \beta \varepsilon_i}) \qquad (27\text{-}28)$$

Therefore

$$Q_{BE} = \prod_i \frac{1}{1 - e^{-\alpha - \beta \varepsilon_i}} \qquad (27\text{-}29a)$$

$$Q_{FD} = \prod_i (1 + e^{-\alpha - \beta \varepsilon_i}) \qquad (27\text{-}29b)$$

We find from (27-28) that

$$\frac{\partial \ln Q}{\partial \beta} = \mp \sum_i \frac{(\mp)(-\varepsilon_i) e^{-\alpha - \beta \varepsilon_i}}{1 \mp e^{-\alpha - \beta \varepsilon_i}} = -\sum_i \frac{\varepsilon_i}{e^{\alpha + \beta \varepsilon_i} \mp 1}$$

and therefore we see from (27-27b) that

$$U = -\frac{\partial \ln Q}{\partial \beta} \qquad (27\text{-}30)$$

Similarly we can show that

$$n_i = -\frac{1}{\beta} \frac{\partial \ln Q}{\partial \varepsilon_i} \qquad (27\text{-}31)$$

$$N = -\frac{\partial \ln Q}{\partial \alpha} \qquad (27\text{-}32)$$

Thus the function Q plays a role for these results which is similar to that of the partition function Z_0 of our previous discussions.

We define our entropy by (21-51), and therefore

$$S = k \ln W_m = k \sum_i [(n_i \pm 1) \ln (1 \pm n_i) - n_i \ln n_i] \qquad (27\text{-}33)$$

because of (27-18); this sum is to be evaluated with the distribution (27-24) corresponding to maximum probability.

If we substitute (27-24) into (27-33) and use (27-27) and (27-28), we find that

$$S = \beta k U + k \ln Q + Nk\alpha \qquad (27\text{-}34a)$$

$$= \frac{U}{T} + k \ln Q + Nk\alpha \qquad (27\text{-}34b)$$

since we shall show shortly that $\beta = 1/kT$, as would be expected. The Helmholtz function as obtained from (27-34b) is

$$F = U - TS = -kT \ln Q - NkT\alpha \qquad (27\text{-}35)$$

27-5 Boltzmann limit

In order to see the connection between these results and our previous ones, let us consider the case

$$e^{-\alpha} \ll 1, \quad e^{\alpha} \gg 1 \qquad (27\text{-}36)$$

Therefore

$$\ln (1 \mp e^{-\alpha - \beta \varepsilon_i}) \simeq \mp e^{-\alpha - \beta \varepsilon_i} \qquad (27\text{-}37)$$

and (27-28) becomes

$$\ln Q \simeq e^{-\alpha} \sum_i e^{-\beta \varepsilon_i} = e^{-\alpha} Z_0 \qquad (27\text{-}38)$$

because of (26-9).

Substituting (27-38) into (27-30), (27-31), and (27-32), we obtain

$$U = -e^{-\alpha} \frac{\partial Z_0}{\partial \beta}, \quad n_i = -\frac{e^{-\alpha}}{\beta} \frac{\partial Z_0}{\partial \varepsilon_i}, \quad N = e^{-\alpha} Z_0$$

so that

$$e^{-\alpha} = \frac{N}{Z_0}, \quad U = -N \frac{\partial \ln Z_0}{\partial \beta}, \quad n_i = -\frac{N}{\beta} \frac{\partial \ln Z_0}{\partial \varepsilon_i} \qquad (27\text{-}39)$$

which are identical with the earlier equations (21-32), (21-36), and (21-37), so that we are back to the case of Boltzmann statistics; this also shows that $\beta = 1/kT$.

We could, of course, have seen this directly from the distribution (27-24) under the condition (27-36), since then

$$n_i \simeq e^{-\alpha - \beta \varepsilon_i}$$

which is exactly our earlier starting point (21-30). Consequently, we have justified our previous results by the more exact calculations of this chapter in which we have used Stirling's formula more legitimately.

We see from (27-38) and (27-39) that we also have

$$\ln Q \simeq e^{-\alpha} Z_0 = N$$

so that

$$\alpha = \ln Z_0 - \ln N$$

When these expressions are substituted into (27-34b), we obtain

$$S_{\text{Boltz}} = \frac{U}{T} + Nk + Nk \ln Z_0 - Nk \ln N = \frac{U}{T} + k \ln \frac{Z_0^N}{N!}$$

which is the same as (21-53d). Thus our calculations which now have taken into account the identity of the particles have *automatically* introduced corrected Boltzmann counting in the Boltzmann limit.

We now estimate the physical conditions which correspond to the expression (27-36) for the validity of the Boltzmann distribution. Combining (27-1) with the first equation in (27-39), we can estimate e^α for an ideal monatomic gas by

$$e^\alpha \simeq \frac{V(2\pi mkT)^{3/2}}{Nh^3} \tag{27-40}$$

This is exactly the quantity we evaluated previously so that for helium under standard conditions $e^\alpha \approx 240,000$. Consequently, we see that classical Boltzmann statistics is a very good approximation under these fairly typical circumstances.

It would be of interest to determine the conditions for which $e^\alpha \approx 1$ or even $e^\alpha \ll 1$, for then we could expect to find significant deviations from the Boltzmann case. We see from (27-40) that generally the conditions are high density, small mass, and low temperature. In particular, the electron has a very small mass, and we might expect these deviations to become important for electrons. Although (27-40) can be used as an approximation, the value of α can in principle always be determined from (27-27a).

A "non-degenerate" gas is one to which we can apply the "corrected" Boltzmann statistics developed in Chapters 21 and 26. If this is not possible and we must use the more exact results summarized in (27-24) and subsequent equations, the gas is called "degenerate." We have seen that generally ordinary gases under ordinary conditions are non-degenerate, while electrons, for instance, may be highly degenerate.

Exercises

27-1. Repeat the calculations leading to (27-12) and (27-17), but use a different number of cells in each group and thus show that the same results are obtained.

27-2. For a monatomic gas, estimate the energy difference between neighboring cells in μ-space which will be of significance, and thereby justify our assumption that N_j and g can be chosen to be large while the energy within a group will be approximately constant.

28 Deviations of ideal gases from the Boltzmann limit

Before we consider some specific applications of our results, we shall see how the thermodynamic properties of the monatomic ideal gas composed of independent particles deviate from those found in the Boltzmann limit. These functions can be found by approximating the sums involved by integrals. This procedure will be satisfactory for any reasonable conditions except for the very degenerate Bose-Einstein gas which will be considered separately.

28-1 General expressions for thermodynamic functions

If we define the density of states $c(\varepsilon)$ so that the number of states with energy between ε and $\varepsilon + d\varepsilon$ is $c(\varepsilon)\,d\varepsilon$, we can express the sum over states of a quantity $F(\varepsilon_i)$ as an integral over energy by

$$\sum_i F(\varepsilon_i) = \int_0^\infty F(\varepsilon)c(\varepsilon)\,d\varepsilon \qquad (28\text{-}1)$$

Since we are interested in ideal gases, we require $c(\varepsilon)$ for a free particle in a box which is large enough that the energies of the states are almost continuously distributed. Comparing (26-2) and (25-31), we see that we can use the result (25-34) which we have already found for the number dN_ν of standing waves in a given frequency interval by making the substitutions:

$$\nu^2 \to \varepsilon, \quad d\nu \to d\varepsilon/2\sqrt{\varepsilon}$$
$$c^2 \to h^2/2m, \quad g\,dN_\nu \to c(\varepsilon)\,d\varepsilon \qquad (28\text{-}2)$$

where g is a possible degeneracy factor which gives the number of different states which correspond to each translational state of energy given by (26-2); the need for g is analogous to the necessity of multiplying dN_v by the number of possible polarizations of a given wave as we did in (25-35) and (26-46). After the substitutions listed in (28-2) are made, we obtain

$$c(\varepsilon)\, d\varepsilon = C\sqrt{\varepsilon}\, d\varepsilon \qquad (28\text{-}3)$$

where

$$C = 2\pi g V \left(\frac{2m}{h^2}\right)^{3/2} \qquad (28\text{-}4)$$

Applying (28-1) and (28-3) to (27-27) and (27-28), we obtain

$$N = C \int_0^\infty \frac{\sqrt{\varepsilon}\, d\varepsilon}{e^{\alpha + \beta\varepsilon} \mp 1} \qquad (28\text{-}5)$$

$$U = C \int_0^\infty \frac{\varepsilon^{3/2}\, d\varepsilon}{e^{\alpha + \beta\varepsilon} \mp 1} \qquad (28\text{-}6)$$

$$\ln Q = \mp C \int_0^\infty \sqrt{\varepsilon}\, \ln\left(1 \mp e^{-\alpha - \beta\varepsilon}\right) d\varepsilon \qquad (28\text{-}7)$$

If we introduce the dimensionless variable x by

$$x = \beta\varepsilon = \frac{\varepsilon}{kT} \qquad (28\text{-}8)$$

and let

$$Z_B = \frac{V}{h^3} (2\pi m k T)^{3/2} \qquad (28\text{-}9)$$

be the partition function for an ideal monatomic Boltzmann gas according to (26-29), we can use (28-4) to write (28-7) in the form

$$\ln Q = Z_B \chi(\alpha) \qquad (28\text{-}10)$$

where

$$\chi(\alpha) = \mp \frac{2g}{\sqrt{\pi}} \int_0^\infty \sqrt{x}\, \ln\left(1 \mp e^{-\alpha - x}\right) dx \qquad (28\text{-}11)$$

Using (27-30), (28-9), and (28-10), we find that

$$U = \tfrac{3}{2} k T Z_B \chi(\alpha) = \tfrac{3}{2} k T \ln Q \qquad (28\text{-}12)$$

Similarly, we find from (27-35), (11-6b), and (28-10) that

$$p = \frac{kT \ln Q}{V} \qquad (28\text{-}13)$$

so that we can also write

$$\ln Q = \frac{pV}{kT} \qquad (28\text{-}14)$$

which gives us a physical interpretation of the function Q. Combining (28-12) and (28-14), we find

$$pV = \tfrac{2}{3}U \qquad (28\text{-}15)$$

The last result is independent of the kind of statistics involved and hence is a universal result for ideal gases; we have already found this to be valid for the classical case, as can be seen from (22-12) and (22-15).

If we substitute (28-14) into (27-35) and use (11-4), the Gibbs function G is found to be

$$G = F + pV = -NkT\alpha \qquad (28\text{-}16)$$

and therefore

$$\alpha = -\frac{G}{NkT} = -\beta\frac{G}{N} \qquad (28\text{-}17)$$

so that α has the physical significance of being directly proportional to the Gibbs function per particle. When we recall the result (26-75) for thermal radiation, we see that $\alpha = 0$ in this case, and then (27-25) becomes

$$n_i = \frac{1}{e^{\beta\varepsilon_i} - 1} \qquad (28\text{-}18)$$

If the thermal radiation is interpreted as being composed of "particles" called *photons*, each of which has the energy $h\nu$, the total energy in each state of a given frequency is

$$n_i h\nu = \frac{h\nu}{e^{\beta h\nu} - 1} \qquad (28\text{-}19)$$

Except for the zero point energy, (28-19) is the starting point (26-36) for the derivation of Planck's law (26-63) and is essentially the basis for describing photons as Bose-Einstein particles. We also see by the derivation of (27-24) from (27-22) that the significance of $\alpha = 0$ is that the condition of constant number of particles is not applicable, the basic reason being that the number of photons need not be conserved since the photons can be changed in number and frequency by absorption, by emission, and by scattering.

28-2 Nearly non-degenerate gases

Using (26-70) and (18-9), we find that

$$\begin{aligned}
\chi(\alpha) &= \mp \frac{2g}{\sqrt{\pi}} \sum_{n=1}^{\infty} \frac{(\pm 1)^n e^{-n\alpha}}{n} \int_0^{\infty} \sqrt{x}\, e^{-nx}\, dx \\
&= g \sum_{n=1}^{\infty} \frac{(\pm 1)^{n+1} e^{-n\alpha}}{n^{5/2}} = g\left(e^{-\alpha} \pm \frac{e^{-2\alpha}}{2^{5/2}} + \cdots\right) \qquad (28\text{-}20)
\end{aligned}$$

The deviations from the Boltzmann limit will be calculated only to the first correction term in order to illustrate the method and to determine the qualitative differences between the two classes of particles. From (28-10) and (28-20), we find

$$\ln Q \simeq g Z_B \, e^{-\alpha} \left(1 \pm \frac{e^{-\alpha}}{2^{3/2}} \right) \tag{28-21}$$

and therefore (27-32) yields

$$N \simeq g Z_B \left(e^{-\alpha} \pm \frac{e^{-2\alpha}}{2^{3/2}} \right) = g Z_B \, e^{-\alpha} \left(1 \pm \frac{e^{-\alpha}}{2^{3/2}} \right) \tag{28-22}$$

so that

$$e^{-\alpha} = \frac{(N/g Z_B)}{[1 \pm (e^{-\alpha}/2^{3/2})]} \simeq \frac{N}{g Z_B} \left(1 \mp \frac{e^{-\alpha}}{2^{3/2}} \right) \tag{28-23}$$

However, $e^{-\alpha} = N/g Z_B$ to first order and this can be substituted for $e^{-\alpha}$ in the right side of (28-23); in this way the series expansion for $e^{-\alpha}$ which is correct to second order terms is found to be

$$e^{-\alpha} \simeq \frac{N}{g Z_B} \left[1 \mp \frac{1}{2^{3/2}} \left(\frac{N}{g Z_B} \right) \right] \tag{28-24}$$

and can be used to eliminate α from other equations.

For example, if we substitute (28-24) into (28-21) and keep only correction terms linear in $N/g Z_B$, we find that

$$\ln Q \simeq N \left[1 \mp \frac{1}{2^{3/2}} \left(\frac{N}{g Z_B} \right) \right] \left[1 \pm \frac{1}{2^{3/2}} \left(\frac{N}{g Z_B} \right) + \cdots \right]$$

$$\simeq N \left[1 \mp \frac{1}{2^{5/2}} \left(\frac{N}{g Z_B} \right) \right] \tag{28-25}$$

which, when combined with (28-14) and (28-9), gives the equation of state:

$$\frac{pV}{NkT} = 1 \mp \frac{1}{2^{5/2}} \left(\frac{N}{g Z_B} \right) = 1 \mp \frac{N h^3}{2^{5/2} g V (2\pi m k T)^{3/2}} \tag{28-26}$$

In essence, we have obtained the virial expansion of the equation of state since (28-26) is in the general form (23-6). Equation (28-26) shows that first order deviations from the ideal gas equation of state $pV = NkT$ are equal and opposite for the Bose-Einstein and Fermi-Dirac ideal gases; this simple relation no longer holds when higher order correction terms are included.

Similarly, we find the energy from (28-12) and (28-25) to be

$$U = \frac{3}{2} NkT \left[1 \mp \frac{N}{2^{5/2} g Z_B} \right] = \frac{3}{2} Nk \left[T \mp \frac{N h^3}{2^{5/2} g V (2\pi m k)^{3/2} T^{1/2}} \right] \tag{28-27}$$

The second form is useful for calculating the heat capacity:

$$C_v = \left(\frac{\partial U}{\partial T}\right)_V = \frac{3}{2} Nk\left[1 \pm \frac{1}{2^{7/2}}\left(\frac{N}{gZ_B}\right)\right] \tag{28-28}$$

Both these expressions approach the Boltzmann values $\frac{3}{2}NkT$ and $\frac{3}{2}Nk$ in the limits of high temperature and low density; the deviations from the Boltzmann limits are again found to be equal and opposite for the two cases. It is clear that we could go on and calculate the other thermodynamic functions in the same fashion in order to find the complete description of almost non-degenerate ideal gases, that is, gases which are given by the Boltzmann limit as a first approximation.

28-3 Degenerate Bose-Einstein gas

We shall briefly consider the Bose-Einstein gas for the case in which it is the most different from the Boltzmann limit. According to (27-36), this degenerate state will correspond to the smallest possible value of α. Since n_i cannot be negative, we see from (27-25) that $\alpha + \beta\varepsilon_i > 0$. If the lowest energy of the particle is ε_1, then

$$\alpha > -\beta\varepsilon_1 \tag{28-29}$$

Therefore we are interested in the properties of the gas as α approaches its limiting value $-\beta\varepsilon_1$; hence we shall assume that

$$\alpha + \beta\varepsilon_1 \ll 1$$

and also that

$$\alpha + \beta\varepsilon_1 \ll \beta(\varepsilon_2 - \varepsilon_1)$$

where ε_2 is the next higher energy.

From (27-19) and (27-25), we therefore find that

$$
\begin{aligned}
N = \sum_i n_i &= \frac{1}{e^{\alpha+\beta\varepsilon_1} - 1} + \frac{1}{e^{\alpha+\beta\varepsilon_2} - 1} + \cdots \\
&= \frac{1}{e^{\alpha+\beta\varepsilon_1} - 1} + \frac{1}{e^{\alpha+\beta\varepsilon_1+\beta(\varepsilon_2-\varepsilon_1)} - 1} + \cdots \\
&\simeq \frac{1}{\alpha + \beta\varepsilon_1} + \frac{1}{e^{\beta(\varepsilon_2-\varepsilon_1)} - 1} + \cdots \\
&= \frac{1}{\alpha + \beta\varepsilon_1}\left(1 + \frac{\alpha + \beta\varepsilon_1}{e^{\beta(\varepsilon_2-\varepsilon_1)} - 1} + \cdots\right) \simeq \frac{1}{\alpha + \beta\varepsilon_1}
\end{aligned}
$$

On the other hand,

$$n_1 = \frac{1}{e^{\alpha+\beta\varepsilon_1} - 1} \simeq \frac{1}{\alpha + \beta\varepsilon_1} \simeq N$$

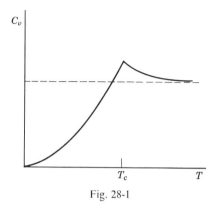

Fig. 28-1

In other words, in this limit of extreme degeneracy all the particles tend to occupy the lowest energy state, practically none being found in the higher energy states. This phenomenon is known as the *Einstein condensation*.

If the effect is investigated in more detail, it is found, for example, that the heat capacity is continuous but has a discontinuous slope at a transition temperature T_c, much as is shown in Fig. 28-1; this behavior is sometimes called a *lambda transition* because of the similarity of this figure to a capital lambda. We can see from our classifications in Sec. 15-3 that such a behavior would also be one of the expected characteristics of a third order phase transition. The transformation of liquid helium to liquid helium II, which occurs at 2.19 degrees absolute, is thought to be an example of a Bose-Einstein condensation because the quantum mechanical properties of He⁴ nuclei require that they be described by Bose-Einstein statistics.

The ordinary condensation of a vapor into a liquid is a condensation in configuration space, because the particles tend to collect within limited

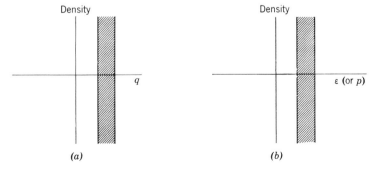

Fig. 28-2

values of the coordinates as illustrated schematically in Fig. 28-2*a*. The Einstein condensation, on the other hand, is a condensation in energy (or momentum) space, with no particular restrictions on the coordinates other than that the particles stay in the volume *V*; this effect is illustrated in Fig. 28-2*b*.

Exercises

28-1. Obtain (28-3) by beginning with (26-2) and by using the method we used to find (25-34). Compare the general features of (28-3) with (18-20).

28-2. Show that

$$\frac{C_p}{C_v} = \frac{5}{3}\left[1 \pm \frac{1}{2^{5/2}}\left(\frac{N}{gZ_B}\right)\right]$$

[*Hint:* Recall (9-21).]

28-3. By comparing with the discussion of the second virial coefficient in Sec. 23-4, show that (28-26) can be interpreted as demonstrating that there is, in effect, an attraction between Bose-Einstein particles and a repulsion between Fermi-Dirac particles.

29 *Free electron theory of metals*

The most important application of Fermi-Dirac statistics is to systems of electrons, since they obey the Pauli exclusion principle. Drude first made the suggestion that electrons in a metal act like gas molecules and participate in the thermal equilibrium and also are the carriers of the electric current. The first calculations of metallic properties based on this general classical model were fairly successful and thereby tended to increase the acceptance of the model; examples of these calculations are given in (I: Sec. 34-3). However, this model initially failed completely in predicting the heat capacity of metals. If the electron were described by classical Boltzmann statistics, each electron should contribute $\frac{3}{2}k$ to the heat capacity according to the equipartition theorem result (25-22). If we assume that there is about one free electron per metallic atom, the contribution of the electrons to the molar heat capacity would be $c_{ve} = \frac{3}{2}R$. If we added this to the Dulong-Petit value (25-28) for the lattice c_{vl}, we would find the total molar heat capacity c_{vt} to be

$$c_{vt} = c_{vl} + c_{ve} \simeq 3R + \frac{3}{2}R = \frac{9}{2}R \tag{29-1}$$

Metals, however, obey the Dulong-Petit law quite well and have a heat capacity of about $3R$. Consequently, it was initially thought that for some reason the electrons did not contribute to the heat capacity although they were necessary to account for the electrical conductivity.

About 1928, Sommerfeld suggested that the electrons should actually be described by the newly developed Fermi-Dirac statistics rather than by the classical Boltzmann results. It was shown that calculations based on these ideas were able to resolve many of the early difficulties.

29-1   General considerations

We shall use a somewhat oversimplified picture, which, however, does lead to useful results which can be obtained with comparative ease. We assume initially that the electrons in the metal can be treated as an ideal gas in a box whose volume V is that of the metal and that they have a constant (zero) potential energy in the box and infinite potential energy at the walls. In doing this, we are assuming in effect that the interactions of the electrons with each other as well as their interactions with the metal ions which are spaced periodically throughout the volume can be regarded as averaging out to a uniform potential corresponding to no net force on an electron.

If we use our previous formula (27-40) to estimate e^α, we can see why we might expect to have to treat the electrons as a degenerate Fermi-Dirac gas. If we assume about one free electron per atom, the density will be $N/V \approx 10^{23}$, and we find that (27-40) becomes

$$e^\alpha \approx \left(\frac{T}{6 \times 10^4}\right)^{3/2} \tag{29-2}$$

The condition for applicability of Boltzmann statistics is $e^\alpha \gg 1$; we see from (29-2) that this corresponds to temperatures large compared to about 10^5 degrees absolute. Therefore, at ordinary temperatures, $e^\alpha \ll 1$ and the electrons are highly degenerate. To put this another way, we can say that at ordinary temperatures the electrons are comparatively at absolute zero; accordingly, most of their properties can be investigated by considering series expansions about their values at $T = 0$.

We also need to take into account the degeneracy factor g which arises from the quantum mechanical properties of electrons. Just as transverse electromagnetic waves can have two states of polarization, electrons of a given translational state can have two possible values of a coordinate describing an intrinsic angular momentum or "spin." We need not go into the precise meaning of electron spin here, but simply accept the fact that we must take $g = 2$; thus the number of states in a given energy range is doubled, and therefore instead of (28-4) we must now use

$$C = 4\pi V \left(\frac{2m}{h^2}\right)^{3/2} \tag{29-3}$$

in formulas such as (28-3) through (28-7).

It is also convenient to define the *Fermi energy* ζ or *Fermi level* by

$$\alpha = -\beta\zeta \tag{29-4}$$

We see from (28-17) that ζ is the Gibbs function per particle. Then, for example, we can write (28-5) as

$$N = C\int_0^\infty \frac{\sqrt{\varepsilon}\,d\varepsilon}{e^{\beta(\varepsilon-\zeta)} + 1} = \int_0^\infty n(\varepsilon)\,d\varepsilon \tag{29-5}$$

where $n(\varepsilon)\,d\varepsilon$ is the number of particles with energies between ε and $\varepsilon + d\varepsilon$. Using (28-3) and (29-5), we can put this number in the form

$$n(\varepsilon)\,d\varepsilon = C\sqrt{\varepsilon}\,f(\varepsilon)\,d\varepsilon = c(\varepsilon)f(\varepsilon)\,d\varepsilon \tag{29-6}$$

where

$$f(\varepsilon) = \frac{1}{e^{\beta(\varepsilon-\zeta)} + 1} \tag{29-7}$$

can be interpreted as the *fraction* of the total number of possible states $c(\varepsilon)\,d\varepsilon$ which are *actually occupied* by electrons, or as the *probability* that the state of energy ε will be occupied. In principle, (29-5) determines the value of the Fermi energy.

29-2   Properties at absolute zero

We let ζ_0 be the value of the Fermi energy at absolute zero. As $T \to 0$, $\beta \to \infty$ and then

$$\begin{array}{llll} \text{if} & \varepsilon < \zeta_0, & e^{\beta(\varepsilon-\zeta_0)} \to 0, & f \to 1 \\ \text{if} & \varepsilon > \zeta_0, & e^{\beta(\varepsilon-\zeta_0)} \to \infty, & f \to 0 \end{array} \tag{29-8}$$

according to (29-7). This dependence of $f(\varepsilon)$ on ε is shown in Fig. 29-1. We see that there is a discontinuity in the probability of occupation of the states—all the states are completely occupied up to the limiting Fermi energy ζ_0 and none of the states is occupied for greater energy. The system of electrons *as a whole* is in its lowest possible energy state, but because of the exclusion principle there are individual electrons in particle states of finite energy even at $T = 0$.

We can determine ζ_0 from (29-5) and (29-8) as follows:

$$N = C \int_0^{\zeta_0} \sqrt{\varepsilon} \, d\varepsilon = \frac{2}{3} C \zeta_0^{3/2} \qquad (29\text{-}9)$$

Therefore, if we also use (29-3), we find that

$$\zeta_0 = \left(\frac{3N}{2C}\right)^{2/3} = \frac{h^2}{2m}\left(\frac{3N}{8\pi V}\right)^{2/3} \qquad (29\text{-}10)$$

which shows that ζ_0 depends only on the density of electrons.

Similarly, the zero point energy U_0 can be found from (28-6), (29-8), and (29-9) to be

$$U_0 = C \int_0^{\zeta_0} \varepsilon^{3/2} \, d\varepsilon = \tfrac{2}{5} C \zeta_0^{5/2} = \tfrac{3}{5} N \zeta_0 \qquad (29\text{-}11)$$

so that the average energy per electron is $\tfrac{3}{5}\zeta_0$. The zero point pressure p_0 can be obtained from (28-15) and (29-11); the result is

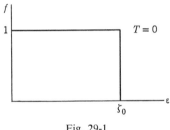

Fig. 29-1

$$p_0 = \frac{2}{5}\left(\frac{N}{V}\right)\zeta_0 = \frac{8\pi h^2}{15m}\left(\frac{3N}{8\pi V}\right)^{5/3} \qquad (29\text{-}12)$$

These quantities are not negligible. For example, if (29-12) is evaluated for copper, it is found that $p_0 \approx 4 \times 10^5$ atmospheres. This large zero point pressure corresponds to the electrical attraction between the electrons and metallic ions since this is what keeps the electrons within the metal in spite of the large value of p_0.

29-3 Properties for finite temperatures

We shall evaluate the quantities of interest by approximate methods which will be valid as long as $kT \ll \zeta_0$, that is,

$$\beta \zeta_0 \gg 1 \qquad (29\text{-}13)$$

If we use (29-10), we see that (29-13) is equivalent to

$$T \ll \frac{h^2}{2mk}\left(\frac{3N}{8\pi V}\right)^{2/3} \approx 10^5 \text{ degrees} \qquad (29\text{-}14)$$

which will certainly be valid for any situation we shall want to consider.

The equation which determines ζ is (29-5), which we can also write as

$$N = C \int_0^\infty f(\varepsilon)\sqrt{\varepsilon}\, d\varepsilon \tag{29-15}$$

If we integrate (29-15) by parts, we obtain

$$N = \left[\frac{2}{3} Cf(\varepsilon)\varepsilon^{3/2}\right]_0^\infty - C \int_0^\infty \frac{2}{3} \varepsilon^{3/2} \frac{df}{d\varepsilon}\, d\varepsilon$$

$$= -C \int_0^\infty \frac{2}{3} \varepsilon^{3/2} \frac{df}{d\varepsilon}\, d\varepsilon \tag{29-16}$$

with the use of (29-7).   Many quantities of interest in this field can be written in the form

$$I = \int_0^\infty \frac{dF(\varepsilon)}{d\varepsilon} f(\varepsilon)\, d\varepsilon = - \int_0^\infty F(\varepsilon) \frac{df}{d\varepsilon}\, d\varepsilon \tag{29-17}$$

where $F(\varepsilon)$ vanishes when $\varepsilon = 0$;   this result enables us to devise a useful series expansion for I.

The general appearance of $f(\varepsilon)$ for $T \neq 0$ is shown in Fig. 29-2a.   We see that f is either almost 1 or zero except for a small region about ζ; consequently, the derivative of f is almost zero everywhere except near ζ, as shown in Fig. 29-2b.   Therefore it is appropriate to expand $F(\varepsilon)$ in a series about the Fermi energy.

We introduce the dimensionless variable $x = \beta(\varepsilon - \zeta)$ so that

$$f = \frac{1}{e^x + 1}, \qquad -\frac{df}{d\varepsilon} = \beta \frac{e^x}{(e^x + 1)^2} \tag{29-18}$$

We also find that (29-17) becomes

$$I = \int_{-\beta\zeta}^\infty F\left(\zeta + \frac{x}{\beta}\right) \frac{e^x}{(e^x + 1)^2}\, dx \tag{29-19}$$

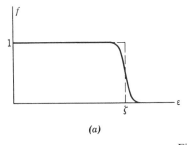

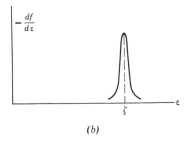

(a)   (b)

Fig. 29-2

Since we expect ζ to be not very different from ζ_0, then $\beta\zeta \gg 1$ because of (29-13) and we can replace the lower limit of integration in (29-19) by $-\infty$. If we expand F in a power series about ζ, we obtain

$$F\left(\zeta + \frac{x}{\beta}\right) = F(\zeta) + \frac{x}{\beta}\left(\frac{dF}{d\varepsilon}\right)_\zeta + \frac{1}{2}\frac{x^2}{\beta^2}\left(\frac{d^2F}{d\varepsilon^2}\right)_\zeta + \cdots \quad (29\text{-}20)$$

and, when (29-20) is substituted into (29-19), we obtain

$$I = F(\zeta)I_0 + \frac{1}{\beta}\left(\frac{dF}{d\varepsilon}\right)_\zeta I_1 + \frac{1}{2\beta^2}\left(\frac{d^2F}{d\varepsilon^2}\right)_\zeta I_2 + \cdots \quad (29\text{-}21)$$

where

$$I_0 = \int_{-\infty}^{\infty} \frac{e^x\,dx}{(e^x + 1)^2} = 1 \quad (29\text{-}22)$$

$$I_1 = \int_{-\infty}^{\infty} \frac{xe^x\,dx}{(e^x + 1)^2} = 0 \quad (29\text{-}23)$$

because

$$\frac{e^{-x}}{(e^{-x} + 1)^2} = \frac{e^x}{(e^x + 1)^2}$$

making the integrand of I_1 an odd function of x. Also,

$$I_2 = \int_{-\infty}^{\infty} \frac{x^2 e^x\,dx}{(e^x + 1)^2} = 2\int_0^{\infty} \frac{x^2 e^{-x}\,dx}{(1 + e^{-x})^2}$$

$$= 2\int_0^{\infty} x^2 e^{-x}(1 - 2e^{-x} + 3e^{-2x} - \cdots)\,dx$$

$$= 4\left(1 - \frac{1}{2^2} + \frac{1}{3^2} - \cdots\right) = 2\zeta(2) = \frac{\pi^2}{3} \quad (29\text{-}24)$$

with the help of (26-57) and the definition of the zeta function. Substituting these results into (29-21), we obtain

$$I = \int_0^{\infty} \frac{dF(\varepsilon)}{d\varepsilon} f(\varepsilon)\,d\varepsilon \simeq F(\zeta) + \frac{\pi^2}{6}(kT)^2\left(\frac{d^2F}{d\varepsilon^2}\right)_\zeta + \cdots \quad (29\text{-}25)$$

as our desired approximation.

Applying this result to (29-16), we see from (29-17) that, when $I = N$,

$$F(\varepsilon) = \frac{2}{3}C\varepsilon^{3/2}, \qquad \frac{d^2F}{d\varepsilon^2} = \frac{C}{2\sqrt{\varepsilon}}$$

If we use these results in (29-25) and also use (29-9), we obtain

$$N = \frac{2}{3}C\zeta_0^{3/2} = \frac{2}{3}C\zeta^{3/2} + \frac{\pi^2}{6}(kT)^2\frac{C}{2\sqrt{\zeta}}$$

so that

$$\zeta^{3/2} = \zeta_0^{3/2} - \frac{\pi^2}{8} \frac{(kT)^2}{\sqrt{\zeta}} \simeq \zeta_0^{3/2} - \frac{\pi^2}{8} \frac{(kT)^2}{\sqrt{\zeta_0}}$$

$$= \zeta_0^{3/2} \left[1 - \frac{\pi^2}{8} \left(\frac{kT}{\zeta_0} \right)^2 \right]$$

and therefore

$$\zeta = \zeta_0 \left[1 - \frac{\pi^2}{8} \left(\frac{kT}{\zeta_0} \right)^2 \right]^{2/3} \simeq \zeta_0 \left[1 - \frac{\pi^2}{12} \left(\frac{kT}{\zeta_0} \right)^2 \right] \qquad (29\text{-}26)$$

is our expression for the Fermi energy as a function of temperature.

In order to calculate U, we compare (28-6) and (29-17) and we see that, when $I = U$,

$$\frac{dF}{d\varepsilon} = C\varepsilon^{3/2}, \quad F = \frac{2}{5} C\varepsilon^{5/2}, \quad \frac{d^2F}{d\varepsilon^2} = \frac{3}{2} C\varepsilon^{1/2}$$

and (29-25) becomes

$$U = \frac{2}{5} C\zeta^{5/2} \left[1 + \frac{5\pi^2}{8} \left(\frac{kT}{\zeta} \right)^2 \right] \qquad (29\text{-}27)$$

We find that $C = 5U_0/2\zeta_0^{5/2}$ from (29-11) and may be used in (29-27). In the bracket of (29-27), ζ can be replaced by ζ_0 because this bracket already involves a second order term. If we use (29-26) in addition and keep only second order terms in kT/ζ_0 so that $(1 + x)^n \simeq 1 + nx$, we find that (29-27) becomes

$$U \simeq U_0 \left(\frac{\zeta}{\zeta_0} \right)^{5/2} \left[1 + \frac{5\pi^2}{8} \left(\frac{kT}{\zeta_0} \right)^2 \right]$$

$$\simeq U_0 \left[1 - \frac{5\pi^2}{24} \left(\frac{kT}{\zeta_0} \right)^2 \right] \left[1 + \frac{5\pi^2}{8} \left(\frac{kT}{\zeta_0} \right)^2 \right]$$

$$\simeq U_0 \left[1 + \frac{5\pi^2}{12} \left(\frac{kT}{\zeta_0} \right)^2 \right] \qquad (29\text{-}28)$$

The heat capacity of the system of electrons then is found to be

$$C_v = \frac{dU}{dT} = Nk \frac{\pi^2}{2} \left(\frac{kT}{\zeta_0} \right) \sim T \qquad (29\text{-}29)$$

with the use of (29-11). The ratio of the molar heat capacity to the Dulong-Petit value of $3R$ is therefore

$$\frac{c_{v\,\text{elec}}}{c_{v\,\text{D-P}}} = \frac{\pi^2}{6} \left(\frac{kT}{\zeta_0} \right) \qquad (29\text{-}30)$$

and, since $kT/\zeta_0 \ll 1$ by (29-13), we see that ordinarily the electrons make only a negligible contribution to the heat capacity of a metal. We have now satisfied the earlier objection to the electron theory of metals for which the classical equipartition theorem predicted too large a contribution from the electrons.

The situation is quite different, however, at extremely low temperatures where the heat capacity of the lattice is proportional to T^3 as given by the Debye theory result (26-60b). Since the electron contribution is linearly proportional to T according to (29-29), we see that the electrons will be the source of practically all the heat capacity once the temperature is low enough to make the term linear in T dominant over the T^3 term. This is the general behavior found for the heat capacity of metals; at low enough temperatures, $c_v \sim T$ as previously mentioned near the end of Sec. 26-5.

We can also calculate the low-temperature entropy of the electrons from (29-29) in order to show that the third law of thermodynamics (13-1) is now satisfied:

$$S = \int_0^T \frac{C_v\, dT'}{T'} = Nk\frac{\pi^2}{2}\left(\frac{kT}{\zeta_0}\right) + \cdots \xrightarrow[T\to 0]{} 0 \qquad (29\text{-}31)$$

The results we have obtained for a finite temperature can be understood and interpreted more easily in terms of our next calculation, in which we wish to find the fraction of the electrons at $T \neq 0$ which have been excited above the Fermi energy ζ_0. If we let δN be the number whose energy is greater than ζ_0, we find from (29-5) and (29-9) that the fraction of interest is

$$\frac{\delta N}{N} = \frac{C}{N}\int_{\zeta_0}^{\infty}\frac{\sqrt{\varepsilon}\,d\varepsilon}{e^{\beta(\varepsilon-\zeta)}+1} = \frac{3}{2(\beta\zeta_0)^{3/2}}\int_{\beta(\zeta_0-\zeta)}^{\infty}\frac{(x+\beta\zeta)^{1/2}\,dx}{e^x+1} \qquad (29\text{-}32)$$

We are going to determine only the lowest order approximation to (29-32) which we can obtain by replacing the lower limit of integration by zero because of (29-26) and by taking $(x+\beta\zeta)^{1/2} \simeq (\beta\zeta)^{1/2} \simeq (\beta\zeta_0)^{1/2}$; we therefore find that

$$\frac{\delta N}{N} \simeq \frac{3}{2\beta\zeta_0}\int_0^{\infty}\frac{dx}{e^x+1} = \frac{3}{2}\left(\frac{kT}{\zeta_0}\right)\ln 2 = 1.04\frac{kT}{\zeta_0} \qquad (29\text{-}33)$$

Therefore the fraction kT/ζ_0 very nearly equals the fraction of the electrons which have been thermally excited above the absolute zero state, so that, in effect, only this small number of the total electrons are responsible for the properties of the system. For example, (29-29) is approximately equal to the classical heat capacity of a system of $N(kT/\zeta_0)$ effective electrons rather than of the number N actually present.

29-4 Thermionic emission

When a metal is heated, it is found that some of the electrons are able to escape through the surface; the resulting current is called the *thermionic emission current*. We have already mentioned that our assumption that the electrons move about in the interior as if there were no net force acting on them is equivalent to an assumption of constant potential energy in the interior and which we have taken to be zero. At the surface of the metal, strong attractive forces balance the electron pressure, so that the potential energy must increase very rapidly and then become constant again outside the metal where the electron can again be regarded as free. The model we shall accordingly adopt is that represented by the potential energy curve of Fig. 29-3. Therefore E_0 is the total difference in energy between the lowest state of an electron inside and one outside. At $T = 0$ the energy states are occupied up to ζ_0 as indicated by the shading; the difference

$$\phi = E_0 - \zeta_0 \qquad (29\text{-}34)$$

is called the *work function* of the metal.

When the electron energy becomes sufficiently large, the electrons are able to escape and we wish to calculate the resultant current density. The energy is $\varepsilon = p^2/2m$; the velocity component perpendicular to the wall is p_z/m. Since the current density of the electrons in the ith state is the product of the charge density ρ_i and the velocity according to (6-2), the component of the total current density perpendicular to the wall is

$$J_z = \sum_i \rho_i u_{iz} = \sum_i \left(\frac{en_i}{V}\right)\left(\frac{p_{zi}}{m}\right) \qquad (29\text{-}35)$$

since n_i is the total number of particles in the ith state and e is the electron

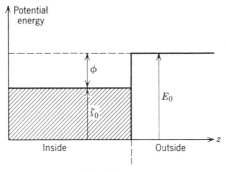

Fig. 29-3

charge. We can convert (29-35) to an integral by multiplying it by

$$\frac{2d\Omega_\mu}{h^3} = \frac{2dp_x\,dp_y\,dp_z\,dx\,dy\,dz}{h^3} \qquad (29\text{-}36)$$

The factor 2 arises because of the spin degeneracy; hence there are two total states for each cell in the μ-space. If we substitute (27-26), (29-4), and (29-36) into (29-35), integrate x, y, and z over the total volume V, and note that an electron cannot escape unless it has a velocity component in the z direction *and* a kinetic energy at least equal to E_0, so that $p_z^2/2m \geqslant E_0$, we obtain

$$J_z = \frac{2e}{mh^3} \int_{-\infty}^{\infty} \int_{-\infty}^{\infty} \int_{(2mE_0)^{1/2}}^{\infty} \frac{p_z\,dp_z\,dp_x\,dp_y}{e^{\beta(p^2/2m-\zeta)} + 1} \qquad (29\text{-}37)$$

We can put this into a more convenient form by noting that

$$p_z = m\frac{\partial}{\partial p_z}\left(\frac{p^2}{2m}\right) = m\frac{\partial\varepsilon}{\partial p_z}$$

which enables us to write (29-37) as

$$J_z = \frac{2e}{h^3} \int_{-\infty}^{\infty} dp_x \int_{-\infty}^{\infty} dp_y \int_{(2mE_0)^{1/2}}^{\infty} \frac{(\partial\varepsilon/\partial p_z)\,dp_z}{e^{\beta(p^2/2m-\zeta)} + 1}$$

$$= \frac{2e}{h^3} \int_{-\infty}^{\infty} dp_x \int_{-\infty}^{\infty} dp_y \int_{E_0+(p_x^2+p_y^2)/2m}^{\infty} \frac{d\varepsilon}{e^{\beta(\varepsilon-\zeta)} + 1} \qquad (29\text{-}38)$$

The integral over ε in (29-38) becomes

$$\int_{E_0+(p_x^2+p_y^2)/2m}^{\infty} \frac{e^{-\beta(\varepsilon-\zeta)}\,d\varepsilon}{1 + e^{-\beta(\varepsilon-\zeta)}} = \frac{1}{\beta}\ln\left[1 + e^{-\beta(E_0-\zeta)-\beta(p_x^2+p_y^2)/2m}\right] \qquad (29\text{-}39)$$

At ordinary temperatures,

$$\beta(E_0 - \zeta) \simeq \beta(E_0 - \zeta_0) = \beta\phi \gg 1 \qquad (29\text{-}40)$$

so that $e^{-\beta\phi} \ll 1$ and we can use the approximation $\ln(1 + x) \simeq x$ for $x \ll 1$ in (29-39); when this is done, (29-38) becomes

$$J_z \simeq \frac{2e}{\beta h^3} e^{-\beta\phi} \int_{-\infty}^{\infty} e^{-\beta p_x^2/2m}\,dp_x \int_{-\infty}^{\infty} e^{-\beta p_y^2/2m}\,dp_y$$

so that, if we use (18-9) and (21-60), we finally obtain

$$J_z = \frac{4\pi emk^2}{h^3} T^2 e^{-\phi/kT} \qquad (29\text{-}41)$$

which is known as the *Richardson equation*.

It has been shown experimentally that the velocity distribution of the electrons which have left the metal is approximately a Maxwell distribution. This may seem surprising at first because the electrons inside have a Fermi-Dirac distribution; however, the observed distribution can be obtained quite easily from our model. The number of electrons in the energy range $d\varepsilon$ at ε is given by (29-6). This equation applies also to those electrons which leave the metal and for which $\varepsilon \geqslant E_0$. If we let $\varepsilon' = \varepsilon - E_0$ be the kinetic energy of the electrons *outside* the metal, their distribution as obtained from (29-6) is

$$n'(\varepsilon')\,d\varepsilon' = \frac{C(\varepsilon' + E_0)^{1/2}\,d\varepsilon'}{e^{\beta(\varepsilon' + E_0 - \zeta)} + 1} \simeq \frac{C(\varepsilon' + E_0)^{1/2}\,d\varepsilon'}{e^{\beta(\varepsilon' + \phi)} + 1} \tag{29-42}$$

which can be approximated with the use of (29-40) and $\varepsilon' \ll E_0$ as

$$n'(\varepsilon')\,d\varepsilon' \simeq C\sqrt{E_0}\,e^{-\beta\phi - \beta\varepsilon'}\,d\varepsilon' = C'\,e^{-\beta\varepsilon'}\,d\varepsilon' \tag{29-43}$$

where C' is a new constant for a given temperature. Equation (29-43), giving the distribution of the energies ε' observed outside the metal, is exactly the classical distribution function.

29-5 Thermal and electrical conductivities

We shall discuss these non-equilibrium phenomena for a metal in a brief and simplified manner which, however, will yield results which differ only by small numerical factors from those obtained from a more exact theory.

In our discussion of transport phenomena in a gas in Chapter 19, we found a formula for the heat flux $\bar{Q}$ given by the first expression of (19-17). If we use (25-2) and (17-12), we can write

$$n\left(\frac{\partial\bar{\varepsilon}_t}{\partial y}\right)_0 = \frac{N}{V}\frac{d\bar{\varepsilon}_t}{dT}\left(\frac{\partial T}{\partial y}\right)_0 = \frac{N\bar{c}_v}{V}\left(\frac{\partial T}{\partial y}\right)_0 = \frac{C_v}{V}\left(\frac{\partial T}{\partial y}\right)_0,$$

which, when substituted into (19-17) and compared with (19-18), gives us the more general expression for the thermal conductivity K:

$$K = \frac{l\bar{u}C_v}{3V} \tag{29-44}$$

Using $\varepsilon = \tfrac{1}{2}mu^2$, we can find $\bar{u}$ from (29-6) as

$$\bar{u} = \frac{1}{N}\int_0^\infty \left(\frac{2\varepsilon}{m}\right)^{1/2} n(\varepsilon)\,d\varepsilon = \frac{C}{N}\left(\frac{2}{m}\right)^{1/2}\int_0^\infty \varepsilon f(\varepsilon)\,d\varepsilon \tag{29-45}$$

Since the average speed $\bar{u}$ is very large even when $T = 0$ and changes very little with temperature, it will be sufficient for our purposes to evaluate $\bar{u}$ at $T = 0$. By using (29-8) and (29-9), we find that

$$\bar{u}_0 = \frac{3}{2\zeta_0^{3/2}} \left(\frac{2}{m}\right)^{1/2} \int_0^{\zeta_0} \varepsilon \, d\varepsilon = \frac{3}{4} \left(\frac{2\zeta_0}{m}\right)^{1/2} = \frac{3}{4} u_0 \qquad (29\text{-}46)$$

where u_0 is the speed of an electron with the Fermi energy. Using (29-29), (29-44), and (29-46), we obtain

$$K = \frac{\pi^2 N l k^2 T}{4Vmu_0} \qquad (29\text{-}47)$$

Before discussing (29-47), let us turn to the calculation of the electrical conductivity. In the absence of an electric field, the electrons have random directions of motion so that the average z component of the velocity vanishes according to (16-14'). Since $\bar{u}_z = 0$, there will be no average current. If there is now a field E in the z direction, each electron of charge e has an acceleration

$$a_z = \frac{eE}{m} \qquad (29\text{-}48)$$

by (5-1) and (6-46). If we assume that the average effect of a collision is to give the electrons a random direction of motion, and if τ is the average time between collisions, we see from (29-48) that by the time the next collision occurs an average electron will have acquired a velocity component in the direction of the field given by $u_z = a_z\tau$. During the time between collisions, its average velocity along E is therefore

$$\bar{u}_z = \tfrac{1}{2} a_z \tau = \frac{e\tau E}{2m} \qquad (29\text{-}49)$$

The average current density J_z in the direction of E is then obtained from (6-2) as

$$J_z = \rho \bar{u}_z = \left(\frac{Ne}{V}\right)\left(\frac{e\tau E}{2m}\right) = \left(\frac{Ne^2\tau}{2Vm}\right)E = \sigma E \qquad (29\text{-}50)$$

where σ is the electrical conductivity. Therefore we have

$$\sigma = \frac{Ne^2\tau}{2Vm} \simeq \frac{Ne^2 l}{2Vm\bar{u}} = \frac{2Ne^2 l}{3Vmu_0} \qquad (29\text{-}51)$$

if we take $\tau \simeq l/\bar{u}$ and use (29-46).

Both K and σ depend on the ratio l/u_0. If we calculate the ratio of the conductivities, we obtain

$$\frac{K}{\sigma} = \frac{3\pi^2}{8}\left(\frac{k}{e}\right)^2 T \sim T \qquad (29\text{-}52)$$

which shows that this ratio should be proportional to the temperature but otherwise *independent of the metal*; the general nature of this result is reminiscent of (19-20). Equation (29-52) is known as the *Wiedemann-Franz law*; it was obtained empirically by them in 1853, long before the development of the electron theory of metals. Experimentally it is found that the ratio K/σ is constant to within about 15 per cent for different metals at the same temperature. The fact that the electron theory of metals predicts this result (29-52) is additional strong evidence of its basic validity.

Exercises

29-1. By following the procedure which led to (29-25), show that, to the next higher order approximation, ζ and U are given by

$$\zeta = \zeta_0\left[1 - \frac{\pi^2}{12}\left(\frac{kT}{\zeta_0}\right)^2 - \frac{\pi^4}{80}\left(\frac{kT}{\zeta_0}\right)^4\right]$$

$$U = U_0\left[1 + \frac{5\pi^2}{12}\left(\frac{kT}{\zeta_0}\right)^2 - \frac{\pi^4}{16}\left(\frac{kT}{\zeta_0}\right)^4\right]$$

rather than by (29-26) and (29-28).

29-2. Show that the average energy of the thermionic electrons which escape perpendicular to the surface is kT.

29-3. A typical number density of electrons in a vacuum tube may be about 10^{17} (meter)$^{-3}$. Should one use the Fermi-Dirac results to discuss this case, or will the Boltzmann limit be adequate?

30 *Semiconductors*

In spite of the success of the free electron theory of metals in accounting for the low-temperature heat capacity and in providing a plausible model for conductivities, it is unsatisfactory in the sense that it does not directly provide a way of predicting whether a given solid will have a high conductivity and thus be classed as a metal or whether it will have a very low conductivity and be classed as an insulator. Modern developments in solid state theory have gone a long way toward resolving this difficulty. In addition, materials of intermediate properties, known as semiconductors, have become of great interest and importance. Our aim in this chapter will be to discuss these materials briefly as another application of statistical mechanics by accepting and using the current quantum mechanical models. Since we shall be interested only in the properties of the electrons as they relate to the electrical conductivity, we shall use the Fermi-Dirac distribution. As we can see from our basic formulas (27-27), (27-28), and (28-1), the information which we require is the distribution and energies of the electronic states.

30-1   Energy band picture of crystals

One of the principal effects which is neglected in the free electron theory is the interaction of the electrons with the positively charged metallic ions. Since these ions are located at the various lattice points of the crystal, the potential energy of the electrons will also be *periodic* with the spatial periodicity and symmetry of the crystal structure. The basic quantum mechanical problem is then to solve the Schroedinger wave equation for a *periodic potential*.

The results of this calculation show that the possible electron energies are very close together and can be treated as almost continuously spaced, much as we have been doing for the free particle in a large box. In addition, the energies can be divided into *bands*. In other words, certain ranges of energy values are possible for the electron moving in a periodic potential, whereas other ranges of the energies are not possible. Those of the first type are called *allowed* energies, and those of the latter are called *forbidden* energies; the corresponding sets of bands are *allowed bands* and *forbidden bands*. This situation is illustrated in the conventional schematic manner in Fig. 30-1 in which energy is plotted versus some position coordinate through the crystal. The energy states are represented by horizontal lines to indicate that the electron is not localized but can be found anywhere within the crystal; the spacing is of course much closer than that shown.

The periodic nature of the crystal structure is the basic reason for the division into bands. Similar results can be obtained when the normal frequencies of coupled mechanical systems are calculated. An example of such a system is the *weighted string* consisting of equal masses spaced equal distances apart and coupled to each other by like forces; this system is discussed in (I: Chapters 13 and 15). It is found that waves cannot be propagated along the weighted string if the frequency is greater than some maximum value, but that such a frequency corresponds to an attenuated disturbance instead. Thus frequencies are divided into two bands for this system, an allowed band for which $0 \leqslant \nu \leqslant \nu_{max}$, and a forbidden band for which $\nu > \nu_{max}$.

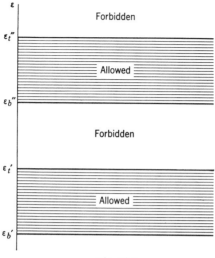

Fig. 30-1

The formation of bands can also be understood qualitatively from a different approach which is illustrated in Fig. 30-2. When the atoms are far apart, each atom has its own discrete energy states and the system will have correspondingly discrete levels; two of these levels are shown in the figure. For N electrons, there are a total of $2N$ states in each level because of the electron spin. As it is imagined that the atoms are brought closer

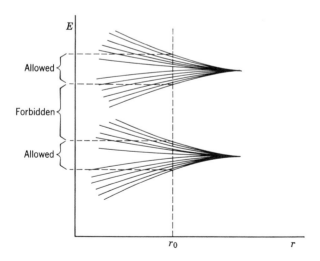

Fig. 30-2

together as the crystal is formed, the forces between the atoms begin to become important. The energies of the previously degenerate states are thus altered, and they begin to separate as shown. The net result when the equilibrium distance r_0 is reached is that a band of energies has originated from each level; there will be a total of $2N$ states in each band, and hence a total of $2N$ electrons will "fill" the band. In any event, the exact values of the locations of the bands and their widths will depend on the particular crystal.

When the *effect of external fields* on an electron in an allowed state of a band is investigated, it is found that the electron can be quite accurately described as reacting much like a free particle, except with an *effective mass m** which is different from the mass of an unbound electron. The exact magnitude of m^* depends on the details of the band structure, and it will be sufficient for our purposes to accept it as one of the state parameters. The situation is somewhat analogous to the problem of a sphere moving in an ideal incompressible fluid which is discussed in (I: Sec. 18-6); in this case it is also found that the net result of all the interactions of the sphere with the fluid is, in effect, to alter the inertia of the sphere as far as its behavior with respect to external forces is concerned.

Since the electron in an allowed band has these attributes of a free particle, we can use the expression for the density of states obtained from (28-3) and (29-3), except that now ε is to be replaced in the formula by the amount the electron energy exceeds the energy of the bottom of the band. For example, if we have a situation like that of Fig. 30-1 and if we consider the band for which $\varepsilon_b'' \leqslant \varepsilon \leqslant \varepsilon_t''$, the density of states in this band will be assumed to be given by

$$c(\varepsilon)\,d\varepsilon = 4\pi V \left(\frac{2m^*}{h^2}\right)^{3/2} (\varepsilon - \varepsilon_b'')^{1/2}\,d\varepsilon = C^*(\varepsilon - \varepsilon_b'')^{1/2}\,d\varepsilon \quad (30\text{-}1)$$

In the absence of external fields there is no net transfer of charge; hence for every state in an allowed band which corresponds to an electron moving in a given direction there must be a state corresponding to motion in the opposite direction. Consequently, the total current of a completely filled band is zero:

$$\mathbf{I} = \sum_{\text{band}} e\mathbf{u}_i = 0 \quad (30\text{-}2)$$

which can also be written

$$\mathbf{I} = e\mathbf{u}_j + \sum_{i \neq j} e\mathbf{u}_i = 0 \quad (30\text{-}3)$$

Suppose now that the *j*th electron is missing from the band for some reason; the total current then is

$$\mathbf{I'} = \sum_{i \neq j} e\mathbf{u}_i = -e\mathbf{u}_j \qquad (30\text{-}4)$$

because of (30-3). In other words, the motions of the electrons in the band no longer exactly cancel and there is a net current equivalent to that carried by a single carrier whose charge is opposite to that of an electron and hence is positive. Thus a band with an electron missing acts *as if* it were equivalent to a positive charge $|e|$; this resultant behavior is called a *hole*, and it provides us with a simplified and useful picture of the over-all situation by enabling us to ascribe independent existence to a hole as a definite and single carrier of positive charge. In the presence of an electric field, therefore, a hole will move in the direction of the field, whereas an electron will move opposite to the field.

The completely filled band of highest energy is called the *valence band*; the next band above this is called the *conduction band*. Suppose now that each of the N atoms contributes one electron to the band; there will be a total of N electrons available for the $2N$ states of the band and, at $T = 0$, the conduction band will be exactly half full as illustrated in Fig. 30-3a. Even a small electric field applied to the material will be able to give the electrons energy because there are possible states just above the topmost filled one. Thus the electrons will be set in motion by an arbitrarily small field, and the material will have the conductivity properties of a *metal*. Suppose, instead, that each atom contributes two electrons to the band; there will be a total of $2N$ electrons and the valence band will be completely filled as shown in Fig. 30-3b. Consequently, an applied electric field will not generally be able to make the electrons change their states because those immediately above the topmost filled one are forbidden. Therefore the field will not produce a current, the conductivity will be zero, and the material will be an *insulator*.

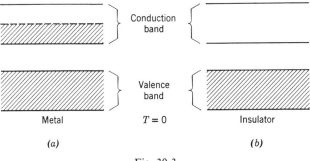

Fig. 30-3

It is clear that, if some of the electrons in the filled valence band could somehow be given enough energy to excite them into the conduction band, they could be accelerated by the field and the conductivity would be different from zero. At the same time, the holes left in the valence band could also be accelerated and could contribute to the conductivity. The most common method of increasing the electron energies is to raise the temperature. In the next section, therefore, we shall calculate the conductivity resulting from thermal excitation.

30-2   Insulators and intrinsic semiconductors

We neglect any possible effects arising from filled bands with energy below the uppermost or valence band; the band picture we assume therefore is that illustrated in Fig. 30-4 for $T \neq 0$. In this figure we also illustrate the conventional pictorialization of electrons in the conduction band and the resultant holes in the valence band.

We can find the total number of electrons N_e in the conduction band by adapting (29-5) to this case with the use of (29-7) and (30-1); the result is

$$N_e = C_e^* \int_{\varepsilon_c}^{\varepsilon_t} f(\varepsilon)(\varepsilon - \varepsilon_c)^{\frac{1}{2}} \, d\varepsilon \qquad (30\text{-}5)$$

where C_e^* is given by (30-1) in terms of the effective electron mass m_e^*. Our experience with the properties of $f(\varepsilon)$ for a finite temperature as illustrated in Fig. 29-2a leads us to think that the Fermi energy ζ will be located somewhere between the bands, as shown in Fig. 30-4; we shall verify this surmise later. As a result, the most important contributions to (30-5) can be expected to come from near the bottom of the band, and we

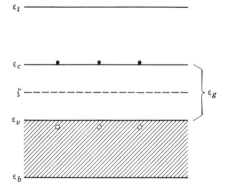

Fig. 30-4

can replace the upper limit by $+\infty$. Generally, we shall also have $\varepsilon_c - \zeta \gg kT$, so that $f(\varepsilon)$ can be approximated by $e^{\beta(\zeta - \varepsilon)}$ and (30-5) becomes

$$N_e \simeq C_e^* \int_{\varepsilon_c}^{\infty} f(\varepsilon)(\varepsilon - \varepsilon_c)^{\frac{1}{2}}\, d\varepsilon$$

$$\simeq C_e^* \int_{\varepsilon_c}^{\infty} e^{\beta(\zeta - \varepsilon)}(\varepsilon - \varepsilon_c)^{\frac{1}{2}}\, d\varepsilon$$

$$= C_e^* \, e^{\beta(\zeta - \varepsilon_c)} \int_0^{\infty} x^{\frac{1}{2}} e^{-\beta x}\, dx$$

$$= \frac{\sqrt{\pi}\, C_e^* \, e^{\beta(\zeta - \varepsilon_c)}}{2\beta^{\frac{3}{2}}}$$

$$= \frac{2V}{h^3} (2\pi m_e^* kT)^{\frac{3}{2}} \, e^{(\zeta - \varepsilon_c)/kT} \tag{30-6}$$

with the use of (18-9) and (30-1).

The number of holes, N_h, can be obtained in a similar manner if we realize that the free particle behavior of a hole is given by its energy distance *below* the top of the valence band; thus in (30-1) we must use $(\varepsilon_v - \varepsilon)^{\frac{1}{2}}$ in place of $(\varepsilon - \varepsilon_b'')^{\frac{1}{2}}$. Since a hole represents a missing electron, the probability of a hole is equal to the probability that an electron is not occupying the state and is therefore $1 - f(\varepsilon)$. Thus, instead of (30-5), we obtain

$$N_h = C_h^* \int_{\varepsilon_b}^{\varepsilon_v} [1 - f(\varepsilon)](\varepsilon_v - \varepsilon)^{\frac{1}{2}}\, d\varepsilon$$

$$\simeq C_h^* \int_{-\infty}^{\varepsilon_v} \frac{(\varepsilon_v - \varepsilon)^{\frac{1}{2}}\, d\varepsilon}{1 + e^{\beta(\zeta - \varepsilon)}} \simeq C_h^* \int_{-\infty}^{\varepsilon_v} (\varepsilon_v - \varepsilon)^{\frac{1}{2}} \, e^{\beta(\varepsilon - \zeta)}\, d\varepsilon$$

$$= \frac{\sqrt{\pi}\, C_h^* \, e^{\beta(\varepsilon_v - \zeta)}}{2\beta^{\frac{3}{2}}}$$

$$= \frac{2V}{h^3} (2\pi m_h^* kT)^{\frac{3}{2}} \, e^{(\varepsilon_v - \zeta)/kT} \tag{30-7}$$

Since each electron raised to the conduction band leaves a hole behind, we must have

$$N_e = N_h \tag{30-8}$$

Thus we can find ζ by substituting (30-6) and (30-7) into (30-8) with the result that

$$\zeta = \tfrac{1}{2}(\varepsilon_c + \varepsilon_v) + \frac{kT}{2} \ln \frac{C_h{}^*}{C_e{}^*}$$

$$= \varepsilon_v + \tfrac{1}{2}\varepsilon_g + \frac{3}{4} kT \ln \frac{m_h{}^*}{m_e{}^*} \qquad (30\text{-}9)$$

where

$$\varepsilon_g = \varepsilon_c - \varepsilon_v \qquad (30\text{-}10)$$

is known as the *gap width*. If $T = 0$ or if $m_h{}^* = m_e{}^*$, the Fermi level lies exactly halfway between the top of the valence band and the bottom of the conduction band.

The number of conduction electrons and holes can be found by substituting (30-9) into (30-6) and (30-7) or by multiplying (30-6) and (30-7) together and using (30-8); the result is

$$N_e = N_h = \frac{2V}{h^3} (2\pi kT)^{3/2} (m_e{}^* m_h{}^*)^{3/4} \, e^{-\varepsilon_g/2kT} \qquad (30\text{-}11)$$

which is much like a Boltzmann distribution except that only half the gap width ε_g appears in the exponent.

Our previous expression for conductivity for one type of charge carrier is given by (29-51). It is generally convenient to write this in the form

$$\sigma = n \, |e| \, \mu \qquad (30\text{-}12)$$

where $n = N/V$ is the density of carriers and μ is called the *mobility* and is defined as the ratio of the magnitude of the average velocity produced in the direction of the applied electric field to the field. For the simple case of (29-49), the mobility is

$$\mu = \frac{|e| \tau}{2m} \qquad (30\text{-}13)$$

The processes determining the mobility are generally more complicated than they were assumed to be in obtaining (30-13); however, (30-13) gives one an idea of what parameters of the system are of importance in determining μ.

In the present case, when there are two types of carriers, (30-12) can be generalized to

$$\sigma = |e| \, (n_e\mu_e + n_h\mu_h) = |e| \, (\mu_e + \mu_h)n_e \qquad (30\text{-}14)$$

because of (30-8). Substituting (30-11) into (30-14), we obtain

$$\sigma = \frac{2 \, |e|}{h^3} (\mu_e + \mu_h)(2\pi kT)^{3/2} (m_e{}^* m_h{}^*)^{3/4} \, e^{-\varepsilon_g/2kT} \qquad (30\text{-}15)$$

It is customary to regard $\ln \sigma$ as a function of $1/T$; if we neglect any possible temperature dependence of the mobilities, we find from (30-15) that

$$\ln \sigma = \text{const.} - \frac{\varepsilon_g}{2kT} - \frac{3}{2} \ln \frac{1}{T} \qquad (30\text{-}16)$$

Since the term $\ln (1/T)$ varies slowly with $1/T$, the curve (30-16) is essentially a straight line with slope $-\varepsilon_g/2k$ as shown in Fig. 30-5. The figure also demonstrates that the conductivity increases as the temperature increases, in contrast to the behavior found for metals. We see from (30-14) that the essential reason for this is that the carrier density increases very rapidly with temperature; for metals, on the other hand, the carrier density stays fairly constant while the average time between collisions decreases with increasing temperature, and hence the mobility decreases by (30-13).

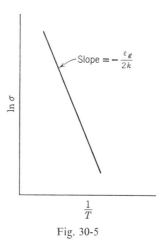

Fig. 30-5

Equation (30-15) shows that the predominant factor determining σ is the value of the gap width ε_g, and this has made it possible to classify materials roughly into two groups. If ε_g is large, there will be comparatively few carriers excited and the solid will be an *insulator*; if ε_g is smaller, there will be an appreciable number of electrons excited into the conduction band and the conductivity will be larger than that of an insulator but not so large as that of a metal—such a material is called an *intrinsic semiconductor*. The distinction between the two is clearly a relative matter, although all intrinsic semiconductors will be insulators at $T = 0$. The gap width is usually given in electron volts; one electron volt equals 1.60×10^{-19} joule. A good insulator such as diamond has a gap width of about 7 electron volts, while typical intrinsic semiconductors such as germanium and silicon have gap widths of about 1 electron volt; by way of comparison, $kT \simeq 0.025$ electron volt for room temperature.

30-3 Impurity semiconductors

The conductivity of most semiconductors is not intrinsic but rather is due to impurities which may be atoms of a type different from those normally in the crystal lattice or may be due to an excess of one constituent.

Since such impurities will destroy the periodicity of the crystal, it may be possible to have allowed electron energies in the previously forbidden band between the valence and conduction bands.

It has been found that these impurity levels are of two general types. In one type there may be electronic levels which are occupied at $T = 0$; the bound electrons in these levels are *localized* near the impurities, and consequently the levels are represented by short bars on a diagram such as Fig. 30-6. These electrons do not contribute to the conductivity unless they are excited to the conduction band, as is shown for one level in the figure; these levels are therefore called *donor levels*. An electron excited from a donor level does not leave a hole behind because the electron was initially localized and was not in a filled band. Similarly, there may be levels which represent a state which lacks one electron of being a normal situation for the particular crystal. These are called *acceptor levels* since it is possible for them to be filled with an electron excited from the valence band. Such a process will produce a hole, and conductivity will be possible; the electron shown excited to the acceptor level in Fig. 30-6 will not contribute to the conductivity because it is localized at this position in the lattice.

Such levels as these often result when an impurity atom of valence different from that of the original constituent of the crystal is substituted into the lattice. If the impurity atom has a higher valence, there will be one more electron than is needed to form the valence bonds; this electron will generally be loosely bound and will correspond to a donor level. Similarly, an acceptor level can result from an impurity of valence less than that of the atoms of the host crystal. It is perfectly possible, of course, for a material to have both types of levels present, and, in addition, the levels need not all have the same energy—the ε_d or ε_a of Fig. 30-6.

As an example of the type of calculations involved for an impurity semiconductor, let us assume that there are only donor levels present. In

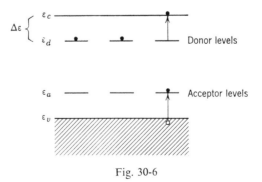

Fig. 30-6

addition, let us initially assume that the temperature is low enough that we can neglect any possible excitation of electrons from the valence band. The number of conduction electrons, N_e, will again be given by the expression (30-6), except that ζ will now be different. If N_d is the number of donor levels present and all are occupied at $T = 0$, then N_e also equals the number of donor levels which are unoccupied when $T \neq 0$; therefore

$$N_e = N_d[1 - f(\varepsilon_d)] = \frac{N_d}{1 + e^{\beta(\zeta - \varepsilon_d)}} \tag{30-17}$$

The Fermi level can be found by equating (30-6) and (30-17); hence

$$\frac{N_d}{1 + e^{(\zeta - \varepsilon_d)/kT}} = \frac{2V}{h^3}(2\pi m_e^* kT)^{3/2} e^{(\zeta - \varepsilon_c)/kT} \tag{30-18}$$

We can solve this approximately for ζ under the conditions $\zeta - \varepsilon_d \gg kT$, since then the denominator on the left becomes $e^{-(\zeta - \varepsilon_d)/kT}$ in the numerator and we find

$$\zeta = \varepsilon_d + \frac{\Delta\varepsilon}{2} + \frac{kT}{2}\ln\left[\frac{N_d}{V}\frac{h^3}{2(2\pi m_e^* kT)^{3/2}}\right] \tag{30-19}$$

where

$$\Delta\varepsilon = \varepsilon_c - \varepsilon_d \tag{30-20}$$

represents the energy required to ionize a donor level by removing its electron to the conduction band. When $T = 0$, $\zeta = \varepsilon_d + \frac{1}{2}\Delta\varepsilon$ and therefore is exactly halfway between the donor levels and the bottom of the conduction band.

The density of conduction electrons can be found from (30-17) and (30-19) with the result

$$n_e = \frac{N_e}{V} \simeq \left(\frac{N_d}{V}\right) e^{-\beta(\zeta - \varepsilon_d)}$$

$$= \left(\frac{2N_d}{V}\right)^{1/2}\left(\frac{2\pi m_e^* kT}{h^2}\right)^{3/4} e^{-\Delta\varepsilon/2kT} \tag{30-21}$$

so that n_e is proportional to the square root of the density of donor levels. Again we find half the energy difference $\frac{1}{2}\Delta\varepsilon$ entering in the Boltzmann type of exponential factor. The conductivity for the donor case is given by $\sigma = |e|\,\mu_e n_e$ and will be approximately described by a straight line of slope $-\Delta\varepsilon/2k$ if $\ln \sigma$ is plotted against $1/T$. This property of the curve is the basis of a method for determining the value of $\Delta\varepsilon$.

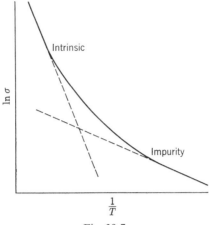

Fig. 30-7

There is always a contribution to the conductivity from the valence band, however, and at high temperatures it can become dominant over the impurity contribution because the number of electrons in the valence band is so much larger than the number of impurity levels that this effect can outweigh the disparity between ε_g and $\Delta\varepsilon$. The result is that the $\ln\sigma$ versus $1/T$ curve can show a change from a slope characteristic of impurity behavior to that characteristic of intrinsic behavior as illustrated in Fig. 30-7.

Exercises

30-1. If there are N_a acceptor levels of energy ε_a as in Fig. 30-6, and if they are all empty at $T = 0$, show that the density of free holes in the valence band is

$$n_h = \left(\frac{2N_a}{V}\right)^{1/2}\left(\frac{2\pi m_h{}^* kT}{h^2}\right)^{3/4} e^{-(\varepsilon_a - \varepsilon_v)/2kT}$$

30-2. Calculate the total conductivity when donor levels and the valence band are both included, and verify the general appearance of Fig. 30-7. What is the approximate temperature corresponding to the intermediate behavior of the curve?

30-3. Assume that only a small fraction of the possible donor levels are occupied by electrons at $T = 0$. Show that under these conditions the density of free electrons is proportional to $(N_d/V)e^{-\Delta\varepsilon/kT}$, and compare your result with (30-21). What are the experimental consequences of this result? How might you be able to distinguish between these two possibilities in the laboratory?

31 General systems and the canonical ensemble

Our specific results so far are applicable only to isolated systems composed of independent subsystems, and we naturally would like to formulate statistical mechanics so that it can also be used to treat more complicated systems such as dense gases or liquids for which the interactions among the particles are important.

We recall that when we originally introduced the concept of an ensemble we wanted to construct it in a way which would represent our knowledge of the system of interest as accurately as possible. Then we defined the microcanonical ensemble (20-23) as a suitable representation of an isolated system and based all our subsequent calculations on this ensemble. However, we realize that the concept of an isolated system is somewhat unrealistic for many cases, and we need to be able to discuss systems which are able to interact with and come to thermal equilibrium with their surroundings. In particular, we are interested in systems which are kept at *constant temperature* by thermal contact with a heat reservoir so that mutual exchanges of energy are possible. Therefore our system can no longer be regarded as having constant energy, and the microcanonical ensemble is not suitable in principle for calculating the system properties. The ensemble which is appropriate for describing the equilibrium properties of a system in contact with a heat reservoir and therefore at constant temperature is called a *canonical ensemble*. Our aim is to define the canonical ensemble accurately and then to determine its characteristics. We were faced with a similar situation in thermodynamics when we tried to formulate the basic results as given for isolated systems in terms of the properties of a system free to interact with its surroundings, and many of the considerations we used in Sec. 11-3 will be very helpful in indicating how we should presently proceed.

31-1   Derivation of the canonical ensemble from the microcanonical ensemble

Figure 11-1 illustrates the basic idea of our thermodynamic treatment in that we regarded the isolated system as being composed of the system of interest plus the heat reservoir. A microcanonical ensemble is evidently what we want to use for the isolated system.

Suppose that we assume our ensemble to be composed of a very large number $\mathscr{M}$ of imaginary copies of the system of interest. Since these copies are mental constructs, they can be treated as *independent* and *distinguishable* and we can apply exactly the same considerations to the ensemble as we did in Sec. 21-1 to the N independent subsystems in μ-space. In fact, since each member is represented by a single point in Γ-space, the full ensemble is represented by $\mathscr{M}$ points in Γ-space. Thus we can actually regard this ensemble *as a whole* as itself a microcanonical ensemble of $\mathscr{M}$ members, and then Γ-space for the system is actually the μ-space for this ensemble; the total constant energy E of this microcanonical ensemble will be

$$E = \mathscr{M}U = \text{const.} \tag{31-1}$$

where U is the average energy of each member which represents the system of interest. The ensemble as a whole can be represented as a single point in a "super" Γ-space which bears the same conceptual relation to Γ-space as Γ-space did to μ-space in Chapter 21; the condition (31-1) then represents a surface of constant energy in this super Γ-space. There will be no problems about the applicability of Stirling's formula, because we are free to choose $\mathscr{M}$ as large as we please and we can let $\mathscr{M} \to \infty$; nor do we need to employ corrected Boltzmann counting, since the ensemble members are *distinguishable* mental constructs.

We can assume in addition that there is a very slight interaction among the members of the ensemble. The reason for this assumption is that, if we look at any particular member of the ensemble, it will be interacting slightly with the remaining members. In other words, a given member of the ensemble can be regarded as being in contact, and able to exchange energy, with a *heat reservoir composed of the other $\mathscr{M} - 1$ members of the ensemble.* The parallel to Fig. 11-1 is now complete and is shown in these terms in Fig. 31-1. What we are interested in is the probability p_n of finding a *system* in the particular cell in Γ-space corresponding to the energy E_n; therefore

$$p_n(E_n) = \frac{N_n}{\mathscr{M}} \tag{31-2}$$

where N_n is the number of ensemble members in this particular region of Γ-space.

We can proceed exactly as before and look for the state of the *ensemble as a whole* which has maximum probability subject to the conditions (31-1) and $\mathscr{M} = \text{const.}$; in this way we find the distribution N_n of ensemble members which gives maximum probability. If we review the calculations in μ-space which we did in Sec. 21-3, we see that the problem we want to

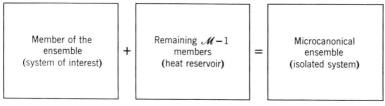

Fig. 31-1

solve now is *exactly* the one we have already solved in Sec. 21-3 by using (21-26) through (21-28) and that the probability (31-2) which we want can be obtained at once from (21-33) and (21-35) by a straightforward change in symbols, namely,

$$p_n(E_n) = \frac{e^{-\beta E_n}}{Z} \tag{31-3}$$

where p_n is the probability of finding the system of interest in the nth cell of energy E_n and where

$$Z = \sum_n e^{-\beta E_n} \tag{31-4}$$

is called the *partition function* for the canonical ensemble.

In spite of the similarity of these formulas to those of Chapter 21, there are essential differences which are important to keep in mind: the probabilities p_n refer to a cell in Γ-space, and E_n is the energy of the system as a whole. Also, we can extend this result at once to the quantum case by using (22-20) and associating a quantum state n of *the system as a whole* with each cell in Γ-space of volume

$$\Delta\Omega_\Gamma = h^{\mathcal{N}} \tag{31-5}$$

where $\mathcal{N}$ is the number of degrees of freedom of the system. Then, as in (26-8), we can write (31-4) as

$$Z = \sum_{\text{cells}} e^{-\beta E_n} = \sum_{\substack{\text{quantum} \\ \text{states}}} e^{-\beta E_n} = \sum_n e^{-\beta E_n} \tag{31-6}$$

If circumstances allow it, we can also evaluate Z as an integral by using (31-5) and (31-6); the result is

$$Z = \frac{1}{h^{\mathcal{N}}} \int e^{-\beta H} \, d\Omega_\Gamma \tag{31-7}$$

where H is the Hamiltonian of the whole system and the integral is taken over *all* Γ-*space* and is not restricted to the single energy surface given by (20-21) as it was before. For convenience, we shall continue to write many of our results as sums rather than integrals.

As we expect by now, the quantities characteristic of the equilibrium state of the system can be found from the partition function Z. For example, the *average energy* U is

$$U = \bar{E} = \sum_n E_n p_n = \frac{\sum\limits_n E_n e^{-\beta E_n}}{\sum\limits_n e^{-\beta E_n}} = -\frac{\partial \ln Z}{\partial \beta} \tag{31-8}$$

We need to speak of U as the average energy because our system is able to exchange energy with its surroundings; we shall return to this point when we discuss fluctuations in the next chapter.

In order to identify the temperature and the entropy, we can proceed much as we did in Sec. 21-4. In general, the energies E_n will depend on various parameters a_λ; hence we can write $E_n(a_1, \ldots, a_\lambda, \ldots)$. If we define the corresponding average generalized force $\bar{F}_\lambda$ by

$$\bar{F}_\lambda = \frac{\overline{\partial E}}{\partial a_\lambda} = \sum_n \frac{\partial E_n}{\partial a_\lambda} p_n \tag{31-9}$$

we find from (31-3) and (31-6) that

$$\bar{F}_\lambda = -\frac{1}{\beta} \frac{\partial \ln Z}{\partial a_\lambda} \tag{31-10}$$

Let us now consider a small change in the quantity $\beta U + \ln Z$; if we use (31-8), (31-10), (21-56), (9-1), and (10-27), we obtain

$$d(\beta U + \ln Z) = \beta \, dU + U \, d\beta + \frac{\partial \ln Z}{\partial \beta} d\beta + \sum_\lambda \frac{\partial \ln Z}{\partial a_\lambda} da_\lambda$$

$$= \beta \, dU - \beta \sum_\lambda \bar{F}_\lambda \, da_\lambda = \beta(dU - dW)$$

$$= \beta \, dQ = \beta T \, dS$$

and therefore, if we define $k = 1/\beta T$ as before, we obtain

$$dS = k \, d(\beta U + \ln Z)$$

which leads to

$$S = \frac{U}{T} + k \ln Z \tag{31-11}$$

The Helmholtz function F is

$$F = U - TS = -kT \ln Z \tag{31-12}$$

so that the equation of state as obtained from (11-6b) is

$$p = kT \frac{\partial \ln Z}{\partial V} \tag{31-13}$$

Thus we have succeeded in expressing our thermodynamic properties in terms of quantities defined for the canonical ensemble.

Our results can be summarized in an interesting and easily remembered fashion by eliminating Z from (31-12) and (31-6); the result is

$$e^{-F/kT} = \sum_n e^{-E_n/kT} \qquad (31\text{-}14)$$

31-2   Quantum mechanical basis for the third law

Now that we are easily able to discuss properties of the system as a whole, we can briefly show how the third law of thermodynamics has a simple and natural origin.

Our basic assumption is that there exists a lowest energy state of the system whose energy is E_1. We want to investigate S as $T \to 0$, that is, as $\beta \to \infty$. If we write the energy of the next higher state as $E_2 = E_1 + \Delta$ where Δ is finite, we find that

$$Z = e^{-\beta E_1} + e^{-\beta E_2} + \cdots = e^{-\beta E_1}(1 + e^{-\beta \Delta} + \cdots)$$

Let us assume that the temperature is already so low that $\beta \Delta \gg 1$ and hence $e^{-\beta \Delta} \ll 1$. Then we can get a good approximation to Z by keeping only the first two terms:

$$Z \simeq e^{-\beta E_1}(1 + e^{-\beta \Delta}) \qquad (31\text{-}15)$$

$$\ln Z = -\beta E_1 + \ln(1 + e^{-\beta \Delta}) \simeq -\beta E_1 + e^{-\beta \Delta} \qquad (31\text{-}16)$$

If we substitute (31-16) into (31-8) and (31-11), we find that

$$U = E_1 + \Delta e^{-\beta \Delta}$$
$$S = k(\beta \Delta + 1) e^{-\beta \Delta} \qquad (31\text{-}17)$$

and therefore

$$\lim_{\beta \to \infty} S = \lim_{\beta \to \infty} k(\beta \Delta + 1) e^{-\beta \Delta} = 0 \qquad (31\text{-}18)$$

This result is exactly in accord with the third law (13-1) and justifies the choice (31-11) for the entropy expression.

We also see from our method of obtaining (31-18) that it depended on the existence of a definite non-degenerate state of lowest energy separated by a discrete amount from the next higher state (or states) and thus it is basically of quantum mechanical origin. An example of such a lowest state for the system as a whole is the $T = 0$ state for free electrons in a metal discussed in Sec. 29-2.

31-3   Independent subsystems

Now let us see how the canonical ensemble results are related to those obtained for the less general system of N independent subsystems previously discussed. The Hamiltonian of the system as a whole has the form (21-1), so that the total energy is simply a sum of the individual subsystem energies ε_k:

$$E = \sum_{k=1}^{N} \varepsilon_k \tag{31-19}$$

If we let ε_i be the energy of the ith quantum state of the subsystem, and n_i be the number in the ith state, we can transform the sum (31-19) to one over the states, and we find that the energy E_n of the corresponding state of the system is

$$E_n = \sum_i n_i \varepsilon_i \tag{31-20}$$

The expression (31-6) for the partition function becomes

$$Z = \sum_n e^{-\beta \sum_i n_i \varepsilon_i} \tag{31-21}$$

and the terms in (31-20) and (31-21) are subject to the restriction of a definite number of subsystems, N,

$$N = \sum_i n_i \tag{31-22}$$

The problem now is to evaluate the sums in (31-21).

Let us consider first the case of Boltzmann statistics which we originally discussed and for which we considered the subsystems to be distinguishable. A given energy E_n can be obtained in a variety of ways, and we see from (31-20) that we obtain a new distinguishable state, but with the same energy, for each permutation of the distinguishable subsystems in the given distribution n_i. If we let $Z_{d(B)}$ be the partition function for the Boltzmann case of distinguishable particles, we can regroup the terms in (31-21) to obtain

$$Z_{d(B)} = \sum_{(n_i)} \left(\sum{}' e^{-\beta \sum_i n_i \varepsilon_i} \right) \tag{31-23}$$

where, as in (21-6), the symbol (n_i) means a sum over all the possible distributions (macrostates) n_i compatible with (31-22). The primed sum is meant to include all the possibilities for a given set of n_i, since they correspond to the same energy $E_n = \sum_i n_i \varepsilon_i$; the number of terms in $\sum{}'$, however, is exactly the number of ways the N particles can be arranged within the given distribution, and this equals W_B given by (21-4). Therefore (31-23) becomes

$$Z_{d(B)} = \sum_{(n_i)} \frac{N!}{n_1! \, n_2! \cdots n_i! \cdots} \, e^{-\beta \Sigma_i n_i \varepsilon_i} \tag{31-24}$$

If we set $x_i = e^{-\beta \varepsilon_i}$ and use the binomial theorem, (31-24) can be written

$$Z_{d(B)} = \sum_{(n_i)} \frac{N!}{n_1! \, n_2! \cdots n_i! \cdots} \, x_1^{n_1} x_2^{n_2} \cdots x_i^{n_i} \cdots$$

$$= (x_1 + x_2 + \cdots + x_i + \cdots)^N$$

$$= \left(\sum_i e^{-\beta \varepsilon_i} \right)^N = Z_0^{\,N} \tag{31-25}$$

where Z_0 is the independent particle partition function defined in (21-35). When (31-25) is used in (31-11) and (31-12), we obtain (21-64) and (21-65), as we expect.

Although the last result will be useful to us very soon, it cannot be the correct approximation when the independent subsystems are identical because we assumed that the subsystems are distinguishable in order to obtain (31-25), and we know from Chapter 27 that we must treat them as indistinguishable. Hence we must reconsider the problem.

We can again regroup the terms in (31-21) and obtain (31-23). Now, however, each permutation of the n_i will *not* correspond to a new state because the new arrangement will be indistinguishable from the first. Therefore there will be only *one* term in the sum Σ' rather than the W_B of (31-24), since each distribution n_i corresponds to only one different state. Therefore, if we let Z_i be the canonical partition function for indistinguishable particles, we obtain

$$Z_i = \sum_{(n_i)} e^{-\beta \Sigma_i n_i \varepsilon_i} \tag{31-26}$$

instead of (31-24). The sum in (31-26) is still over all distributions n_i which are compatible with the constraint (31-22); it is very difficult to carry out this sum because of (31-22), although a method devised by Darwin and Fowler can be used for this purpose. Instead of considering the general problem, therefore, we shall content ourselves with evaluating (31-26) approximately in the high-temperature or Boltzmann limit for indistinguishable particles.

We recall our previous result after (27-1) that only about one cell in every 240,000 is occupied by a molecule for a gas under normal conditions. Therefore practically all the n_i are either 0 or 1, and only a negligible fraction of the cells have values of n_i as large as 2 or 3. Hence we shall not make much error by neglecting the latter cells and including in our sum only cells for which n_i is 0 or 1; for the cells which we do include, all the $n_i! = 1$ since $0! = 1! = 1$. Therefore we can approximate (31-26) as

$$
\begin{aligned}
Z_{i(B)} &\simeq \sum_{(n_i = 0, 1)} e^{-\beta \Sigma_i n_i \varepsilon_i} \\
&= \frac{1}{N!} \sum_{(n_i = 0, 1)} \frac{N!}{n_1! \, n_2! \cdots} e^{-\beta \Sigma_i n_i \varepsilon_i} \\
&= \frac{Z_{d(B)}}{N!} = \frac{Z_0^N}{N!}
\end{aligned}
\tag{31-27}
$$

with the use of (31-24) and (31-25). Thus, in the high-temperature limit, the canonical partition function for a system of independent indistinguishable subsystems can be approximately expressed in terms of the partition function Z_0 in μ-space. For an ideal gas, for example, we find from (31-27) and (26-29) that

$$
Z_{i(B)} = \frac{V^N (2\pi m k T)^{3N/2}}{N! \, h^{3N}}
\tag{31-28}
$$

which one could also verify by direct integration of (31-7) throughout all Γ-space.

If we use (31-27) in (31-8) and (31-11), we obtain

$$
U \simeq -N \frac{\partial \ln Z_0}{\partial \beta}, \quad S \simeq \frac{U}{T} + k \ln \frac{Z_0^N}{N!}
$$

which agree exactly with the formulas (21-36) and (21-53*d*) previously obtained by dealing entirely with μ-space and corrected Boltzmann counting, again showing how the necessity of using (21-5) rather than (21-4) is due to the basic indistinguishability of atoms and molecules. To show the corresponding equivalence of our μ-space calculations for the Bose-Einstein and Fermi-Dirac cases with the general canonical ensemble requires much more complicated mathematical methods than we have been using, and hence we shall satisfy ourselves with the assertion that it can be done and that our results of Chapter 27 can be similarly rederived.

31-4   Theorem of van Leeuwen

As a specific example of the application of the canonical ensemble, we consider a result of classical statistical mechanics which illustrates the generality of this approach and also is quite instructive in the way in which it requires that we combine many separate results of Hamiltonian mechanics, electrodynamics, and statistical mechanics. The theorem asserts that, if we treat matter in a completely classical way, the component of its magnetic moment in the direction of an applied magnetic field is *always* zero. In other words, if we assume that matter consists solely of charged particles which can be completely described by classical mechanics, electrodynamics, and statistical mechanics, a material can *never* be magnetized.

If we consider our material to consist of N charges $q_1, q_2, \ldots, q_N$ with position vectors $\mathbf{r}_1, \mathbf{r}_2, \ldots, \mathbf{r}_N$ the total magnetic dipole moment $\mathcal{M}$ of the system is given by

$$\mathcal{M} = \sum_{j=1}^{N} \frac{q_j}{2m_j} \mathbf{l}_j = \sum_j \tfrac{1}{2} q_j (\mathbf{r}_j \times \mathbf{u}_j) \tag{31-29}$$

according to (I: 38-18 and 38-20), where $\mathbf{l}_j = \mathbf{r}_j \times m_j \mathbf{u}_j$ is the angular momentum of the jth charge of velocity $\mathbf{u}_j$.

Let us now suppose that the material is subject to homogeneous electric and magnetic fields $\mathbf{E}$ and $\mathbf{B}$ which, for simplicity, we assume are along the positive z axis. These fields can be derived from the potentials

$$\phi = -Ez, \quad \mathbf{A} = \tfrac{1}{2} \mathbf{B} \times \mathbf{r} \tag{31-30}$$

according to (I: 21-8 and 38-17). We also know from (I: 38-15) that the Hamiltonian of this system in the presence of electromagnetic fields is

$$H = \sum_j \left[\frac{1}{2m_j} (\mathbf{p}_j - q_j \mathbf{A}_j)^2 + q_j \phi_j \right] \tag{31-31}$$

where the potentials are evaluated at the positions of the charges, so that from (31-30) we find

$$\phi_j = \phi_{j0} - Ez_j, \quad A_{xj} = \tfrac{1}{2} By_j, \quad A_{yj} = \tfrac{1}{2} Bx_j, \quad A_{zj} = 0 \tag{31-32}$$

where ϕ_{j0} is determined solely by the mutual electrostatic forces between the individual charges. We are neglecting the effect of the magnetic field produced by one moving charge on the motion of another charge. This effect is really very small compared to the electrostatic forces; furthermore, it would make the vector potential depend on the charge velocities as well as on position, and then we could not describe this problem within the framework of Hamiltonian mechanics.

Substituting (31-32) into (31-31), we obtain

$$H = \sum_j \left\{ \frac{1}{2m_j} \left[(p_{jx} + \tfrac{1}{2} Bq_j y_j)^2 \right. \right.$$
$$\left. \left. + (p_{jy} - \tfrac{1}{2} Bq_j x_j)^2 + p_{jz}^2 \right] + q_j (\phi_{j0} - Ez_j) \right\} \tag{31-33}$$

We also know from (I: 38-14) that

$$\mathbf{p}_j - q_j \mathbf{A}_j = m_j \mathbf{u}_j \tag{31-34}$$

If we now differentiate (31-33) with respect to B and use (31-34) and (31-29), we find that

$$-\frac{\partial H}{\partial B} = \sum_j \frac{q_j}{2m_j} \left[-(p_{jx} + \tfrac{1}{2}Bq_j y_j)y_j + (p_{jy} - \tfrac{1}{2}Bq_j x_j)x_j\right]$$

$$= \sum_j \frac{q_j}{2}(x_j u_{jy} - y_j u_{jx}) = \mathscr{M}_z = \mathscr{M} \tag{31-35}$$

where $\mathscr{M}$ is the component of the total moment in the direction of the field for a given state of the system.

For a system in thermal equilibrium at constant temperature, the pertinent quantity is the canonical ensemble average. We find from (31-35), (31-3), and (31-7) that

$$\bar{\mathscr{M}} = \frac{1}{Zh^{\mathscr{N}}} \int \left(-\frac{\partial H}{\partial B}\right) e^{-\beta H} \, dp_{1x} \cdots dz_N = \frac{1}{\beta}\frac{\partial \ln Z}{\partial B} \tag{31-36}$$

which is similar to the result (24-4) and where

$$Z(E, B, T) = \frac{1}{h^{\mathscr{N}}} \int e^{-\beta H(E, B, p_{1x}, \ldots, z_N)} \, dp_{1x} \cdots dz_N \tag{31-37}$$

The theorem can now be easily proved. In the absence of a magnetic field, the Hamiltonian is $H_0 = H_0(\mathbf{p}_1, \ldots, \mathbf{r}_N)$. In the presence of a field, the Hamiltonian is given by

$$H = H_0(\mathbf{p}_1 - q_1\mathbf{A}_1, \ldots, \mathbf{p}_N - q_N\mathbf{A}_N; \ \mathbf{r}_1, \ldots, \mathbf{r}_N) \tag{31-38}$$

according to (31-31); the same functional form H_0 is used in both cases. The partition function in the field is then

$$Z(B, T) = \frac{1}{h^{\mathscr{N}}} \int e^{-\beta H_0(\mathbf{p}_1 - q_1\mathbf{A}_1, \ldots, \mathbf{r}_1, \ldots)} \, dp_{1x} \cdots dx_1 \cdots \tag{31-39}$$

If we define new variables $\mathbf{p}_j{}'$ by

$$\mathbf{p}_j{}' = \mathbf{p}_j - q_j\mathbf{A}_j, \quad dp_{jx}{}' = dp_{jx}, \quad \text{etc.,} \tag{31-40}$$

then (31-39) becomes

$$Z(B, T) = \frac{1}{h^{\mathscr{N}}} \int e^{-\beta H_0(\mathbf{p}_1', \ldots, \mathbf{r}_1, \ldots)} \, dp_{1x}{}' \cdots dx_1 \cdots = Z(0, T) \tag{31-41}$$

where $Z(0, T)$ is the partition function in zero field. This result follows because the limits of integration for the momentum components extend from $-\infty$ to ∞ in both (31-39) and (31-41). Therefore the partition function is independent of the magnetic field, and (31-36) becomes

$$\overline{\mathcal{M}} = \frac{1}{\beta} \frac{\partial \ln Z(B, T)}{\partial B} = \frac{1}{\beta} \frac{\partial \ln Z(0, T)}{\partial B} = 0 \qquad (31\text{-}42)$$

which proves the theorem.

This theorem dates back to about 1905. It was extremely disturbing at that time because it indicated a basic disagreement between experiment and the then current formulation of theoretical physics. The situation was finally resolved, however, with the introduction of the concept of electron spin and its associated magnetic moment. These non-classical variables cannot be included in the proof above, of course, so the theorem does not apply.

Exercises

31-1. Another method of deriving (31-3) is based on the assumption that two coupled systems in equilibrium will remain in equilibrium in the limiting case of vanishingly small coupling. Show that, if the Hamiltonians of the two systems are H_1 and H_2 and the coupling term is δH, the probability of the combined system is

$$p(H) = p(H_1 + H_2 + \delta H) \simeq p_1(H_1)p_2(H_2)$$

Consider the limit $\delta H \to 0$, and then use the methods of Chapter 18 and Sec. 21-4 to show that $p(H) = \text{const.} \, e^{-\beta H}$, where β is some constant.

31-2. Using the notation of Exercise 14-3, show that the formulas for the electric case which are analogous to (31-35) and (31-36) are

$$\mathscr{P} = -\partial H/\partial E \quad \text{and} \quad \overline{\mathscr{P}} = kT(\partial \ln Z/\partial E)$$

31-3. Show that the entropy as given by the canonical ensemble distribution can also be written

$$S = -k \, \overline{\ln p_n} = -k \sum_n p_n \ln p_n$$

Compare with Exercise 21-3.

32 Fluctuations and noise

The energy U as given by (31-8) was called the average energy because a system at constant temperature can exchange energy with its surroundings. One naturally wonders therefore how we are able to identify the average energy with the thermodynamic energy U since the very concept of an average value implies the possibility that any single measurement of the energy will yield a value which is larger or smaller than the average. The good agreement which is found between the statistical average values and the macroscopic measurements indicates that the fluctuations or deviations from the average are generally quite small. Although we briefly touched on this matter with (21-45), we now want to discuss these fluctuations in a more systematic manner.

32-1   Fluctuations in the energy

We can define the fluctuation ΔE in the energy as the difference between a given value E and the average so that

$$\Delta E = E - \bar{E} = E - U \tag{32-1}$$

because of (31-8). The average fluctuation is zero, of course, as we can quickly find from (32-1)

$$\overline{\Delta E} = \overline{E - \bar{E}} = \bar{E} - \bar{E} = 0 \tag{32-2}$$

The *mean square fluctuation* is of more use and is defined as the average of the square of the fluctuation from the average; thus

$$\overline{(\Delta E)^2} = \overline{(E - \bar{E})^2} = \overline{E^2 - 2E\bar{E} + (\bar{E})^2} = \overline{E^2} - (\bar{E})^2 \tag{32-3}$$

We see from (31-3), (31-6), and (31-8) that

$$\overline{E^2} = \frac{1}{Z} \sum_n E_n{}^2 e^{-\beta E_n} = \frac{1}{Z} \frac{\partial^2 Z}{\partial \beta^2}$$

$$= \frac{\partial}{\partial \beta} \frac{\partial \ln Z}{\partial \beta} + \left(\frac{\partial \ln Z}{\partial \beta}\right)^2$$

$$= \frac{\partial^2 \ln Z}{\partial \beta^2} + (\bar{E})^2 \tag{32-4}$$

and therefore

$$\overline{(\Delta E)^2} = \frac{\partial^2 \ln Z}{\partial \beta^2} = -\frac{\partial U}{\partial \beta} = kT^2 \frac{\partial U}{\partial T} = kT^2 C_v \tag{32-5}$$

since $\beta = 1/kT$ and C_v is the heat capacity of the system. We see from (32-5) that the mean square energy fluctuation is determined by the *thermodynamic* parameters of the system. The relative magnitude of these quantities can be estimated if we consider a reasonable example.

Example. Monatomic Ideal Gas. According to (22-12), $C_v = \frac{3}{2}Nk$ so that (32-5) yields

$$\overline{(\Delta E)^2} = \frac{3}{2}Nk^2T^2 \tag{32-6}$$

Although this quantity can be quite large in absolute value because it is proportional to N, what is of more significance is the fractional fluctuation which compares (32-6) with the system energy $U = \frac{3}{2}NkT$; we find

$$\frac{\overline{(\Delta E)^2}}{(\bar{E})^2} = \frac{\overline{(\Delta E)^2}}{U^2} = \frac{2}{3N} \tag{32-7}$$

and therefore

$$\frac{|\Delta E|}{U} \approx \frac{1}{\sqrt{N}} \approx 10^{-13} \tag{32-8}$$

These results show that the average fluctuation is so small as to be completely unobservable because of the *large number of particles involved.* Hence we are well justified in identifying the average energy with the thermodynamic equilibrium energy; even though there is a finite probability of finding our system to have any value of the energy, this chance will be so small that in actual practice the energy will have a well-defined value.

We also see from (32-5) that it is a consequence of the third law that the energy fluctuations will vanish at absolute zero; that is

$$\overline{(\Delta E)^2} \xrightarrow[T \to 0]{} 0 \tag{32-9}$$

because the heat capacity remains finite as $T \to 0$ according to (13-20). On the other hand, the relative fluctuation in the energy will generally not vanish, for we see from (32-7) that the ratio $|\Delta E|/U$ is independent of the temperature.

32-2 Fluctuations in other quantities

Let us now consider fluctuations in the generalized forces $\bar{F}_\lambda$ which, according to (31-9), (31-10), and (31-12), are given by

$$\bar{F}_\lambda = \frac{\overline{\partial E}}{\partial a_\lambda} = -\frac{1}{\beta}\frac{\partial \ln Z}{\partial a_\lambda} = \frac{\partial F}{\partial a_\lambda} \tag{32-10}$$

A convenient starting point is (31-14), which can be written

$$\sum_n e^{\beta(F-E_n)} = 1 \tag{32-11}$$

If we differentiate this expression with respect to a_λ, we obtain

$$\sum_n \left(\frac{\partial F}{\partial a_\lambda} - \frac{\partial E_n}{\partial a_\lambda} \right) e^{\beta(F - E_n)} = \bar{F}_\lambda - \bar{F}_\lambda = 0 \qquad (32\text{-}12)$$

as we already know. Now, however, let us differentiate (32-12) with respect to the parameter a_μ; the result is

$$0 = \sum_n \left(\frac{\partial^2 F}{\partial a_\mu \, \partial a_\lambda} - \frac{\partial^2 E_n}{\partial a_\mu \, \partial a_\lambda} \right) e^{\beta(F - E_n)}$$

$$+ \beta \sum_n \left(\frac{\partial F}{\partial a_\lambda} - \frac{\partial E_n}{\partial a_\lambda} \right) \left(\frac{\partial F}{\partial a_\mu} - \frac{\partial E_n}{\partial a_\mu} \right) e^{\beta(F - E_n)}$$

$$= \frac{\partial^2 F}{\partial a_\mu \, \partial a_\lambda} - \overline{\left(\frac{\partial^2 E}{\partial a_\mu \, \partial a_\lambda} \right)} + \beta \, \overline{(\bar{F}_\lambda - F_\lambda)(\bar{F}_\mu - F_\mu)} \qquad (32\text{-}13)$$

because of (31-3), (31-12), and (31-14). Therefore we find from (32-13) that

$$\overline{\Delta F_\lambda \, \Delta F_\mu} = \overline{(F_\lambda - \bar{F}_\lambda)(F_\mu - \bar{F}_\mu)}$$

$$= kT \overline{\left(\frac{\partial^2 E}{\partial a_\mu \, \partial a_\lambda} - \frac{\partial^2 F}{\partial a_\mu \, \partial a_\lambda} \right)} \qquad (32\text{-}14)$$

and is a generalized fluctuation theorem involving possibly different generalized forces.

If $\lambda = \mu$ and if we also use (32-10), we find that (32-14) becomes

$$\overline{(\Delta F_\lambda)^2} = \overline{(F_\lambda - \bar{F}_\lambda)^2} = kT \overline{\left(\frac{\partial^2 E}{\partial a_\lambda{}^2} - \frac{\partial \bar{F}_\lambda}{\partial a_\lambda} \right)} \qquad (32\text{-}15)$$

If we apply this to the pressure so that $a_\lambda = V$ and $\bar{F}_\lambda = -p$, we find from (32-15) that

$$\overline{(\Delta p)^2} = kT \overline{\left(\frac{\partial^2 E}{\partial V^2} + \frac{\partial p}{\partial V} \right)} \qquad (32\text{-}16)$$

It is sometimes more convenient to express (32-16) in terms of the isothermal compressibility κ_T defined in (8-2); we then find that

$$\overline{(\Delta p)^2} = kT \overline{\left(\frac{\partial^2 E}{\partial V^2} - \frac{1}{V \kappa_T} \right)} \qquad (32\text{-}17)$$

Example.   Monatomic Ideal Gas.   If, for simplicity, we consider the gas to be contained in a cube of sides $L_x = L_y = L_z = L$ and of volume $V = L^3$, we find from (26-2) that the energy levels of a particle are given by

$$\varepsilon_{n_x n_y n_z} = \frac{a}{L^2} = \frac{a}{V^{2/3}} \tag{32-18}$$

where a is a quantity independent of the volume. The energy levels of the whole system will be a linear combination of terms like (32-18), according to (31-20), and, since each term in the sum depends on the volume in the same way, we can conclude that

$$E_n = \frac{A}{V^{2/3}} \tag{32-19}$$

where A is independent of the volume. Therefore

$$\frac{\partial E_n}{\partial V} = -\frac{2A}{3V^{5/3}} = -\frac{2E_n}{3V} \tag{32-20}$$

and hence the average pressure as obtained from (32-10) is given by

$$p = -\frac{\overline{\partial E}}{\partial V} = \frac{2\bar{E}}{3V} = \frac{2U}{3V} \tag{32-21}$$

and is the same as (28-15), which we obtained by other means.

We also find from (32-20) that

$$\frac{\partial^2 E_n}{\partial V^2} = \frac{10A}{9V^{8/3}} = \frac{10E_n}{9V^2}$$

so that

$$\frac{\overline{\partial^2 E}}{\partial V^2} = \frac{10\bar{E}}{9V^2} = \frac{5p}{3V} \tag{32-22}$$

Since $p = NkT/V$, we find that

$$\frac{\partial p}{\partial V} = -\frac{NkT}{V^2} = -\frac{p}{V} \tag{32-23}$$

and, when the last two results are substituted into (32-16), we obtain

$$\overline{(\Delta p)^2} = \frac{2pkT}{3V} = \frac{2p^2}{3N} \tag{32-24}$$

and the fractional fluctuation in the pressure is therefore

$$\frac{\overline{(\Delta p)^2}}{p^2} = \frac{2}{3N} \tag{32-25}$$

which is exactly what was found in (32-7) for the energy fluctuation.

Since $p = nkT$ by (17-12) and (17-15), we can obtain the density fluctuation for our isothermal system directly from (32-25):

$$\frac{\overline{(\Delta n)^2}}{n^2} = \frac{2}{3N} \approx \frac{1}{N} \tag{32-26}$$

It is evident that considerations similar to these could be applied to other thermodynamic variables. In addition, higher order fluctuations could be found by extending the type of calculation which led to (32-14) by including further differentiation with respect to the parameters a_λ.

32-3   "Thermal noise"

The title of this section describes another type of phenomenon which is often referred to as a fluctuation, although it does not apply to the system as a whole. This effect is generally calculated by applying the equipartition theorem to separate degrees of freedom. We shall discuss only a few examples rather briefly.

The earliest example is called *Brownian motion*; it was first observed by the botanist Brown, who noted the constant motion of pollen particles which were suspended in water. Since these small particles are in thermal equilibrium with their surroundings, we can use the equipartition theorem result (25-22)

$$\tfrac{1}{2}m\overline{u^2} = \tfrac{3}{2}kT$$

which leads to an rms speed

$$u_{\rm rms} = (\overline{u^2})^{1/2} = \left(\frac{3kT}{m}\right)^{1/2} \tag{32-27}$$

For a mass of about 10^{-18} kilograms, $u_{\rm rms}$ as found from (32-27) is about 0.10 meter/second, which is about what is observed. The magnitude of $u_{\rm rms}$ is virtually unobservable for more massive bodies; for example, if $m = 1$ kilogram, $u_{\rm rms} \simeq 3 \times 10^{-3}$ meter/year.

This thermal motion may be magnified, however, in some measuring equipment, and the useful sensitivity of the apparatus thereby limited. A simple example of such a situation is provided by a galvanometer mirror. If φ is the angular displacement, the elastic restoring torque in the suspension is $-c\varphi$, where c is a constant of proportionality. The potential energy associated with this angular displacement is $\tfrac{1}{2}c\varphi^2$ by (I: 5-3); hence

$$\tfrac{1}{2}c\overline{\varphi^2} = \tfrac{1}{2}kT \tag{32-28}$$

by (25-22). Therefore there will be a random deflection superimposed on the steady deflection of the mirror. The rms value as obtained from (32-28) is

$$\varphi_{\text{rms}} = \sqrt{\frac{kT}{c}} \tag{32-29}$$

Accordingly, deflections less than φ_{rms} will be hidden by the random thermal motion and cannot be detected by the apparatus. One cannot avoid this problem by simply increasing the sensitivity, because we see that, as c is decreased, φ_{rms} is increased.

The derivation of the equipartition theorem in Sec. 25-2 shows that its application is not limited to mechanical degrees of freedom because it depended only on very general properties of the Hamiltonian description of the system; for example, we have already applied it to electromagnetic normal modes. As another example, a short-circuited inductance L possesses a random thermal electric current I which is found from (25-22) and (I: Exercise 26-2) to be given by

$$\tfrac{1}{2}L\bar{I^2} = \tfrac{1}{2}kT$$

so that

$$I_{\text{rms}} = \sqrt{\frac{kT}{L}} \tag{32-30}$$

Similarly, a short-circuited condenser whose energy can be written in terms of its capacitance C and potential difference V as $\tfrac{1}{2}CV^2$ by (I: Exercise 23-2) has a random potential difference given by

$$V_{\text{rms}} = \sqrt{\frac{kT}{C}} \tag{32-31}$$

These random currents and potential differences are called thermal or *Johnson noise*. This noise often limits the amplification which can be applied to a given signal and is consequently quite important in communication or detecting equipment. It is important to know the general properties of such noise; one feature of interest is the frequency distribution. For the simple case of a resonant circuit consisting of a condenser shorted by an inductance, the rms amplitudes given by (32-30) and (32-31) will apply to the resonant frequency. In the next section, we obtain the noise frequency distribution for a less restricted situation.

32-4 Nyquist's theorem

Let us consider a very long lossless transmission line of length l which has the same kind of termination at each end. A mechanical example would be a very long continuous string fastened at the ends. An acoustic example would be a long pipe through which sound could be transmitted. Electromagnetic examples would be a hollow wave guide or a coaxial line. In any event, we know from previous experience that the effect of the boundary conditions for this essentially one-dimensional problem will be to determine the many possible normal modes of oscillation of the system. Typically, the normal mode can be expressed as a standing wave with a form such as

$$a \sin \frac{n\pi x}{l} \sin 2\pi \nu_n t = a \sin \frac{2\pi x}{\lambda_n} \sin 2\pi \nu_n t$$

where a is the amplitude and n is an integer. If v is the speed of the wave, the frequency of the nth mode is related to the wavelength by (I: 15-7)

$$\nu_n = \frac{v}{\lambda_n} = \frac{nv}{2l} \tag{32-32}$$

and hence the number of modes, Δn, of this type in the frequency interval $\Delta \nu$ is found from (32-32) to be

$$\Delta n = \frac{2l}{v} \Delta \nu \tag{32-33}$$

The average energy of such a mode is given by the expression (26-36) for the average oscillator energy $\bar{\varepsilon}_{osc}$ provided that we drop the zero point energy as usual. Therefore the total energy in the frequency range $\Delta \nu$ is

$$U_\nu \, \Delta \nu = \bar{\varepsilon}_{osc} \, \Delta n = \frac{2l\bar{\varepsilon}_{osc}}{v} \Delta \nu$$

so that the average energy density per unit length is

$$u_\nu \, \Delta \nu = \frac{2\bar{\varepsilon}_{osc}}{v} \Delta \nu \tag{32-34}$$

Each standing wave can be written as two traveling waves, one in each direction, as shown, for example, in (I: 15-4). The energy flux in each traveling wave equals the average energy density times the speed of the wave by (I: 28-54). Therefore the power in a given frequency interval in a given direction $P_\nu \, \Delta \nu$ can be obtained from (32-34) as

$$P_\nu \, \Delta \nu = \tfrac{1}{2} v u_\nu \, \Delta \nu = \bar{\varepsilon}_{osc} \, \Delta \nu = \frac{h\nu \, \Delta \nu}{e^{h\nu/kT} - 1} \tag{32-35}$$

which is the basic formula for the frequency distribution of Johnson noise. Nyquist's theorem refers to the form of (32-25) which corresponds to the Rayleigh-Jeans approximation to Planck's law; that is, $\bar{\varepsilon}_{osc} \simeq kT$ or $h\nu/kT \ll 1$, so that (32-35) becomes

$$P_\nu \, \Delta\nu = kT \, \Delta\nu \tag{32-36}$$

and gives a noise distribution whose density is independent of the frequency and agrees well with experiment in those situations where it can be expected to be applicable.

Exercises

32-1. Calculate the mean square fluctuational deviation from the vertical of a suspended simple pendulum.

32-2. Find the fractional fluctuation in energy of a Debye crystal at low temperatures.

32-3. A good human ear can detect sound if the power is as low as 10^{-17} watt for frequencies between 10^3 and 3×10^3 (second)$^{-1}$. If one listened at the end of a long tube, would the thermal noise be detectable? Repeat this estimate for the familiar example of hearing the roar of the sea by holding a large seashell to the ear.

32-4. In what sense can thermal radiation be described as electromagnetic noise?

32-5. Show that the fluctuations in n_i for Bose-Einstein and Fermi-Dirac systems are

$$\overline{(\Delta n_i)^2} = n_i(1 \pm n_i)$$

What does this become in the Boltzmann limit?

32-6. Show that $\overline{(\Delta E)^3} = -\partial^3 \ln Z/\partial\beta^3$, and evaluate it for a monatomic ideal gas.

Index